W9-AFL-370

WITHDRAWN

520
B17a

20631

DATE DUE			

WITHDRAWN

REGION OF ORION

The photograph was made with a small lens with an exposure of ten hours. It covers nearly one twentieth of the whole sky. The Hyades, in Taurus, are near the upper right corner. Sirius appears at the lower left. Faintly luminous nebulosity is abundant in the vicinity of Orion. (From a photograph by Edwin Hubble, Mount Wilson Observatory)

Astronomy

An Introduction

By

ROBERT H. BAKER, Ph.D.

Professor of Astronomy in the University of Illinois

SECOND EDITION—SECOND PRINTING

CARL A. RUDISILL
LIBRARY
LENOIR RHYNE COLLEGE

NEW YORK
D. VAN NOSTRAND COMPANY, Inc.
250 FOURTH AVENUE

520
B17a

Copyright, *1930, 1933*
by
D. *Van Nostrand Company, Inc.*

———

*All rights reserved, including that of translation
into the Scandinavian and other foreign languages.*

First Published, May *1930*
Reprinted, August *1930,* April *1931*
Second Edition, May *1933*
Reprinted, August *1934*

20631
Sept '45

Printed in U. S. A.

PRESS OF
BRAUNWORTH & CO., INC.
BOOK MANUFACTURERS
BROOKLYN, NEW YORK

PREFACE TO THE SECOND EDITION

In the three years that have elapsed since the appearance of the first edition, astronomy has made important advances in almost every field. The revised edition is intended to bring the book again abreast of the times. As examples of the new features, the reader will find accounts of two asteroids which approach the earth closer than Eros, of recently discovered meteor craters, of globular clusters around the Andromeda nebula, of the celebrated "red shift" and the theory of the expanding universe.

The treatments of the galactic system and the exterior systems have been amplified and further systematized. Advantage has been taken of the discussions at the 1932 meeting of the International Astronomical Union, in Cambridge, which served to crystallize viewpoints on these and other subjects.

New illustrations include photographs of the solar eclipse of 1932, Dr. Millman's meteor spectrum, two of Dr. Ross' superb Milky Way photographs, and reproductions of Mount Wilson spectrograms of distant extra-galactic nebulae, showing the enormous displacements to the red. The size of the book remains unchanged. The addition of new material is offset by the omission of an equal amount which with the seasoning of the book has proved to be somewhat less useful in the classroom and to the general reader.

Grateful acknowledgment is made of the favorable comments on the first edition. For suggestions of improvements the author is indebted to many colleagues, particularly to Dr. B. J. Bok, Dr. W. J. Fisher, Dr. S. G. Barton, and Dr. B. W. Sitterly. The excellent appearance of this book and the copious illustrations bear witness in part to the complete cooperation of the D. Van Nostrand Company, Inc.

ROBERT H. BAKER

University of Illinois Observatory,
May, 1933.

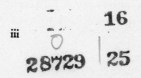

28729 | 16 25

PREFACE

This book is intended for use as a text in introductory college courses in astronomy. In its preparation, the author has kept in mind the requirements of his own classes, in which many of the students have had little previous acquaintance with physical science, and limited preparation in elementary mathematics.

It is believed that the book can be read with understanding, in general, by students of this description; and that the treatment is sufficiently mature to afford a profitable introduction to astronomy to those who are more advanced in preparation. It is believed also that the inclusion of the most recent discoveries and viewpoints and the excellence of the illustrations will make this book acceptable for general reading and reference.

The account begins with various aspects of the sky, some of which are known to everyone. Small scale maps of the constellations are included for reference in connection with the reading. Larger star maps suitable for systematic studies of the constellations in the evening can be readily obtained. They will be more satisfactory for outdoor use than maps bound in a book of this size.

By the time the constellations have been studied it will have become apparent that there is much more to be learned by observing the sky with the unaided eye. Many of the facts considered in Chapter I, and in subsequent chapters, can be verified directly. If a telescope is available, its use can be begun early in the course. Accordingly, a brief account of the telescope, and of great telescopes, including the projected 200-inch reflector, is given in the opening chapter.

The account of the earth's motions, in the second chapter, explains the apparent motions of the heavens and of the sun, previously described, and anticipates the study of planetary motions in general. In Chapter III the earth and the moon are considered, and the subject of eclipses as well. Beyond a brief reference, the field of geology is not entered. In order to keep the size of the book within bounds and to allow ample space for recent developments in sidereal astronomy, it has been decided to omit almost entirely the problems of practical astronomy relating to determinations of latitude, longitude, and azimuth. Considerable space has been devoted to the earth's atmosphere and its astronomical effects.

The organization of the solar system is treated in Chapter IV, preparing the way for studies of its individual members, which follow. The historical development leads naturally to the subject of celestial mechanics which is dealt with briefly in such a manner that it will not be beyond the grasp of the non-mathematical reader. During the reading of the fifth chapter, in which the planets except the earth are described in order of their distance from the sun, it will be profitable to refer frequently to the two Tables at the end of the chapter, and to study carefully the beautiful examples of planetary photography which illustrate the chapter, most of them of very recent date. Comets, meteors, meteorites, and hypotheses concerning the early history of the solar system are the chief subjects of the sixth chapter. Photographs of Meteor Crater from the air and of the great Grootfontein meteorite will be noted among those which have not previously appeared in textbooks.

The second half of the book deals principally with the stars, their motions and distances (Chapter VIII), the quantity and quality of their light, their constitution, and their organization into vast systems. It begins, in Chapter VII, with a description of the sun, because the proximity of this star to the earth makes it the most favorable of all for detailed investigation. With the introduction of these self-luminous bodies into the account, it becomes necessary to consider various phenomena of light, and the means by which astronomers interpret the messages that the starlight brings to us from its remote sources. The light of the stars is the subject of the ninth chapter.

The greater part of the material of the last three chapters could not have been presented a dozen years ago, because it was not then available. In this short interval, the description of the universe around us has been greatly clarified and extended. Previously, the story ended in disappointing uncertainty and vague speculation. Now it rises to a convincing climax, with the hint of greater revelations to come. In these new fields the developments will be rapid, and details in the present account will doubtless require some revision.

In the preparation of this book the author has consulted original sources wherever it was possible, particularly in the more recent developments. He has drawn freely from many scientific publications.

The photographs which are reproduced in this book have been generously furnished by institutions and individuals in various parts of the world. For the photographs the author owes acknowledgment to:

Professor A. S. Eddington, Professor Carl Störmer, Dr. Max Wolf, the Astronomer Royal, M. F. Quénisset, M. de Kerolyr; the directors of the Meudon, Hamburg, Potsdam, Kodaikanal, and Union observatories; Carl Zeiss, Inc., Adam Hilger, Ltd.; the associate director of the Lick Observatory, the directors of the Harvard, Lowell, Dominion Astrophysical, Mount Wilson, University of Michigan, Washburn, Sproul, Yerkes, and Naval observatories, and other astronomers in these observatories; Dr. George E. Hale, Dr. Donald B. MacMillan, Mr. Ernest A. Grunsfeld, Jr.; Bureau of Standards, U. S. Army Air Corps, American Museum of Natural History, Carnegie Institution of Washington; Sperry Gyroscope Company.

Grateful acknowledgment is made to Professor Frank Schlesinger for reading parts of the manuscript and for helpful comments, and to the late Professor Ralph H. Curtiss for reading and criticizing other parts. The author is deeply indebted to Professor Philip Fox who read all the manuscript and suggested many improvements.

Robert H. Baker

University of Illinois Observatory,
May, 1930.

CONTENTS

vii

LIST OF TABLES

LIST OF ILLUSTRATIONS

The zodiacal light 24

255
Kant's
Nebular H
256
Hypothesis
258

FIGURE		PAGE
7.29.	Direct Photograph and Spectroheliogram of the Sun	287
7.30.	A Sun-Spot Region at Three Levels	288
7.30A.	Very Bright Solar Eruption	289
7.31.	Prominence Observed at the Total Eclipse of May 29, 1919	290
7.32.	Very High Prominence, November 19, 1928	291
7.32A.	Prominence Observed at the Total Eclipse of May 9, 1929	292
7.34.	Photograph of the Corona, September 21, 1922	294
7.34A.	Drawing of the Corona, January 14, 1926	295
7.36.	Variations in Number of Sun-Spot Groups and in Intensity of Ultra-Violet Solar Radiation	296
7.39.	Energy Curves of a Perfect Radiator	298
	Hydrogen Lines in the Spectrum of ζ Tauri	301
8.1.	Parallaxes of the Stars	302
8.3.	Eye End of the 40-inch Refractor of the Yerkes Observatory	304
8.4.	The Heliocentric Parallax of a Star	305
8.7.	Proper Motion and Radial Velocity	308
8.10.	Proper Motion of Proxima Centauri	310
8.11.	Doppler Shift in the Spectrum of Procyon	310
8.11A.	Micrometer for Measuring Stellar Spectra	311
8.12.	Annual Variation in the Radial Velocity of a Star	312
8.13.	Relation between Space Velocity, Tangential Velocity, Radial Velocity, Proper Motion and Distance of a Star	313
8.14.	Common Motion of Stars in Ursa Major	313
8.15.	Convergence of the Taurus Cluster	314
8.15A.	Track of Taurus Cluster	315
8.16.	The Pleiades	316
8.18.	Parallactic Motions of the Stars	318
8.19.	The Earth's Motion in a Helix	319
8.22.	The Two Star Streams	321
8.25.	Effects of the Rotation of the Galactic System on the Radial Velocities of the Stars	323
8.27.	The Binary System Krueger 60	325
8.28.	Orbit of Krueger 60	326
8.29.	Micrometer of the 36-inch Refractor, Lick Observatory	327
8.33.	Orbit of Sirius	331

The Light of Star

To the Student who uses this Textbook:

This textbook represents many years of learning and experience on the part of the authors. It does not treat of an ephemeral subject, but one which, since you are studying it in college, you must feel will have a use to you in your future life.

Unquestionably you will many times in later life wish to refer to specific details and facts about the subject which this book covers and which you may forget. How better could you find this information than in the textbook which you have studied from cover to cover?

Retain it for your reference library. You will use it many times in the future.

The Publishers.

INTRODUCTION

Astronomy, the "science of the stars," is concerned not merely with the stars, but with all the celestial bodies which together comprise the known physical universe. It deals with planets and their satellites, with comets, meteors, stars, and nebulae; with the star-clusters, the great star-clouds which form the Milky Way, and the galaxies which lie beyond the Milky Way. Its province extends into space as far as the largest telescope can penetrate, including the earth, of course, as one of the planets, and as the abode of those who observe and reflect on the things around them.

The most comprehensive of the sciences, astronomy is regarded also as the oldest of all. People of ancient times were attentive watchers of the skies. They were attracted by the splendor of the celestial scenery, as we are today, and by its mystery which entered into their religions and mythologies. Astrology, the pseudo-science which held that the destinies of nations and individuals were revealed by the stars, furnished at times another motive for the study of the heavens.

Still another incentive to the early cultivation of astronomy was its usefulness in relation to ordinary pursuits. The daily rotation of the heavens provided means of telling time. The cycle of the moon's phases and the westward march of the constellations with the changing seasons were convenient for calendar purposes. The invariable pole of the heavens in the north, around which the Dippers wheel, and whose place is now marked roughly by the north star, served as a guide to the traveler on land and sea. These are some of the ways in which the heavens have been useful to man, from the earliest times to the present.

But the value of astronomy must not be measured in terms of economic applications. Astronomy is concerned primarily with an aspiration of mankind, which is fully as impelling as the quest for survival and material welfare, namely, the desire to know about the universe around us, and our relation to it. The importance of this service is clearly demonstrated by the widespread public interest in astronomy, and by the generous financial support which has promoted the construction and effective operation of great telescopes in rapidly increasing numbers. Nowhere in the college curricula can the value of learning for its own sake be more convincingly presented than in the introductory courses in astronomy.

It is the purpose of astronomy to furnish a description of the physical universe, in which the characteristics and relationships of its various parts are clearly shown. At present, the picture is incomplete. Doubtless it will remain incomplete always, subject to improvements in the light of new explorations and new viewpoints. The advancing years will bring additional grandeur and significance to our view of the universe, as they have in the past.

The Sphere of the Stars. As early as the sixth century B.C., Greek philosophers regarded the earth as a globe standing motionless in the center of the universe. The boundary of the universe was a spherical shell, on whose inner surface the stars were set. This *celestial sphere* was supported by an inclined axis through the earth, on which the sphere rotated daily, causing the stars to rise and set. Within the sphere of the stars seven celestial bodies moved around the earth; they were the sun, the moon, and the five bright planets.

For more than two thousand years thereafter, this view of the universe, the universe of appearances, remained practically unchanged. The chief problem of astronomy was to account for the motions of the seven wandering bodies, so that their places in the heavens could be predicted for the future. The outstanding solution of the problem, on the basis of the central, motionless earth, was the Ptolemaic system.

Copernicus, in the sixteenth century, proposed the theory that the planets revolve around the sun rather than the earth, and that the earth is simply one of the planets. The rising and setting of the stars was now ascribed to the daily rotation of the earth. The new theory placed the sun and its family of planets sharply apart from the stars. With its gradual acceptance, the stars came to be regarded as remote suns, at different distances from us and in motion in different directions. The ancient sphere of the stars remained only as a convention; and the way was prepared for explorations into the star-fields, which have led to the more comprehensive view of the universe that we hold today.

The Solar System. The earth is one of a number of relatively small planets which revolve around the sun, accompanied by smaller bodies, the satellites, of which the moon is an example. They are dark bodies, shining only as they reflect the sunlight. The nine principal planets, including the earth, are somewhat flattened globes whose average distances from the sun range from four tenths to forty times the earth's distance. Thousands of smaller planets, the asteroids, describe their orbits in the middle distances. Comets and meteor swarms also revolve around the sun. Their orbits are, in general, more elongated than those of the planets, and they extend to greater distances from the sun.

These bodies together comprise the solar system, the only known system of this kind, although others may well exist. A similar planetary system surrounding the very nearest star could not be discerned with the largest telescope. Likewise, the telescopic view of our system from the nearest star would show only the sun, now having the appearance of a bright star.

The Stars. The sun is one of the multitude of stars, representing a fair average of the general run of stars. It is a globe of intensely hot gas 864,100 miles in diameter, and a third of a million times as massive as the earth. Some stars are much larger than the sun; others are smaller, and a few, at least, scarcely exceed the planets in size, though the masses of all do not differ greatly. Blue stars have higher surface temperatures than the sun, which is a yellow star. The red stars are cooler. But all are exceedingly hot, as compared with ordinary standards, and are radiating enormous quantities of energy. The stars are the power houses and the building blocks of the universe.

Vast spaces intervene between the stars. If the size of the sun is represented by a period on this page, the nearest star on this scale is a dot of about equal size five miles away. The distance of the nearest star, Proxima, is 4.2 light-years; that is to say, a ray of light, whose speed is 186,300 miles a second, spends 4.2 years in its journey from this star to the earth.

The sun occupies a fairly central position in the *local system,* a flattened assemblage of stars having a diameter of several thousand light-years. Its membership includes the majority of the lucid stars and of the nearer telescopic stars. Bright nebulae add variety to the star-fields around us, and dark dust-clouds also, which obscure the stars behind them. While there is not complete agreement among astronomers as to the separate existence of the local system, the opinion is widely held that it is a star-cloud resembling those which form the Milky Way.

The Galactic System is the assemblage of stars, star-clusters, star-clouds, and nebulae around us, whose most prominent feature is the Milky Way; it occupies a region of space some 200,000 light-years in diameter. Globular clusters of stars constitute the superstructure of the system. The cluster system has roughly the form of a flattened globe whose center lies in the direction of the great star-cloud in the constellation Sagittarius. The other star-clouds, including the local system, are grouped around the Sagittarius cloud, forming a system much more flattened and somewhat smaller in diameter than the cluster system.

Analogy suggests that the system of the star-clouds has the form of a flat, double-armed spiral. The Sagittarius cloud is the nucleus, from opposite sides of which two streams of star-clouds emerge and coil in the same sense. The local system is a condensation in one of the arms of the spiral. Another hypothesis views the system as a group of galaxies nearly in the same plane and without spiral structure. We await the completion of current surveys.

Extra-Galactic Systems. The galactic system is a unit, or group of units, in a still greater structure which has been called the *meta-galactic system*. Millions of other members lie far beyond the Milky Way, at distances which must be expressed in millions of light-years. The majority have the spiral form, and many of these *spiral nebulae* have been recognized for a long time. It was not until the close of the first quarter of the present century, however, that the spirals and associated nebulae were definitely established as great systems exterior to our own.

Many of the problems which confronted the astronomer two centuries ago, when he began to look beyond the solar system to study the stars systematically, now arise again in enormous enlargement as the explorations are extended beyond the galactic system. The characteristics of the different types of extra-galactic systems and their relation to our own system, their motions, their clustering, and their arrangement in the vaster structure — these are prominent among the problems that claim the attention today.

CHAPTER I

ASPECTS OF THE SKY

THE CELESTIAL SPHERE; ITS APPARENT DAILY ROTATION — DIURNAL CIRCLES OF THE STARS OBSERVED IN DIFFERENT LATITUDES — THE SUN'S APPARENT ANNUAL CIRCUIT — THE CONSTELLATIONS — THE TELESCOPE

Our study of astronomy begins with the sky, and with the celestial bodies that seem to be and to move upon it, as they appear to the unaided eye. The point of view at first will not differ greatly from that of the ancient watchers of the sky, whose astronomy began and ended with appearances.

1.1. The Sky. In the daytime, the sky resembles a blue dome which rests on the earth along the circle of the horizon. The only celestial bodies to be seen ordinarily are the sun, and occasionally the moon. It is understood that the stars are there too, but their faint light does not compete successfully with the sunlight which the atmosphere diffuses from all quarters.

At night the blue of the sky deepens almost to black, and the stars come out — twinkling points of light they seem to be, differing one from another only in direction, brightness, and color. Here and there they form striking figures of dippers, squares, and crosses, which remain unaltered in form year after year. They are the "*fixed stars*," as distinguished from the few brilliant star-like objects which move unblinking among the stars themselves, from one configuration to another. These are the *planets*, literally "the wanderers."

As a whole, the celestial scenery moves steadily toward the west. The stars rise and set, as the sun and moon do, except the stars in the north, whose courses around the pole star never descend below the horizon, for stations in the northern hemisphere. Finally it is noticed that familiar groups of stars are each night a little farther west than they were the previous night at the same hour. As the season advances, these configurations gradually disappear in the west out of the evening sky, while new groups come into view in the east to claim attention.

The Celestial Sphere; Its Apparent Daily Rotation

1.2. The Celestial Sphere. There are two ways of regarding the sky. To many people, especially in the daytime, it seems to be a flattened stationary dome of not very great size. Indeed, for the observations of clouds and other phenomena of the atmosphere two observers several miles apart have different skies. But when the stars come out, and as we watch them rising and setting, it is easy to imagine them set like diamonds upon the surface of a vast sphere, the *celestial sphere,* which completely encloses the earth.

In earlier times, the celestial sphere was regarded as a tangible surface upon which the stars were really fixed, and whose daily rotation caused them to rise and set. With us it survives as a conventional representation of the sky, useful in astronomy for many purposes in which the distances of the stars need not be taken into account. Evidently of very great size, since it is the background of the universe, the celestial sphere has the properties of an infinite sphere. Its center may be anywhere at all; while parallel lines are directed toward the same point of the sphere, regardless of the amount of their separation, just as the rails of a track seem to meet in the distance.

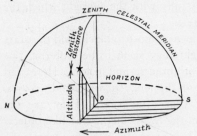

FIG. 1.3. Location of a Star by Azimuth and Altitude. Azimuth is measured westward from the south point along the horizon. Altitude is the star's angular distance above (or below) the horizon. Zenith distance is the complement of the altitude.

1.3. Horizon and Celestial Meridian. The point in the sky that is directly overhead is the *zenith;* it is located by sighting along a plumb line, or vertical line. The *nadir* is the opposite point on the celestial sphere, directly underfoot. The *horizon* is the great circle on the celestial sphere halfway between the zenith and nadir, which divides the sphere into two equal parts. This is the horizon of astronomy, as distinguished from the visible horizon, the frequently irregular line where the earth and sky seem to meet.

The horizon is an example of the circles that are imagined on the celestial sphere for the purpose of describing the places of the stars, just as circles, such as the equator and prime meridian, are imagined on the earth's surface. One of the most useful circles of the sky is the *celestial meridian;* it passes through the zenith and nadir, and crosses the horizon at its north and south points.

Altitude is measured in degrees vertically above, or below, the horizon, from 0° on the horizon to 90° at the zenith. Its complement, *zenith distance,* is measured downward from the zenith, along a vertical circle. *Azimuth* is measured in degrees from the south point westward along the horizon.

1.4. Apparent Places of the Stars. The zenith and nadir are apparent places on the celestial sphere. Every star has likewise its *apparent place,* where it seems to be. These places are represented on celestial globes, or on plane maps which are projections of parts of the sphere. It must be remembered that we are describing in this convenient way nothing more than the directions of the stars. Thus the *apparent distance* between two stars is their difference in direction.

Apparent places and distances are always expressed in angular measure, such as degrees, minutes, and seconds, and never in linear measure, such as feet or miles. The statement that a star appears to be ten feet above the horizon has little meaning. If, however, its altitude is given as 10°, we look for the star one ninth of the way from the horizon to the zenith. The term *angular distance* is often used instead of apparent distance, or the word *distance* alone, when there is no chance for ambiguity.

For estimating distances between stars it is useful to remember that the apparent diameters of the sun and moon are about half a degree. The pointer stars of the Big Dipper are a little more than 5° apart. Near the horizon, however, the scale is enlarged; here the sun, moon, and constellation figures seem to be magnified. This well-known illusion accompanies the apparent flattening of the sky overhead.

1.5. Apparent Daily Rotation of the Celestial Sphere. The westward movement of the sun across the sky, which causes it to rise and set, is an example of a motion in which all the celestial bodies share. It is as though the whole celestial sphere were rotating daily from east to west, as almost everyone before the time of Copernicus supposed that it did. This apparent daily rotation, or *diurnal motion* of the heavens from east to west is an effect of the earth's rotation on its axis from west to east.

Every star describes its *diurnal circle* around the sky daily. All diurnal circles are parallel, and are described in the same length of time, very nearly equal to the sidereal day (2.17). As will be explained later, and as anyone can easily observe, the period of the

FIG. 1.6. Circumpolar Star Trails. Photographed with a 2½-inch portrait lens and an exposure of one hour. The bright trail a little way below the center is that of Polaris. (From a photograph at the Yerkes Observatory)

diurnal motion is about four minutes shorter than the solar day. Thus a star rises four minutes earlier from night to night. The sun, moon, and planets, which change their positions among the stars, have slightly different periods.

The rapidity with which a star proceeds along its diurnal circle depends on the size of the circle that it describes. The motion is fastest for stars that rise exactly in the east; it becomes progressively slower as the rising points are farther from the east point, and it vanishes altogether at the two opposite points in the sky, around which the diurnal circles are described.

1.6. The Celestial Poles. The two points on the celestial sphere having no diurnal motion are the *north and south celestial poles*. They are the points toward which the earth's axis is directed. For observers in the northern hemisphere the north celestial pole is located vertically above the north point of the horizon; its altitude equals the observer's latitude (1.10). This pole is marked approximately by Polaris, the *pole star*, or *north star*, at the end of the handle of the Little Dipper. Polaris is now about a degree from the pole, or twice the apparent diameter of the moon.

The south celestial pole is depressed below the southern horizon as much as the north pole is elevated in the northern sky. This is the elevated pole for observers in the southern hemisphere. Its place is not marked closely by any bright star.

It is possible to photograph the diurnal motions of the stars around the pole with an ordinary camera. Point the camera toward the pole star, and expose a film for several hours on a clear evening, using the full aperture of the lens, and having the focus adjusted for distance. The trails in the picture will be arcs of the diurnal circles whose common center is the celestial pole. Increasing the exposure makes the trails longer, but shows no more stars. With an ordinary camera the trails of only the brightest stars can be photographed.

1.7. Celestial Equator; Directions in the Sky. The *celestial equator* is the great circle of the celestial sphere halfway between the north and south celestial poles. It is directly over the earth's equator, that is to say, in the same plane with it; it is the largest of the diurnal circles.

For the same place on the earth, the celestial equator occupies nearly the same position throughout the day and year, so that its course across the sky can be traced once for all. It is marked approximately by the sun's diurnal motion on March 21, or September 23. The celestial equator crosses the horizon at the east and west points, at an angle which is the complement of the observer's latitude. Thus in latitude 40° the celestial equator is inclined 50° to the horizon at the points of intersection.

Directions in the sky are denoted with reference to this important circle. North is the direction perpendicular to the celestial equator toward the north celestial pole. *West is the direction of the diurnal motion,* which is parallel to the celestial equator. There will now be no confusion as to directions in the sky, even in the vicinity of the pole. As one faces north, the stars circle daily in the counterclockwise direction. Above the pole, north in the sky is downward, and west is toward the left; under the pole, north is upward, and west is toward the right.

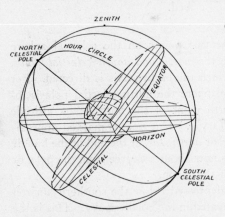

FIG. 1.7. The Celestial Equator in the Plane of the Earth's Equator. The celestial equator is halfway between the celestial poles, the two points in the sky toward which the earth's axis is directed. It crosses the horizon at the east and west cardinal points, at an inclination equal to the complement of the observer's latitude.

1.8. Positions on the Earth and in the Sky. The location of a point on the earth is often given approximately with reference to a natural or conventional division of the earth's surface. Thus Greenwich is in England, and Denver is in Colorado. Similarly, the position of a star on the celestial sphere is denoted approximately by the constellation in which it is situated. Vega, for example, is in the constellation Lyra.

Positions on the earth are described more precisely with reference to imaginary circles, such as the equator. The circles that pass through the north and south poles, and therefore at right angles to the equator, are the *meridians.* The prime meridian is the *meridian of Greenwich,* which passes through the site of the Royal Observatory at Greenwich, near London. The *longitude* of a place is measured in degrees, or hours, east or west of the meridian of Greenwich. The *latitude* is the distance in degrees north or south of the equator.

Corresponding circles are imagined on the celestial sphere. *Hour circles* pass through the celestial poles, and intersect the celestial

equator at right angles. The hour circle that serves the same purpose as the prime meridian is the *equinoctial colure;* it passes through
the vernal equinox, the point where the sun crosses the celestial
equator on March 21 (1.17). Right ascension and declination on the
celestial sphere correspond to longitude and latitude on the earth.

1.9. Right Ascension and Declination; Hour Angle. The *right
ascension* of a star is its angular distance, measured in hours or degrees, from the vernal equinox
eastward along the celestial
equator to the hour circle of the
star. The *declination* is its
angular distance, measured in
degrees along the hour circle,
north or south of the celestial
equator. If the star is north of
the equator, the sign of the
declination is plus; if the star
is south, the sign is minus.
The positions of the celestial
bodies are denoted in this way
in most maps and catalogues.

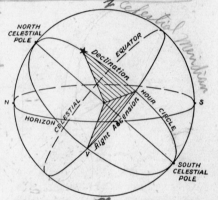

The bright star Sirius, for
example, is in right ascension
$6^h 42^m$, and its declination is
$- 16° 37'$; it is therefore
$6^h 42^m$, or $100° 31'$, east of

FIG. 1.9. Right Ascension and
Declination. Right ascension is
measured eastward from the vernal
equinox, V, along the celestial equator.
Declination is measured north or south
of the celestial equator along an hour
circle.

the vernal equinox, and $16° 37'$ south of the celestial equator. In
order to change from hours to degrees of right ascension, or conversely, since 24 hours equal 360°, we can employ the relations:

$$1^h = 15° \qquad\qquad 15° = 1^h$$
$$1^m = 15' \qquad\qquad 1° = 4^m$$
$$1^s = 15'' \qquad\qquad 1' = 4^s$$

Hour angle is the angular distance of a star from the celestial
meridian, measured along the celestial equator. It increases steadily
as the diurnal motion proceeds. The hour angle of a star at any time
can be found by subtracting its right ascension from the sidereal time
(Fig. 2.27) which is kept by special clocks in the observatory.

Celestial meridian - N Z S n

DIURNAL CIRCLES OF THE STARS OBSERVED IN DIFFERENT LATITUDES

1.10. The Observer's Latitude Equals the Altitude of the North Celestial Pole. The astronomical latitude of any place on the earth is defined as the angle that a vertical line at that place makes with the plane of the earth's equator. It is easily seen, from Fig. 1.10, that this angle is equal to the altitude of the north celestial pole, and also to the declination of the zenith at that place. This is the fundamental

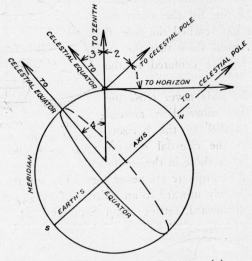

FIG. 1.10. The Observer's Latitude (4) Equals the Altitude of the North Celestial Pole (1), and also the Declination of the Observer's Zenith (3). Angles (1) and (3) are equal, because (1) + (2) and (2) + (3) are both equal to 90°, and (2) is common to both. Angles (3) and (4) are equal, because they are corresponding angles formed by the intersections of two parallel lines and a third line. Thus (4) = (1) = (3).

rule for latitude. Whatever the special method of finding the latitude, as it is employed by the navigator, surveyor, or astronomer, it is always a way of finding the altitude of the pole. Astronomical latitude differs only slightly from the latitude of geography (3.6).

When the latitude is already known, the altitude of the celestial pole is an equal number of degrees, according to the rule. Thus the locations of the celestial poles relative to the horizon are known, and that of the celestial equator midway between the poles. Since the daily rotation of the heavens is parallel to the equator, the directions of the diurnal circles of the stars with respect to the horizon can be described for any specified latitude.

1.11. At the Pole, Diurnal Circles are Parallel to the Horizon.

Viewed from the north pole, latitude 90°, the north celestial pole is directly overhead, and the celestial equator coincides with the horizon. This is the test for the arctic explorer; he has reached the pole, if his observations show that the diurnal circles are centered in the zenith.

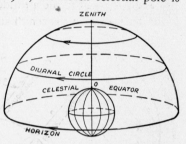

FIG. 1.11. Diurnal Circles Observed at the North (or South) Pole are Parallel to the Horizon.

Here the stars never cross the horizon; they move daily around the sky parallel to the horizon. Stars above the celestial equator never set, while those in the southern celestial hemisphere are never seen. The sun rises about March 21, spirals slowly upward to an altitude of 23½° on June 21; then it spirals downward, setting about September 23. Twilight lasts, however, until the middle of November, and begins again at the end of January. At the south pole, of course, everything is reversed.

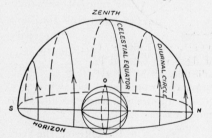

FIG. 1.12. Diurnal Circles Observed at the Equator are Perpendicular to the Horizon.

1.12. At the Equator, Diurnal Circles are Perpendicular to the Horizon.

Viewed from the equator, latitude 0°, the celestial poles are on the horizon at the north and south points. The celestial equator is at right angles to the horizon at the east and west points, and passes directly overhead. All diurnal circles, since they are parallel to the equator, are also perpendicular to the horizon, and are bisected by it. Consequently, every star is above the horizon 12 hours, and below it 12 hours. Days and nights are of equal length throughout the year.

It is to be noticed that places on the equator are the only ones from which the celestial sphere can be seen from pole to pole, so that all parts of the heavens are brought into view by the apparent daily rotation.

1.13. Elsewhere, Diurnal Circles are Oblique.

From points of observation between the poles and the equator, the north celestial pole is elevated a number of degrees equal to the latitude of the place,

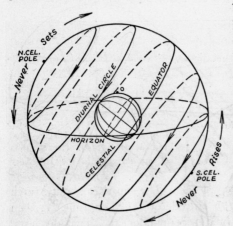

while the south celestial pole is depressed the same amount. Although the celestial equator still cuts the horizon at the east and west points, it no longer passes through the zenith, but leans toward the south in the northern hemisphere by an angle equal to the latitude. Therefore, the diurnal circles of the stars cross the horizon obliquely.

FIG. 1.13. Diurnal Circles Observed in Latitude 40° are Oblique.

The celestial equator is the only one of these circles bisected by the horizon. Northward, the visible portions of the diurnal circles become progressively greater, until the entire circles are in view; southward from the celestial equator they diminish, until they are wholly out of sight. The changing duration of sunlight from summer to winter serves as an illustration.

Owing to its oblique motion with respect to the horizon, the celestial sphere is conveniently divided into three parts: (1) a cap around the elevated celestial pole, whose radius equals the latitude of the place, contains the stars that are always above the horizon; (2) a cap of the same size around the depressed pole contains the stars that never come into view; (3) a band of the sky symmetrical with the celestial equator contains the stars that rise and set. In latitude 40°, for example, the two caps are 40° in radius, while all stars within 50° of the celestial equator rise and set.

As one travels south, the circumpolar caps grow smaller, and finally disappear when the equator is reached, where all stars rise and set. On the other hand, as one travels north, the circumpolar caps increase in radius, until they join when the poles are reached. Here none of the stars rises or sets.

1.14. Circumpolar Stars. If a star is nearer the celestial pole than the pole itself is to the horizon, the star does not cross the horizon; it is a *circumpolar star*. Consequently, for an observer in the northern hemisphere, *a star never sets, if its north polar distance (90° minus*

FIG. 1.14. The Midnight Sun at Etah, Greenland. The exposures were made in July, at intervals of twenty minutes while the sun was describing the lowest part of its diurnal circle above the north horizon. (From a photograph by Donald B. MacMillan)

its declination) is less than the observer's latitude; it never rises, if its south polar distance is less than the latitude. The following examples illustrate the rule:

(1) The Southern Cross, Decl. = − 60°, never rises in latitude 40° N., because its south polar distance of 30° is less than the latitude. It becomes visible south of latitude 30° N., in Florida and southern Texas.

(2) The Bowl of the Big Dipper, Decl. = + 58°, never sets in latitude 40°, because its north polar distance of 32° is less than the latitude. Under the pole it is still 8° above the horizon. It rises and sets south of latitude 32° N.

(3) The sun on June 22, Decl. = + 23½°, rises and sets in latitude 40°, because its north polar distance of 66½° is not less than the latitude; but north of latitude 66½° the sun is circumpolar on this date.

The *midnight sun* is an example of a circumpolar star. The sun may be seen at midnight about June 22 as far south as the arctic circle. Farther north it remains above the horizon for a longer period, while at the north pole it shines continuously for six months.

1.15. Zenith Distance of a Star at Upper Transit. Maps of the constellations are often arranged so as to indicate at what date a star

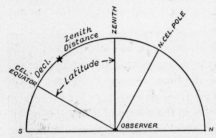

is at upper transit at a specified hour, that is to say, when it is crossing the celestial meridian on the same side of the celestial pole as the zenith. It is useful to know also how far from the zenith one must look at this time in order to find the star. The appropriate rule follows from the relation described in Section 1.10.

FIG. 1.15. The Zenith Distance of a Star at Upper Transit. It is equal to the observer's latitude minus the star's declination. This is evidently true because the observer's latitude equals the declination of his zenith (1.10).

The zenith distance of a star at upper transit equals the observer's latitude minus the star's declination (Fig. 1.15). If the resulting zenith distance is positive, the star is south of the zenith; if it is negative, the star is north of the zenith. In the following examples the observer is in latitude 40° N.

(1) What is the sun's zenith distance at apparent noon on June 22? The sun's declination is then $+23\frac{1}{2}°$. Its zenith distance at upper transit is $40° - 23\frac{1}{2}° = 16\frac{1}{2}°$, south of the zenith.

(2) How close to the zenith does the middle of the Bowl of the Great Dipper pass? The declination is $+58°$. At upper transit the zenith distance is $40° - 58° = -18°$, north of the zenith.

(3) What declination must a star have in order to pass through the zenith? Since the zenith distance is zero, the declination must equal the latitude (40°). Thus stars whose declinations are less than the latitude pass south of the zenith; those whose declinations are greater than the latitude pass north of the zenith. The sun is directly overhead at noon in the latitude which equals the sun's declination.

THE SUN'S APPARENT ANNUAL CIRCUIT

1.16. Westward Advance of the Constellations with the Seasons. Since the stars describe their diurnal circuits in four minutes less than a day, by the sun, every star is a little farther west each evening than it was at the same hour the night before. Thus the constellations steadily advance toward the west as the seasons progress. The familiar quadrilateral of Orion, for example, is seen rising in the east at 7 o'clock in the evening on the first of December. Each night thereafter at 7 o'clock, this constellation is higher in the sky than it was the night before. In March, Orion appears in the south early in the evening. As spring advances, it is found in the west setting soon after sunset, until finally it is lost in the twilight.

This steady westward march of the constellations shows that the sun is moving eastward among them, completing the circuit yearly. If the stars were visible in the daytime, the sun's apparent path among them could be easily traced from day to day; for the sun is displaced about two of its diameters in the course of a day. It is this eastward displacement of the sun which delays by four minutes the completion of its daily circuit.

The sun's annual movement around the celestial sphere is a consequence of the earth's revolution around the sun; but it does not prove that the earth revolves. The earliest astronomers were aware of the sun's motion among the constellations, and explained it readily enough as the sun's actual revolution around a stationary earth.

Not only does the sun move eastward with respect to the stars, but it moves north and south also in the course of the year, so that its path does not coincide with the celestial equator.

1.17. The Ecliptic; Equinoxes and Solstices. The *ecliptic* is the sun's apparent annual path on the celestial sphere. It is a great circle inclined 23½° to the celestial equator.

Four equidistant points on the ecliptic are the two *equinoxes*, where this circle intersects the celestial equator, and the two *solstices* where it is farthest away from the equator. The *vernal equinox* is the sun's position on March 21, when it crosses the celestial equator going north; the *autumnal equinox* is its position on September 23, when it crosses on the way south. The *summer solstice* is the most northern point of the ecliptic, the sun's position on June 22; the *winter solstice* is the most southern point, the sun's position on December 22. Owing to the plan of leap years, these dates vary slightly. The north and south *ecliptic poles* are the two points 90° from the ecliptic; they are 23½° from the celestial poles.

The relation between the ecliptic and the celestial equator will be understood from Fig. 1.17, in which the earth's orbit is viewed nearly edgewise. Since parallel lines meet in the distant sky, the celestial

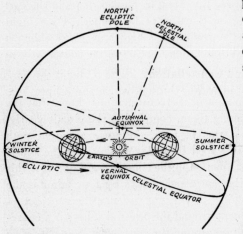

poles, toward which the earth's axis is directed, are not displaced as the earth revolves around the sun; similarly the celestial equator is unaffected. Evidently the angle between the ecliptic and celestial equator is the same as the angle between the earth's orbit and equator. This inclination, or *obliquity,* of the ecliptic is 23° 27'; it is at the present time decreasing at the rate of 1' in 128 years.

FIG. 1.17. Relation of Ecliptic and Celestial Equator. The inclination of the ecliptic to the celestial equator is the same $(23\frac{1}{2}°)$ as the inclination of the earth's equator to its orbit.

1.18. Celestial Longitude and Latitude. The observations of early astronomers were confined for the most part to the sun, moon, and planets, which are never far from the ecliptic. It was customary to describe the positions of these objects with reference to the ecliptic, by giving their celestial longitudes and latitudes. *Celestial longitude* is measured in degrees eastward from the vernal equinox along the ecliptic. *Celestial latitude* is measured in degrees north or south of the ecliptic along a circle at right angles to it. These ancient coordinates still find considerable use; but they are now replaced for most purposes by right ascension and declination, which more nearly resemble longitude and latitude on the earth.

Four different sets of coordinates have now been described for designating the place of a celestial body:

(1) *Azimuth and Altitude* (1.3). They are measured from the south point, along and perpendicular to the horizon. Their use is limited because these coordinates for any star are continually changing, owing to the diurnal motion; and they are not the same for observers in different places.

(2) *Right Ascension and Declination* (1.9). They are measured from the vernal equinox, along and perpendicular to the celestial equator. These

coordinates for any star are more nearly permanent. They have the greatest use.

(3) *Hour Angle and Declination* (1.9). They are measured from the intersection of the celestial meridian and celestial equator. Hour angle is involved in the subject of time (2.16). It is useful in setting the telescope, and in other ways.

(4) *Celestial Longitude and Latitude.* They are measured from the vernal equinox, along and perpendicular to the ecliptic.

1.19. The Zodiac; Signs and Constellations. The zodiac is the band of the celestial sphere, 16° in width, through which the ecliptic runs

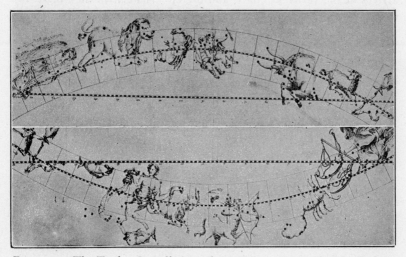

FIG. 1.19. The Twelve Constellations of the Zodiac. As described by Ptolemy about 150 A.D.

centrally. It contains at all times the sun and moon, and the principal planets, with the exceptions of Venus and Pluto; these two and many asteroids are not confined within its limits.

The *signs of the zodiac* are twelve equal divisions, each 30° long, which are marked off eastward from the vernal equinox. The signs are named from the twelve *constellations of the zodiac,* which were located in these divisions in the time of Hipparchus, more than two thousand years ago. The names of the signs and the seasons in which the sun is passing through them are as follows:

Aries		Cancer	
Taurus	Spring	Leo	Summer
Gemini		Virgo	

Libra			Capricornus		
Scorpio	}	Autumn	Aquarius	}	Winter
Sagittarius			Pisces		

Owing to the precession of the equinoxes (2.32), the vernal equinox has moved westward about 30°, and the signs have moved with it, away from the constellations after which they were named. Thus the signs and constellations of the zodiac of the same names no longer have the same positions. When the sun, on March 21, arrives at the vernal equinox, and therefore enters the sign of Aries, it is in the constellation Pisces. The sun does not enter the constellation Aries until the latter part of April.

1.20. Relation Between Ecliptic and Horizon. The position of the celestial equator in the sky is not altered by the diurnal motion. The angle at which it intersects the horizon is always the same, since

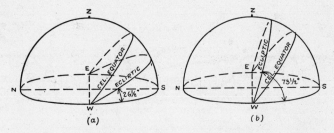

Fig. 1.20. Relation Between the Ecliptic and Horizon. (*a*) The ecliptic is least inclined to the horizon in middle northern latitudes (26½° in latitude 40° N.) when the vernal equinox is rising and the autumnal equinox is setting. (*b*) It is most inclined (73½°) when the autumnal equinox is rising and the vernal equinox is setting.

it is the complement of the latitude of the place. The ecliptic, however, takes different positions in the sky. Since the ecliptic is inclined 23½° to the celestial equator, its inclination to the horizon varies by this amount, at the most, either way from the inclination of the equator. The greatest and least angles between the ecliptic and horizon occur when the equinoxes are rising and setting.

In latitude 40° N., when the vernal equinox is rising and the autumnal equinox is setting, the angle between the ecliptic and horizon is 50° − 23½° = 26½°. The part of the ecliptic that is then in view is entirely below the celestial equator. When the autumnal equinox is rising and the vernal equinox is setting, the angle between the ecliptic and horizon is $50° + 23\frac{1}{2}° = 73\frac{1}{2}°$. The visible half of the ecliptic is now above the celestial equator.

The variation in the angle between the ecliptic and horizon is involved in the explanation of a number of astronomical occurrences, such as the harvest moon (3.31), and the favorable seasons for observing the planet Mercury (5.1) and the zodiacal light (6.26).

THE CONSTELLATIONS

1.21 The Primitive Constellations. *In the original sense, the constellations are configurations of stars.* Two thousand years ago the Greeks recognized 48 constellations, with which they associated

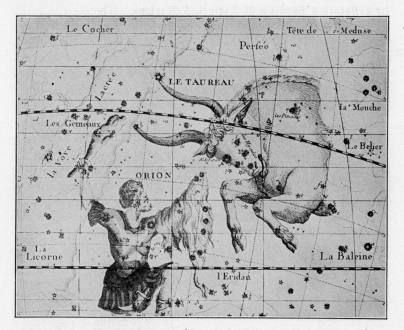

FIG. 1.21. Orion and Taurus. (From *Atlas Céleste de Flamsteed*, 1776)

the names and forms of heroes and animals of their mythology. The earliest nearly complete account of them, that survives, is contained in the *Phenomena*, written about 270 B.C. by the poet Aratus. In the writings of Hesiod, more than five hundred years earlier, and in the Homeric epics the more conspicuous figures, such as Orion, the Pleiades, and the Great Bear, are mentioned familiarly. There are reasons for supposing that practically the whole scheme of constellations was transmitted to the Greeks, having originated thousands of years before among the primitive peoples òf the Euphrates valley.

The 48 original constellations are described in Ptolemy's *Almagest* (about 150 A.D.), which specifies the positions of the stars in the imaginary figures. Owing to the great authority of this book for many centuries afterward, these configurations and their names descended to us with only a few alterations. As examples of changes, the Ptolemaic constellations of the Horse, the Bird, and the Kneeler are with us respectively Pegasus, Cygnus, and Hercules; and the original Argo Navis, the ship of the Argonauts, is now divided into the separate constellations Puppis, Vela, and Carina.

The ancient figures have not much to do with the science of astronomy. But many of them are associated with striking groupings of the stars, which attract the attention now, just as they interested the Sumerian shepherd long ago, and as they will doubtless interest people of the remote future. It is worth while to know the constellations.

1.22. Constellations as Regions of the Celestial Sphere. The original scheme of constellations did not cover the entire sky. Of the 1028 stars listed by Ptolemy, ten per cent were " unformed," that is, not included within the 48 figures. Moreover, a large area of the celestial sphere in the south, that never rose above the horizon of the Greeks, was uncharted. In the various star maps that appeared after the beginning of the seventeenth century, new configurations were gradually added to fill the vacant places. At the present time 88 constellations are recognized, of which seventy are visible, at least in part, from the latitude of New York in the course of a year.

For the purposes of astronomy, *the constellations are regions of the celestial sphere set off by arbitrary boundary lines.* These divisions are useful for describing the approximate locations of the stars and other celestial bodies. The statement that Vega is in the constellation Lyra serves the same purpose as the information that a town is in Ohio. We know about where it can be found.

The boundaries of the majority of the constellations were originally very irregular. Revised by action of the International Astronomical Union, in 1928, the boundaries are now parts of circles parallel and perpendicular to the celestial equator.

1.23. Names of Individual Stars. Fifty or more of the brighter stars are known to us by the names given them long ago, by herdsmen, sailors, and nomads of the desert, as well as by the scholars. Some of the star names, such as Sirius and Capella, are of Greek and Latin origin; others are of Arabic derivation, for example, Vega, Rigel, Aldebaran. The influence of the Arabians in the development of astronomy is indicated by the frequent appearance of their definite article *al* in the names of the stars (Algol, Altair, etc.).

Many of the star names, now regarded as personal, were originally expressions giving the locations of the stars in the imaginary constellation figures. These descriptive terms, transcribed from Ptolemy's catalogue into the Arabic, degenerated later into single words. Examples are Betelgeuse (armpit of the Central One), Fomalhaut (mouth of the Fish), Deneb (tail of the Bird), etc.

1.24. Designations of Stars by Letter and Number. The star maps of Bayer's *Uranometria* (1603) introduced the present plan of designating the brighter stars of each constellation by small letters of the Greek alphabet. In a general way, the stars are lettered in order of brightness, and the Roman alphabet is drawn upon for further letters. The full name of a star in the Bayer system is the letter followed by the genitive (possessive) of the Latin name of the constellation. Thus α Tauri is the brightest star in Taurus. When several stars in the constellation have nearly the same brightness, they are lettered in order of their positions in the figure, beginning at the head. Thus it happens that the stars of the Great Dipper, which are not much different in brightness, are lettered in order of position.

A different plan, adopted in Flamsteed's *Historia Coelestis* (1729), in which the stars are numbered consecutively from west to east across the constellation, permits the designation of a greater number of stars. The star 61 Cygni is an example. In modern maps of the lucid stars it is usual to employ the Bayer letters as far as they go, giving also the specific names of the brightest and most notable stars, and to designate other stars by the Flamsteed numbers.

These are the means of identifying the few thousands of stars visible to the unaided eye. Telescopic stars are referred to by their running numbers in the star catalogues. The location of the star Cordoba 32416, for example, can be found by turning to that number in the Cordoba catalogue.

1.25. Magnitudes of the Stars. For the purpose of describing the relative brightness of a star, Hipparchus and Ptolemy divided the stars arbitrarily into six magnitudes. About 20 of the brightest stars were assigned to the first magnitude. Polaris and stars of the Great Dipper were representatives of the second magnitude; and so on, in order of diminishing brightness. The sixth magnitude comprised the stars that are barely visible to the naked eye under favorable conditions.

With the invention of the telescope, permitting the observation of still fainter stars, the number of magnitudes was increased, while greater precision in the measurements called for the use of decimals in denoting the magnitudes, and for a uniform scale for all observers. Accordingly, the light-ratio, 2.5+, was adopted as the ratio in brightness corresponding to a difference of one magnitude. Thus a star whose magnitude is 3.0 is 2½ times as bright as a star of magnitude 4.0.

The magnitudes assigned to the naked-eye stars by the early astronomers are not altered greatly by modern practice, except those of the brightest stars. The original first magnitude stars differ so much in brightness that the more brilliant ones have been promoted to brighter classes, and so to smaller numbers. The magnitude of the brightest star, Sirius, is − 1.6; Canopus is − 0.9; Vega, Capella, and Arcturus, the brightest stars of the northern hemisphere of the sky, are about 0.2. Altair (0.9) and Aldebaran (1.1) are nearly standard first magnitude stars.

1.26. The North Circumpolar Map. Fig. 1.26 represents the appearance of the sky to one facing north in middle northern latitudes. At the center is the north celestial pole, closely marked by the pole star, Polaris. The lines radiating from the center of the key map are parts of hour circles; they are numbered in order of their right ascensions. The hour circle marked 0 at the top and 12 below is part of the equinoctial colure; extended upward beyond the limits of the map, it passes through the vernal equinox. Parallels of declination are indicated at intervals of ten degrees, from declination 90° at the center to 40° at the circumference.

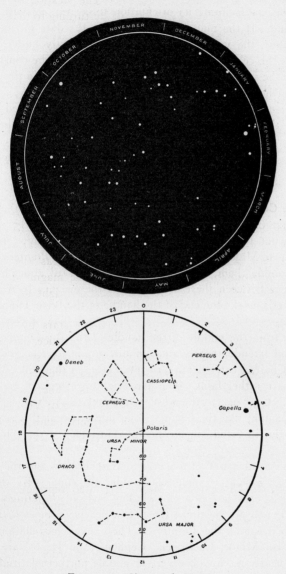

FIG. 1.26. Circumpolar Stars.

The names of the months around the circumference of the map are intended to facilitate its orientation to correspond with the sky at any time. If the map is turned so that the date of observation is uppermost, the vertical line on the map directly under the date represents the celestial meridian at about 8 P.M. The constellations then have the same positions on the map as they have in the northern sky at that hour.

To orient the map for a later hour, it must be turned counterclockwise through as many hours of right ascension as the time is later than 8 P.M. For an earlier hour it must be turned clockwise. Thus the map may be made to represent the appearance of the northern sky at any time during the year.

1.27. The Constellations in the North. At 8 o'clock in the evening on the first of October, the Big Dipper is found nearly right side up somewhat to the left of the north cardinal point. The stars α and β Ursae Majoris in its bowl are known as the Pointers, because the line joining them, when it is extended upward about five times the distance between these stars, directs the eye nearly to the pole star. Polaris marks the end of the handle of the Little Dipper (Ursa Minor).

A line from the middle of the handle of the Big Dipper through Polaris and extended nearly an equal distance beyond points out Cassiopeia's Chair, a configuration of seven stars in the Milky Way, two of which are rather faint. The five brighter ones form an irregular M, or W. Cepheus, to the west, resembles a church spire, as some people imagine; like the Chair it is upside down at this season, the point of the inverted steeple being a little more than 10° above Polaris.

Draco's head is a V of five stars. With Polaris and the Pointers it completes a right triangle whose sides are equal. By the aid of the map it is easy to follow the winding body of the Dragon around the ecliptic pole to the tip of the tail, which lies almost midway between Polaris and the Pointers. These five constellations: Ursa Major, Ursa Minor, Cassiopeia, Cepheus, and Draco, are circumpolar, or nearly so, for observers in middle northern latitudes.

1.28. The Equatorial Map. In the projection of the equatorial region of the sky, in Fig. 1.28, the hour circles are vertical, and the parallels of declination are horizontal. As before, the vertical line

under the date marks the course of the celestial meridian among
the stars at about 8 P.M. on that date. The stars that lie along
this line are then crossing the celestial meridian; their distances from
the zenith are obtained by the rule of Section 1.15. For the position
of the celestial meridian on the map at a later hour, the vertical
line must be carried to the left through as many hours of right
ascension as the time is later than 8 o'clock; and to the right for
an earlier hour.

The section of the map on either side of the celestial meridian
shows the constellations, from the zenith to the horizon, as they
appear to one facing south. Farther to the left on the map are
the constellations of the eastern sky, and to the right are those in
the west. When the map is compared with the sky, it should be
held so that the equator on the map is parallel to the equator in
the sky. Near the meridian the celestial equator is horizontal; near
its intersections with the horizon, at the east and west points, it is
inclined to the horizontal at an angle equal to the complement of
the observer's latitude. When the map is compared with the eastern
or western sky, it should be held at the appropriate angle.

1.29. Learning the Constellations.

In a few evenings anyone can
become acquainted with the more conspicuous constellations, and
with the names of the brightest stars that are visible. As the
seasons advance, and new constellations make their appearance in
the east, these can be identified with reference to the ones already
known, until the circle is completed. The requirements are a clear,
reasonably unobstructed sky, with the moon out of sight, or at least
not near the full phase, freedom from the glare of artificial lights, a
map of the constellations, and some means of illuminating the map.
A number of excellent star maps are available, which are suitable
for detailed constellation studies.

Familiarity with the constellations means the ability to recognize
the different configurations, and to call them by name. Many of the
constellations exhibit characteristic geometrical figures. Some of
them, however, particularly the modern ones, are simply regions
of the sky in which no striking pattern of stars is to be found. All of
the 44 constellations which are listed in Table 1.I can be studied
profitably in middle northern latitudes.

Let us suppose that the constellation studies are begun at 8 o'clock on the
first of October. Under this date, in Fig. 1.28, we find the constellation

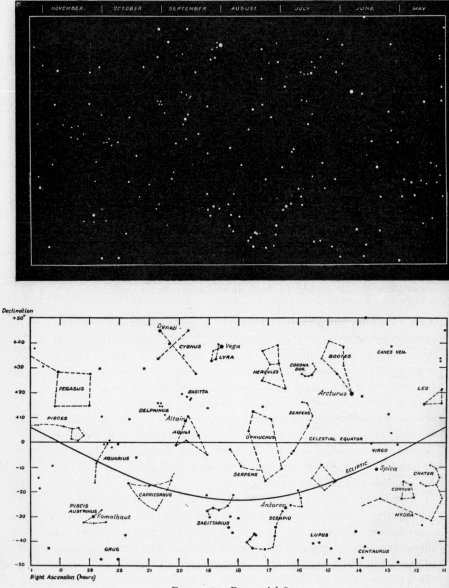

Fig. 1.28. Equatorial Stars.

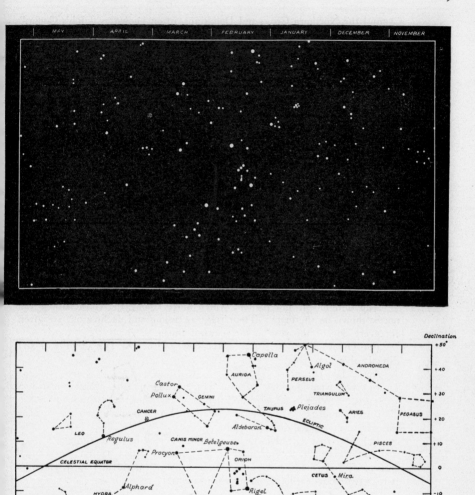

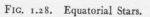

FIG. 1.28. Equatorial Stars.

Cygnus, the Northern Cross, and Delphinus, often known as " Job's Coffin."
These constellations are then on the celestial meridian. 'If the observer is in
latitude 40°, by the rule in Section 1.15 Cygnus (declination + 40°) is in
the zenith, and Delphinus (declination + 15°) is 25° from the zenith
toward the south. There will be no difficulty in finding the two configurations in these positions in the sky resembling those on the map.

With Cygnus and Delphinus known, rules can be made from the map
for pointing out neighboring constellations. It will be noticed, for example,
that a line from Delphinus through the star at the foot of the Cross (β Cygni)
and extended two thirds of the way beyond points out the constellation
Lyra, which contains the bright star Vega. In this way all the conspicuous
constellations that are above the horizon can be identified by means of maps.

1.30. Examples of the Use of Star Maps. (1) Read from Fig. 1.26
the right ascension and declination of δ Ursae Majoris (where the handle
and bowl of the Dipper join).

Ans. Right ascension $12^h 12^m$, declination + 57°.

(2) Locate with respect to the constellations, in Fig. 1.28, a planet having
a right ascension of $5^h 30^m$, and a declination of + 24°.

Ans. The planet is nearly midway between the stars β and ζ Tauri,
which mark the tips of the horns of Taurus.

The sun, moon, and planets, which move among the constellations can
not be shown on the maps. Their right ascensions and declinations are given
for every day of the year in the nautical almanacs.

(3) On what date at 8 P.M. is the bowl of the Big Dipper (Fig. 1.26)
directly above the pole?

Ans. May 15.

(4) On what date is Arcturus (Fig. 1.28) on the celestial meridian
at 8 P.M.? What is its zenith distance at that time in latitude 40° N.?

Ans. June 25. The zenith distance (1.15) is 40° − 19° = + 21°;
the star is 21° south of the zenith.

(5) On what date does Orion rise at 8 o'clock in the evening?

Ans. November 15. It must be remembered that a star on the celestial
equator rises six hours earlier than the time of its meridian transit, and that
it rises two hours earlier from month to month.

TABLE 1.I. THE MORE CONSPICUOUS CONSTELLATIONS VISIBLE IN MIDDLE NORTHERN LATITUDES

Latin Name	Genitive Ending	English Equivalent	On Meridian at 8 P.M.	Declination
Andromeda	dae	Andromeda	December	+ 40°
Aquarius	rii	Water-bearer	November	− 10
Aquila	lae	Eagle	September	0
Aries	etis	Ram	December	+ 20
Auriga	gae	Charioteer	February	+ 40
Boötes	tis	Bear-driver	July	+ 30
Cancer	cri	Crab	April	+ 20
Canes Venatici	num corum	Hunting Dogs	June	+ 40
Canis Major	nis joris	Great Dog	March	− 20
Canis Minor	nis noris	Little Dog	March	+ 10
Capricornus	ni	Sea-goat	October	− 20
Cassiopeia	eiae	Cassiopeia	December	+ 60
Cepheus	ei	Cepheus	October	+ 70
Cetus	ti	Sea-monster	December	− 10
Coma Berenices	mae ces	Berenice's Hair	June	+ 20
Corona Borealis	nae lis	Northern Crown	July	+ 30
Corvus	vi	Crow	May	− 20
Crater	teris	Cup	May	− 20
Cygnus	ni	Swan	September	+ 40
Delphinus	ni	Dolphin	October	+ 10
Draco	conis	Dragon	August	+ 60
Eridanus	ni	River	January	
Gemini	norum	Twins	March	+ 30
Hercules	lis	Hercules	August	+ 30
Hydra	rae	Sea-serpent	April	
Leo	eonis	Lion	April	+ 20
Lepus	poris	Hare	February	− 20
Libra	rae	Scales	July	− 10
Lyra	rae	Lyre	September	+ 40
Ophiuchus	chi	Serpent-holder	August	0
Orion	onis	Orion	February	0
Pegasus	si	Pegasus	November	+ 20
Perseus	sei	Perseus	January	+ 50
Pisces	cium	Fishes	December	+ 10
Piscis Austrinus	cis ni	Southern Fish	November	− 30
Sagitta	tae	Arrow	September	+ 20
Sagittarius	rii	Archer	September	− 30
Scorpio *or* Scorpius	pii	Scorpion	July	− 30
Serpens	entis	Serpent	July	+ 20
Taurus	ri	Bull	January	+ 20
Triangulum	li	Triangle	December	+ 30
Ursa Major	sae joris	Great Bear	May	+ 60
Ursa Minor	sae noris	Little Bear	July	+ 80
Virgo	ginis	Virgin	June	− 10

TABLE I.II. GREEK ALPHABET (SMALL LETTERS)

α alpha	ι iota	ρ rho
β beta	κ kappa	σ sigma
γ gamma	λ lambda	τ tau
δ delta	μ mu	υ upsilon
ε epsilon	ν nu	φ phi
ζ zeta	ξ xi	χ chi
η eta	o omicron	ψ psi
θ theta	π pi	ω omega

1.31. The Planetarium. In the cities the study of the constellations is made difficult by obstructions, smoke, and especially by strong artificial illumination. Even in more favorable places the sky may

FIG. 1.31. Interior of a Planetarium. The appearance of the sky is faithfully reproduced on the interior of the dome by the projection apparatus in the center. The lecturer is calling the attention of the audience to the Hyades in Taurus. (By courtesy of Carl Zeiss, Inc.)

be cloudy. The planetarium, which has recently come into use, represents the appearance of the sky, showing the constellations as they can be seen under the best conditions, and the motions they seem to have because of the earth's motions; it exhibits the sun, moon, and planets in their apparent courses among the constellations, and other astronomical phenomena visible to the naked eye.

The planetarium chamber carries a large dome whose interior is covered with white linen. At the center of the floor a complicated stereopticon projects the stars and other celestial bodies upon the dome which represents the sky. The projection apparatus has the form of a long dumb-bell, containing many parts which move independently, inclined $23\frac{1}{2}°$ to the polar axis around which it turns to represent the diurnal motion of the heavens. The spheres at the ends of the apparatus project the stars, while the cylinder contains projectors for the sun, moon, and planets. Motions which really are performed in long periods of time may be speeded up, so as to be completed in a few minutes, or even seconds.

Since the first public exhibition of this apparatus, in 1924, at the works of the Zeiss Company in Jena, many planetariums have been installed or are under construction in European cities, and elsewhere. The Adler Planetarium and Astronomical Museum in Chicago, under the direction of Professor Philip Fox, contains the first apparatus of this kind in operation in America. Demonstrations are given daily at scheduled hours in the planetarium chamber which has seats for 600 people. The subjects of the lectures are changed from month to month; they are selected so as to utilize the varied possibilities of the instrument as a vehicle for public instruction concerning the more obvious celestial phenomena. Among the many objects of interest in the Museum, the fine Mensing collection of antique scientific instruments is noteworthy.

THE TELESCOPE

Since the greater part of our knowledge of the celestial bodies is derived from observations with the telescope, a description of this important instrument will be next in order. The discovery of the principle of the telescope is generally credited to a Dutch spectacle maker, who found that two spectacle lenses held in certain positions before the eye gave a clearer view of distant objects.

1.32. Development of the Telescope. Galileo, in 1609, was one of the first to use the telescope in the study of the celestial bodies. His list of notable discoveries with the new instrument includes the four bright satellites of Jupiter, the phases of Venus, and the lunar craters.

Two of his telescopes are preserved intact in the Galileo Museum in Florence; the larger one, having a paper tube about four feet long, and less than two inches in diameter, magnifies 32 times. The Galilean telescope has a convex lens at the upper end of the tube, and a concave lens at the eye end; it has the merit of giving an erect image, but its use in astronomy is limited because of the small field with higher powers. In 1611, Kepler proposed the substitution of a convex lens at the eye end, which gives a wider field, although the image is inverted. This *simple astronomical telescope* is the basis of modern refracting telescopes.

About 1670, Gregory, Newton, and Cassegrain explained the construction of the reflecting telescope, which however did not come into extensive use until about fifty years later. Thereafter, owing to its freedom from color effects, the reflecting telescope replaced the refractor, until the construction of achromatic refracting telescopes, beginning in 1758, brought this type again into service. In recent years, the development of silver-on-glass mirrors, and the possibility of making very large mirrors, has raised the reflecting telescope to a commanding place in astronomical research.

1.33. The Refracting Telescope. The *objective,* or object glass, of the refracting telescope is a combination of two or more lenses; its functions are to collect the light and to focus it by refraction (3.15),

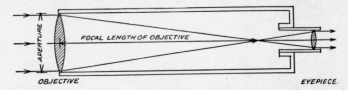

FIG. 1.33. The Simple Refracting Telescope. In its simplest form the refracting telescope consists of two convex lenses whose separation equals the sum of their focal lengths. In modern refracting telescopes both the objective and eyepiece are compound lenses.

forming an image of the object toward which the telescope is pointed. The *aperture,* or clear diameter of the objective, is usually stated in denoting the size of the telescope; thus a 12-inch telescope has an objective 12 inches in diameter. The *focal length* of the objective is the distance from the objective to its focal plane, where the image can be sharply focused on a piece of ground glass. This distance depends on the curvatures and compositions of the lenses. In ordinary refracting telescopes the ratio of the aperture to the focal length is about 1 to 15, so that a 12-inch telescope is likely to be about 15 feet long.

The *eyepiece* is a combination of smaller lenses designed to give a clear view of the image, and to magnify it. Eyepieces are of two kinds, each of which has its special advantages. The *positive eyepiece* is placed just beyond the focus of the objective, where it operates like an ordinary magnifying glass. But the image formed by the objective is between the lenses of the *negative eyepiece;* this type of eyepiece will not serve as a hand magnifier. The eyepiece is set in a sliding tube, so that its distance from the objective can be adjusted to give the clearest possible view. The eyepieces are the same in both refracting and reflecting telescopes.

The hollow *tube* of the telescope, usually of metal, holds the two optical parts rigidly in their appropriate relative positions. If the telescope is of considerable size, a smaller *finder* telescope is attached to the tube of the larger one near the eye end, and adjusted to parallelism with it. It is easier to pick up an object with a short telescope, because its field of view is wider.

1.34. The Achromatic Telescope. Whenever light is refracted, it is also dispersed into the different colors, for the violet light is changed

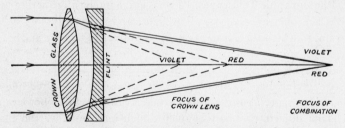

FIG. 1.34. Principle of the Achromatic Objective. The crown lens focuses the different colors at different distances, so that a clear image of the star is not obtained anywhere. The addition of the flint lens increases the focal length, and, since it affects the violet more than the red light, brings the different colors to focus at more nearly the same point.

in direction more than the red light. Thus the refraction of sunlight by drops of water forms the rainbow. When light is focused by a single lens, the different colors are brought to focus at dif-

ferent distances from the lens, violet light at the least distance and
red light farthest away; so that the image of a star formed by the
lens in any color is surrounded by a blur of the other colors. This
is *chromatic aberration.* In the early telescopes both the objective
and the eyepiece were single lenses, and the only known way to
diminish the blurring was to lengthen the telescope. Toward the
end of the seventeenth century, refracting telescopes as long as 150
and 200 feet were in use; but they were so unwieldy that not much
could be done with them.

The new era of the refracting telescope began in 1758, when
John Dollond called attention to the principle of the *achromatic
objective.* By an appropriate combination of lenses of different
curvatures and compositions it is possible to unite a limited range
of colors, but not all of them, at the same focus. The majority of
present telescope objectives are combinations of two lenses. The
upper lens is double convex and of crown glass; the lower lens,
either cemented to the upper one or separated by an air space, is
plano-concave, or usually nearly so, and is of heavier, flint glass. By
the use of two lenses other defects of the single lens may be compensated as well. The achromatic telescope is not entirely free from
color effects. A purple fringe around the image of the moon or of a
bright star is noticeable, especially in a large telescope.

1.35. Photographic Telescopes. The average modern refracting telescope is achromatic only for yellow light, and adjacent colors of the
spectrum, to which the eye is specially sensitive. The blue and violet
light, which most strongly affects the ordinary photographic plate,
can not be brought to focus with the yellow. Thus a refracting
telescope giving fine definition visually produces a blurred photograph, unless special precaution is taken. Successful photographs
of celestial objects of small angular dimensions, such as the planets, are secured by the introduction of a correcting lens a short
distance above the plate. Photographs of larger areas require
the use of a yellow filter which transmits the light that can be
sharply focused, and special plates which are sensitive to yellow
light.

In refracting telescopes intended for photography, such as the
30-inch refractor of the Allegheny Observatory, the objective is made
to focus the blue and violet light sharply. Photographic telescopes
are much more rapid than visual ones, but they give poor definition

visually. The reflecting telescope can be used successfully for both
purposes, because it is achromatic for all colors.

For the photography of large areas of the sky, the ratio of aperture to focal length must be as small as possible. Special telescopes
are designed for this purpose, whose objectives have more than two
lenses. *Doublets* are telescopes in which the objective is a combination of two pairs of lenses. The largest doublet is the 24-inch Bruce
telescope at the Harvard station in Bloemfontein, South Africa. The
10-inch Bruce doublet of the Yerkes Observatory was made famous
by Barnard's remarkable photographs of regions of the Milky Way,
and of comets.

1.36. The Reflecting Telescope. The objective of the reflecting telescope is a concave mirror at the lower end of the tube, which receives
the light of the star and reflects it to the focus near the top of the

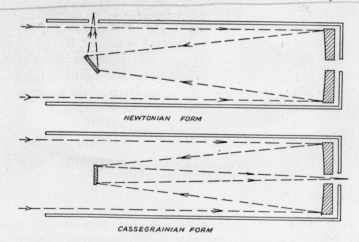

NEWTONIAN   FORM

CASSEGRAINIAN FORM

FIG. 1.36. The Reflecting Telescope in Two Forms. The objective is a concave mirror which reflects the light to focus. In the
Newtonian form the converging beam is diverted to the side of the
tube by a small diagonal plane mirror. In the Cassegrainian form it
is reflected by a small convex mirror through the central aperture
in the large mirror to focus below it.

tube. The objective is a circular block of glass having its front
surface ground to a parabolic curvature and coated with silver. The
light does not pass through the glass, which serves simply to support
and to give the required shape to the silver surface. But the image

formed by the large mirror is in the middle of the tube, where it can not be viewed without obstructing the incoming light. The two types of reflecting telescope in common use employ different devices for diverting the focus to a convenient place.

In the _Newtonian_ form a small plane mirror at an angle of 45° near the top of the telescope receives the converging beam before it comes to focus, and reflects it to an eyepiece outside the tube, at right angles to the direction of the star.

FIG. 1.37. Large Disk of Glass for a Reflecting Telescope. This 70-inch disk, made at the Bureau of Standards, in Washington, is intended for the large mirror of the reflecting telescope at Ohio Wesleyan University. The core which was cut out to make the 8-inch opening is resting on the disk. (From a photograph at the Bureau of Standards)

In the _Cassegrainian_ form a small _secondary_ convex mirror receives the converging beam from the large mirror, and reflects it back again through an opening in the large mirror to the eyepiece below it. In this form the observer looks in the direction of the star, as with the refracting telescope. In the great telescopes of the Mount Wilson Observatory the large mirrors have no openings. The returning light is reflected to the side by a third mirror set diagonally in front of the large mirror. Most reflecting telescopes can be used in either the Newtonian or Cassegrainian form.

1.37. Reflectors have a number of advantages over refractors. They are achromatic for both visual and photographic purposes. Reflectors have shorter tubes (the ratio of aperture to focal length of the mirror is often about 1 to 5), and therefore require smaller mountings and domes, with reduction in the cost of construction. It is easier to make disks of glass for reflectors, because the light does not go through the glass; striae and some other defects in the disks, which would render them useless for lenses, do not make them unfit for mirrors. The optician has to figure only one surface of the reflector objective. Moreover, the back of the mirror is supported; but the lenses of the refractor can be supported only at the edges and, if the lenses are very large, may bend under their own weight, affecting the figure, and therefore the performance of the objective.

Distortions of the mirrors with changes of temperature are reduced by using glass of high silica content, for silica has a low coefficient of expansion. Disks of pure silica, made by fusing quartz crystals, are likely to be available for large mirrors in the near future.

1.38. The Equatorial Telescope. For all except the smallest telescopes and those, such as the transit instrument (2.28), which are designed for special purposes, the equatorial form of mounting is universally adopted. The equatorial telescope turns on two axes at right angles to each other.

The *polar axis* turns in fixed bearings at the top of the pier. It is parallel to the earth's axis, and is therefore inclined to the horizontal at an angle equal to the latitude of the place. Around this axis the telescope is turned parallel to the celestial equator, and so along the diurnal circle of a star. The *declination axis* is supported by the polar axis; around it the telescope can be turned along an hour circle, from one declination to another. Clamps and slow motions in right ascension and declination are operated by handles, or switches, convenient to the observer.

Each axis carries a large graduated circle. The *hour circle,* on the polar axis, denotes the hour angle (1.9) of the object toward which the telescope is pointing. There is often, in addition, a dial on the pier, from which the right ascension of the star can be read directly. The *declination circle* is graduated in degrees of declination. By means of the circles the telescope can be quickly pointed toward a celestial body whose right ascension and declination are known. Once set on the star, and clamped in right ascension, the telescope is made to follow the star accurately in its diurnal motion by driving mechanism in the hollow column that supports the telescope, either a smooth running *driving clock,* or a motor which is synchronized by a clock.

Fig. 1.38. The 36-inch Refractor of the Lick Observatory. This telescope, nearly sixty feet long, is equatorially mounted. The entire floor of the dome can be raised or lowered to a height convenient for observation.

This type of equatorial mounting has been standard since the time of Fraunhofer. The great refractors of the Yerkes and the Lick observatories are mounted in this way. There are, however, a number of important variations. In the *English mounting* a long polar axis is supported by two piers between which the telescope can swing from the east to the west horizon, without striking the pier midway and having to be reversed to the other side, as is the case with the type of mounting above described. The 100-inch reflector at Mount Wilson, and the 72-inch reflector at Victoria are examples of the English type of equatorial. In the *fork* mounting the telescope turns between two tines of a fork whose handle is the polar axis; the 60-inch reflector at Mount Wilson is an example. In the *polar telescopes* of the Harvard and the Yale observatories, and in the *equatorial coudé* of the Paris Observatory the polar axis serves as the tube of the telescope, and the observer sits in a fixed position, as one working with a microscope. These are a few examples of special types of the equatorial mounting.

1.39. Light-Gathering Power. The brightness of the image of a star in the telescope increases in proportion to the area of the objective, or the square of its diameter. This defines the light-gathering power of the telescope, aside from the loss of light in the optical parts. Thus a star appears a hundred times brighter with the 100-inch reflector than with a 10-inch telescope, and 250,000 times brighter than with the eye alone, if we suppose the free aperture of the eye to be one fifth of an inch in diameter. By the concentration of the light, many stars become visible in the telescope, which shine too feebly to be seen with the naked eye. Still fainter stars can be photographed by the cumulative effect of long exposures. By means of the driving clock, and judicious manipulations of slow motions for slight adjustments, the telescope can be made to follow a star accurately, often for many hours, while the plate is being exposed.

It is easy to show that the surface brightness of an extended luminous area, such as the moon's surface, can not be increased by the telescope. The light of the sky is no brighter than it appears to the eye alone. Since the light of a star is concentrated, it is possible to see the brighter stars with the telescope in the daytime.

1.40. Magnifying Power of the Telescope. The *linear scale of the image* formed by the objective increases with the focal length of the objective. Telescopes of long focus are best for observing the details of a planet's surface, or for separating very close double stars. The *apparent size of the object* that is being observed depends also on the distance of the eye from the image. The least distance of distinct vision for the normal eye is about 10 inches. With the eyepiece the eye can be brought closer to the image, which accordingly appears larger. *The magnifying power of a telescope is the focal length of the objective divided by the focal length of the eyepiece.* If, for example, the focal length of the objective is 180 inches, and that of the eyepiece is a half-inch, the object is magnified 360 times.

A telescope is usually equipped with eyepieces of different focal lengths, so that the magnification can be varied as desired. The highest powers are useful only when atmospheric conditions are especially good; for unsteadiness of the image is magnified as well as the image itself. For this and other reasons, even under the best conditions there is little to be gained by increasing the magnification beyond fifty times for each inch of the aperture, and usually lower powers are more satisfactory. While the sun, moon, and planets appear larger with the telescope, no amount of magnification with present telescopes can show the *real* disk of a star.

1.41. Resolving Power. The image of a star, or any other luminous point, is spread by *diffraction* of light in the telescope into a tiny disk which is brightest at the center, and is surrounded by faint concentric rings. Two stars which are closer together than the diameter of the " spurious " disk can not be separated by any amount of magnification. The *resolving power* of a telescope is the angular distance between two stars that can be just separated under the best conditions. Many years ago Dawes showed that the least distance, *d*, in seconds of arc, is related to the aperture of the telescope, *a*, in inches, by the expression: $d'' = 4''.56/a$. Thus with a 4½-inch telescope a double star can not be resolved, if the separation is less than $1''$. With the 36-inch Lick refractor the minimum resolvable separation is $0''.13$; but for somewhat smaller separations Aitken can detect the duplicity of the star by the elongation of the image.

Aside from its ability to show fainter objects, the large telescope has the advantage of higher resolving power; it can show finer detail which runs together in the smaller instrument. On the other hand, the blurring of the image by atmospheric disturbances is more pronounced in the large telescope. In order to profit by the greater resolving power of the larger instrument, its site must be carefully chosen with respect to steadiness of the air.

The correctness of the formula, for two stars of nearly equal brightness, has been demonstrated by observations with telescopes of various apertures. For the eye alone the formula does not hold; it gives the resolving power as about $20''$, but the least separation the eye can resolve is several times greater. In fact, the eye is said to be a good one, if it can separate the two stars of ϵ Lyrae, which are $207''$ apart. The difference is ascribed to the coarse structure of the retina of the eye.

1.42. Value of the Telescope. As the fundamental instrument of astronomical research the telescope has many important uses, some of which we have already noted. It concentrates the light from a celestial body, forming a bright image which can be viewed and magnified with an eyepiece, or else photographed. The magnification and resolving power of the telescope permit observations of details of the sun, moon, planets, and other bodies, the separation of satellites from their planets, and of star-clouds into their individual stars. Owing to the enlarged scale the positions and motions of the celestial bodies can be determined more accurately than with the eye alone.

In addition to the direct study of the object, either visually or photographically, an important use of the telescope is to direct the concentrated light into special physical instruments, such as the spectroscope, photometer, and radiometer. Large telescopes are usually provided with a variety of auxiliary apparatus, which can be attached at the eye end, or in some cases, as with the interferometer and objective prism, in front of the objective. Descriptions of a number of these instruments will be given in connection with the kind of investigation that each one promotes.

1.43. Great Telescopes. The 100-inch reflector of the Mount Wilson Observatory is the largest telescope in operation. The reflecting telescopes of the Dominion Astrophysical Observatory, Victoria, and the Perkins Observatory, Delaware, Ohio, have apertures around six feet in diameter. A 200-inch reflector will be installed in California. A 74-inch reflector is under construction for the University of Toronto, and an 80-inch reflector is planned for the University of Texas.

Refracting telescopes have more moderate apertures. The largest are the 40-inch telescope at the Yerkes Observatory and the 36-inch refractor of the Lick Observatory. In addition, more than a dozen refracting telescopes have apertures of 25 inches or over. Arranged in about the order of size, although not necessarily of effectiveness, for mechanical features and atmospheric conditions must be taken into account, they are located at Meudon, Potsdam, Nice, Pulkowa, Pittsburgh, Greenwich, Bloemfontein, Vienna, Johannesburg, Washington, Charlottesville, Berlin, Tokyo, and Cambridge, England. The wide geographical distribution is noteworthy, although these examples, which are restricted to the largest telescopes of each kind, are inadequate to show the widespread activity in astronomical research with powerful instruments.

Especially valuable is the greater extension of this activity in the southern hemisphere in recent years. In addition to the Royal Observatory at the

Cape of Good Hope, and others long-established in the south, the Union Observatory and the new southern stations of the Harvard, Yale, and Michigan observatories, all in South Africa, and the Bosscha Observatory in Java are equipped with large telescopes for studies of that part of the heavens around the south celestial pole that is invisible in northern latitudes.

FIG. 1.43. Dome of the 100-inch Reflector of the Mount Wilson Observatory. The dome is 100 feet in diameter. It can be turned completely around, so that the telescope may look out in any direction. The top of the telescope is visible through the opened shutter.

1.44. The 100-inch Reflecting Telescope.

The objective of the great reflector on Mount Wilson is a circular block of glass 101 inches in diameter and 13 inches thick, weighing 4½ tons; the upper surface is concave and silvered, having a focal length of 42 feet. The mirror is placed at the lower end of the skeleton tube which is characteristic of large reflectors. The tube is turned in declination in the massive yoke which forms the polar axis. The movable parts of the telescope weigh about 100 tons. A powerful driving clock moves the telescope around the polar axis to follow the stars in their diurnal motions. The telescope is supported by a concrete pier 52 feet wide at the top. When the mirror requires resilvering, the cell which holds it is detached from the tube and lowered into the silvering room within the pier. The dome is 100 feet in diameter. The various motions of telescope, dome, shutters, and observing platforms are operated by motors, forty or more in all, which are controlled from a switchboard.

When photographs are taken with this telescope, the plate can be exposed in any one of four places: (1) directly at the focus of

FIG. 1.44. The 100-inch Reflector of the Mount Wilson Observatory. The largest telescope in the world. It has an equatorial mounting of the English type. When the telescope is used in the Cassegrainian form, the observer occupies the platform to the left near the floor; the platform for the Newtonian form appears near the upper right corner of the picture.

the objective, at the center of the tube near the upper end; (2) at the Newtonian focus, at the side of the tube near the upper end;

(3) at the Cassegrainian focus, at the side of the tube near the lower end; and (4) in the laboratory to which the light is directed along the polar axis. This telescope is employed primarily in investi-

FIG. 1.45. Model of the 200-inch Reflecting Telescope. A tentative design which may undergo extensive modifications before the final design is made. (By courtesy of G. E. Hale)

gations of the stars and nebulae, by direct photography and with the aid of auxiliary apparatus, such as the spectograph, thermocouple, and interferometer.

1.45. Plans for a 200-inch Reflector. The new Astrophysical Observatory of the California Institute of Technology will be equipped with a 200-inch reflecting telescope. It was originally hoped that the objective could be made of fused quartz. The large mirror will have the ratio, aperture to focal length, of 1 to 3.3, which is a smaller ratio than in most reflectors. An equatorial mounting of the fork type is under consideration. This telescope will be located in the most favorable site that can be found within reasonable distance of Pasadena, where an astrophysical laboratory will serve as the headquarters of the observatory staff. Special emphasis will be laid on the development of auxiliary instruments to be used in connection with the telescope, and of laboratory apparatus for reproducing or interpreting celestial phenomena.

Dr. George E. Hale, honorary director of the Mount Wilson Observatory, is the chairman of a committee of four in full charge of this great project, whose completion will be the work of many years. Distinguished astronomers, physicists, chemists, engineers, and experts in other fields are cooperating.

REFERENCES

Suggestions for supplementary reading and reference are given here and at the ends of other chapters. Current contributions to astronomy appear or are referred to in astronomical periodicals, such as:

Popular Astronomy.
The Astrophysical Journal.
The Astronomical Journal.
Publications of the Astronomical Society of the Pacific.
Journal of the Royal Astronomical Society of Canada.
The Observatory (London).
Monthly Notices of the Royal Astronomical Society.
Astronomische Nachrichten.
Astronomischer Jahresbericht (Berlin). A volume for each year since 1899, containing reviews of publications in astronomy and closely allied subjects which appeared during that year.

The work of many observatories is to be found also in their own publications, for example:

Mount Wilson Observatory: *Contributions*, which appear also in *The Astrophysical Journal.*
Harvard Observatory: *Annals, Circulars,* and *Bulletins.*

For general reference the following books will be useful (see also list of general references at the end of Chapter VII):

Agnes M. Clerke, *History of Astronomy During the Nineteenth Century* (Black, 1902).

Arthur Berry, *A Short History of Astronomy* (Murray).

Harlow Shapley and Helen E. Howarth, *A Source Book in Astronomy* (McGraw-Hill, 1929).

H. N. Russell, R. S. Dugan, and J. Q. Stewart, *Astronomy*, in two volumes (Ginn, 1926–27).

References which apply more specially to Chapter I are:

C. A. Young, *Uranography* (Ginn). Suitable for constellation studies. Contains maps and descriptions of constellations visible in middle northern latitudes.

R. Schurig, *Himmels-Atlas* (Gaebler, Leipzig). Eight excellent maps show all stars, star-clusters, and nebulae visible to the naked eye.

S. G. and W. H. Barton, *A Guide to the Constellations* (McGraw-Hill, 1928).

E. Delporte, *Atlas Céleste* (Cambridge University Press, 1930).

Kelvin McKready, *A Beginner's Star Book* (Putnam, 1929).

G. P. Serviss, *Astronomy with an Opera-Glass* (Appleton, 1923).

R. H. Allen, *Star-Names and their Meanings* (Stechert, 1899). An authoritative reference.

Louis Bell, *The Telescope* (McGraw-Hill, 1922).

Amateur Telescope Making (Scientific American, 1933).

T. W. Webb, *Celestial Objects for Common Telescopes* (Longmans, Green, 1917).

Adler Planetarium and Astronomical Museum, Chicago.

CHAPTER II

THE MOTIONS OF THE EARTH

THE EARTH'S ROTATION — THE EARTH'S REVOLUTION — TIME — PRE-CESSION — THE SEASONS AND THE CALENDAR

Our immediate interest in the earth's movements is in their relation to our daily affairs. The alternation of day and night, the changing seasons, and time reckoning are among the obvious consequences of the earth's motions that affect everyone. These motions may well receive attention on their own account also. Although the earth is only one of the countless number of bodies adrift in the universe, it is *our* earth; and it is of more than casual interest to inquire where it is going with us.

From the astronomer's standpoint it is important to know precisely how the earth is moving, because the observations are made here. Any shifting of the point of observation produces corresponding apparent displacements of the celestial bodies, which must be allowed for, if the true motions of these bodies are to be ascertained.

2.1. Four Principal Motions. (1) *The earth rotates* eastward once in very nearly (2.32) 24 sidereal hours on the axis whose extremities are its north and south poles. The axis is inclined $23\frac{1}{2}°$ from the perpendicular to the plane of the earth's orbit; and it maintains nearly the same direction throughout the year.

(2) *The earth revolves* eastward around the sun once in a sidereal year. Its orbit is an ellipse of small eccentricity having the sun in one focus. Its average speed is $18\frac{1}{2}$ miles a second (29.76 km./sec.).

(3) *The earth's precessional motion* is a slow conical movement of its axis, like that of a spinning top, westward around a line joining the ecliptic poles. At the present rate, a single turn is completed in about 26,000 years.

(4) In addition, the earth as a member of the solar system shares in the *solar motion* (8.17). The sun and all its attendants are moving together through the stellar system at the rate of 12 miles

49

a second, straight ahead nearly in the direction of the bright star Vega.

These are the most conspicuous of the earth's motions. Although they are all going on together, it will be less confusing to describe them separately. The discussion of the solar motion is reserved for Chapter VIII.

In astronomy it is the custom to distinguish sharply between the terms rotation and revolution. It is well to keep this in mind because the terms are often used interchangeably in other sciences. *Rotation is motion around an axis.* Thus the earth rotates daily. *Revolution is motion in an orbit.* The earth revolves around the sun annually.

2.2. Absence of Proof of the Earth's Motions in Early Times.

Up to the time of Copernicus, and in fact beyond it, no convincing proof was available that the earth has any motion at all. It is true that some of the early philosophers, Aristarchus of Samos for example, believed that the earth is in motion, but their teachings were not generally received with favor. The great authorities, Aristotle, Hipparchus, and Ptolemy, held for the motionless earth. This in itself would have sufficed for most people. In addition, however, the view was supported by the evidence that the earth certainly appears to be motionless.

Astronomy, from primitive times to the age of Galileo, Kepler, and Newton, was founded on appearances simply; as a thing seems to be, so it is. It was a long journey from the static earth of the past to the dynamic earth as we now regard it. Progress was slow because every step meant disillusionment — the overcoming of appearances. There are indeed few experiences in our ordinary activities to convince us that the earth is not flat and motionless. There is little to suggest that the earth is spinning around at a rate exceeding a thousand miles an hour at the equator; and there is nothing at all in everyday experience to inform us that it is whirling around the sun twenty times faster than the flight of the swiftest modern projectile.

Familiar phenomena, such as the alternation of day and night and the changing seasons, are not in themselves proofs of the earth's rotation and revolution; they leave us in doubt as to whether the sun or the earth is moving. The ancients were as familiar with these phenomena as we are, but they scarcely considered the alternative.

Copernicus favored the earth's rotation, because it seemed to him more reasonable to have the tiny earth turn around daily instead of the immense celestial sphere. He taught the earth's revolution also, because the interpretation of the planets' courses was simplified thereby (4.9). But he could point to no rigorous proof of the earth's motions in which he firmly believed.

THE EARTH'S ROTATION

2.3 Deflection of Objects Moving Along the Earth's Surface.

Since all parts of the earth rotate in the same period, the speed of the rotation varies with the latitude. It is greatest at the equator, where the largest circle is completed, and diminishes toward the poles.

In its flight toward the target, a projectile retains the speed of the eastward rotation at the place from which it started, aside from friction effects. Fired northward in the northern hemisphere, the projectile moves toward a place of slower rotation; it is therefore deflected ahead, or to the east of the target. If it is fired southward instead, the projectile moves toward a place of faster rotation; it now falls behind, or to the west of the target. In either event the deflection is to the right, when the observer faces in the direction of the flight. If the experiment is

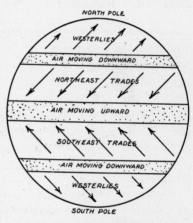

FIG. 2.3. Directions of Prevailing Winds. As a consequence of the earth's rotation, the moving air is deflected to the right in the northern hemisphere, and to the left in the southern hemisphere.

tried in the southern hemisphere, the deviation is always to the left. In general, *objects moving along the earth's surface are deflected to the right in the northern hemisphere and to the left in the southern hemisphere.*

The deflection is relative to a meridian on the earth's surface. What really occurs is that the object continues to move in the same plane, while the earth's rotation skews the meridian around under it. The deviation of the projectile is, of course, affected by the curvature of the earth's surface, as well as by the difference in the speeds of the rotation.

A proof of the earth's rotation consists in observing this deflection. Although it is not a conspicuous effect in the case of the projectile itself, convincing deflections are to be seen in the directions of prevailing winds and ocean currents, and in the spiral motions of cyclones.

2.4. Cyclones Prove the Earth's Rotation. The cyclones of the temperate zones are great vortices in the atmosphere, averaging 1500 miles in diameter, which migrate eastward and are likely to bring stormy weather. Marked "low" on the weather map, they are areas of low barometric pressure, into which the surface air pours from all directions. The inflowing currents are deflected like projectiles, so that they spiral inward, in the *counterclockwise direction in the northern hemisphere* and *clockwise in the southern hemisphere*. This invariable rule is a proof of the earth's rotation.

A cyclone is often accompanied on the west by an anticyclone, or "high," where the surface currents spiral outward in accordance with the rule reversed.

2.5. The Foucault Pendulum. A freely swinging pendulum affords a simple and effective demonstration of the earth's rotation. The experiment was first performed for the public by Foucault in 1851 under the dome of the Panthéon in Paris. The Foucault pendulum, unlike that of a clock, is suspended with the least possible friction at the point of support, in such a manner that it is free to swing in any plane; it is also generally much longer, and the bob is heavier. When the pendulum is set in motion, the plane of its swing slowly rotates, in the clockwise direction in the northern hemisphere, and counterclockwise in the southern. It is an example of the deflection effect of the earth's rotation.

FIG. 2.5. Foucault Pendulum. (By courtesy of the Eastern Science Supply Company)

In the northern hemisphere, where the deflection is to the right, the south end of the swing is carried westward and the north end eastward. This is the *observed* effect. Actually it is the meridian beneath the pendulum that is changing direction; the south end is moved eastward by the earth's rotation faster than the north end.

The deflection is zero at the equator, where the direction of the meridian does not vary as the earth rotates, and is the maximum at the poles, where the meridian changes direction most rapidly. In general, the hourly change in the direction of the swing is 15° times the sine of the latitude. In latitude 40°, therefore, the variation is about 10° an hour.

2.6. Wanderings of the Terrestrial Poles. This effect is known as the *variation of latitude* from the data by which it was detected and subsequently studied. It was discovered in 1888, by Küstner in Germany, and further established by Chandler, that the latitude of any

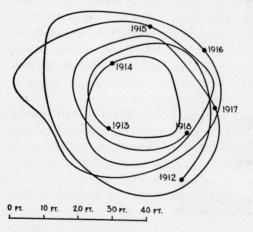

FIG. 2.6. Wandering of the North Pole, 1912–1918. The complicated path of the pole on the earth's surface is shown, with its position at the beginning of each year.

place on the earth is continually changing. Since latitude is measured from the equator which is midway between the poles, it follows that the north and south poles are not stationary points on the earth's surface. Systematic observations of latitude are being made at two chains of stations widely scattered in longitude in the two hemispheres. The central station, at Mizusawa, Japan, is under the direction of H. Kimura.

These motions are very irregular, but they are resolvable roughly into two separate effects; one is a motion in an ellipse 30 feet long in a period of 12 months, the other is a circular motion of slightly less amplitude in a period of 14 months. Neither pole can withdraw from its mean position much more than 40 feet; nor is there any evidence of greater variations in the past that might explain climatic changes. The wanderings of the poles are confined to areas smaller than that of a baseball diamond.

The effect we are considering is a shifting of the earth upon its axis, whose direction in space is not altered thereby. It must not be confused with precession (2.29) which is a change in the direction of the axis.

2.7. Variations in the Speed of the Rotation. The earth's rotation is the master clock by which all terrestrial and celestial happenings are timed. It is accordingly one of the most important problems of astronomy to determine the reliability of this clock — whether it ever runs fast or slow, or both. As early as 1875, Newcomb's review of records of the preceding 250 years brought to light unmistakable fluctuations in the observed times of occultations of stars, and of the moon's meridian transits relative to the times predicted by the theory of the moon's motions. Neither the lunar theory nor an Einstein effect can be held accountable for the discrepancies, according to Brown, who ascribes them to variations in the speed of the earth's rotation. In the meantime, evidence has accumulated that other periodic events, such as transits of Mercury over the sun's disk and the meridian transits of the sun and planets exhibit simultaneous and similar fluctuations.

The variations are resolvable into two effects, one of which is the steady or secular slowing up of the rotation, so that *the sidereal day is lengthening at the rate of 0.001 second in a century.* This is verified by Fotheringham's study of the records of ancient and modern eclipses. Over long periods the slight variation accumulates to considerable differences between observed and predicted times. The secular retardation of the earth's rotation is brought about mostly by the friction of the tides (4.39). Sudden changes in the period of rotation, at times as much as $0^s.003$, constitute the second effect. From 1660 to 1790 the earth ran slow; then it ran fast until 1898 when it became slow again. The maximum observed error in the earth-clock with respect to average readings (allowing for the tidal retardation) is nearly 30 seconds. In addition, there are minor accelerations and retardations of shorter duration. Brown advances the hypothesis that the fluctuations in the rotation rate are caused by expansions and contractions of the earth, which need not alter the radius by more than a few feet.

THE EARTH'S REVOLUTION

2.8. Evidence of the Earth's Revolution. The changing seasons and the sun's annual circuit among the constellations are consequences but not convincing proof of the earth's revolution, for by

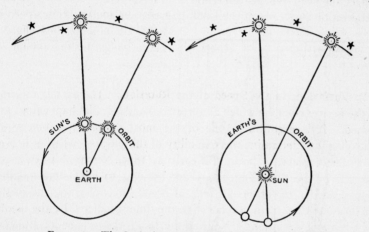

FIG. 2.8. The Sun's Apparent Motion Among the Constellations is not a Conclusive Proof of the Earth's Revolution. The same effect is obtained whether the earth revolves around the sun or the sun around the earth.

themselves they leave reasonable doubt as to whether the earth or the sun is really moving. With the aid of the telescope other annually periodic phenomena are observed which are regarded not only as consequences, but also as proofs that the earth revolves around the sun, for they arise from this cause much more plausibly than from any other that can be assigned. Among the effects of this kind, which are easily available to modern astronomical instruments, but are too minute to be seen without them, the following may be mentioned:

(1) *The annual parallaxes of the stars* (8.1) are the periodic changes in the alignments of the nearer stars relative to the more distant ones. This effect was first detected by Bessel in 1837. It is too minute for the less precise instruments and methods of earlier times.

Inability to observe this effect, coupled with the failure to realize the vast distances of the stars, which make the effect extremely minute, contributed much to the long persistence of the belief in the stationary earth. Aristotle dismissed the heliocentric theory on this basis, and Tycho Brahe, eighteen centuries later, rejected the Copernican system for this reason.

(2) *The aberration of starlight* (2.9) was discovered by Bradley and explained by him in 1727. It is an annually periodic change in the star's direction, nearly thirty times greater than the parallax effect on even the nearest star; it was therefore observed sooner. Aberration proves both the earth's revolution and the finite speed of light. A closely allied effect is made known by the annual oscillations of the lines in the spectra of the stars (8.12).

If any doubt of the earth's revolution remains after this evidence has been considered, it will be removed by reference to Newton's third law of motion (4.12). This law requires that the earth and sun mutually revolve. Consequently, the earth can not be stationary, if the law is correct.

FIG. 2.9. Aberration of Raindrops. The source of the raindrops is apparently displaced in the direction of the observer's motion. (From a drawing by W. H. Steavenson)

2.9. Aberration of Starlight; the Raindrop an Illustration. Raindrops descending vertically on a still day strike the face of the pedestrian. Whatever direction he takes, the source of the rain seems to be displaced from overhead in that direction. If he runs instead, the slanting direction of the rain becomes more noticeable; and if he drives rapidly, it may seem to be almost horizontal. This is a familiar example of aberration.

The amount of the aberration depends on three factors: (1) The displacement increases as the observer's speed increases. (2) It decreases as the speed of the raindrop, or starlight, increases. No one can drive fast enough to displace a star noticeably, because the speed of light is far greater than that of the raindrop. (3) The displacement is greatest when the observer moves at right angles to the direction of the rain, and becomes zero, if he moves in the direction the rain is falling.

The earth's swift motion around the sun produces a corresponding change in a star's position. *Aberration of starlight is the apparent displacement of a star in the direction the earth is moving.* Its maximum value in seconds of arc is:

$$\text{Aberration} = \frac{\text{speed of earth}}{\text{speed of light}} \times 206,264''.8.$$

If the earth were motionless, there would be no aberration of starlight. If it had only uniform motion in a straight line, the displacement of the star would be always the same, and would therefore be unnoticed. If the earth revolves, the changing direction causes the

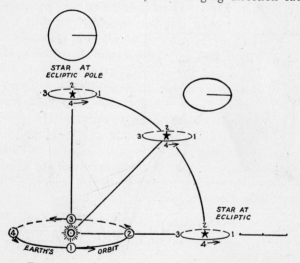

FIG. 2.10. Aberration Orbits of the Stars. The numbers mark corresponding positions of the earth in its orbit and of the stars in their apparent aberration orbits. The outer figures show the observed forms of the aberration orbits.

star's displacement to change direction also, always keeping ahead of us, so that the star describes a little orbit. This is precisely what the telescope shows. The aberration of starlight is a convincing proof of the earth's revolution around the sun.

2.10. Aberration Orbits of the Stars; the Constant of Aberration.

A star at either pole of the ecliptic has a nearly circular apparent orbit, because the earth's motion is always perpendicular to its direction; the star is displaced always the maximum amount. Owing to the lack of uniformity in the earth's revolution, the orbit is not an exact circle.

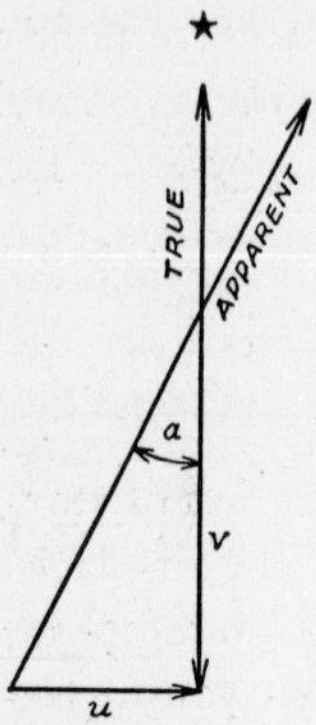

A star on the ecliptic oscillates on a straight line. The maximum displacement occurs only twice a year; twice also, when the earth is moving toward or away from the star, the displacement is zero. Between the ecliptic and its poles the aberration orbit is an ellipse which flattens as the ecliptic is approached. In other words, we view the little orbit flatwise at the ecliptic poles, edgewise on the ecliptic, and at various angles in between.

The constant of aberration is the apparent displacement of a star when the earth is moving at average speed at right angles to the star's direction. It is the same for all stars regardless of their distance or direction; it is the radius of the circle at the ecliptic pole, half the major axis of the ellipse, and half the straight line on the ecliptic. Its approximate value is:

FIG. 2.10A.

Aberration of Starlight. The amount of the aberration, *a*, depends on the velocity of the observer, *u*, and the velocity of light, *V*.

Constant of aberration = 20''.47.

The situation is represented by a right triangle whose side *u* is the earth's average velocity. The side *V* is the velocity of light, and the angle *a* is the aberration constant. By trigonometry the relation is:

$$\tan a = u/V.$$

When the angle is small, as it is in astronomical aberration, it is proper to substitute for the tangent the angle itself *in radians.* A radian equals 206,-264''.8. The relation becomes:

$$a'' = u/V \times 206{,}264''.8.$$

To find the value of *u*, suppose that the earth's orbit is a circle, which is nearly true. The earth's distance from the sun: $R = 92{,}870{,}000$ miles (4.25), multiplied by 2π gives the circumference of the circle. Divide by 31,558,149.5, the number of mean solar seconds in the sidereal year, and we have the *earth's average speed in the orbit:*

$$u = 18.49 \text{ miles a second} = 29.76 \text{ km./sec.}$$

The velocity of light is 186,284 miles a second. Everything is known except the aberration constant whose value is now calculated from the above relation.

Of the three important quantities connected by this relation, namely, *a*, *V*, and *R*, the aberration constant is found by direct observation with less certainty than the others can be determined. There is no advantage at present in calculating the sun's distance from the constant of aberration. Uncertainty in the constant as little as $0''.01$ produces an uncertainty in the sun's distance of nearly 50,000 miles.

If the earth did not revolve, u in the above expression would be zero, and $a = 0$; if light were propagated instantly, V would be infinite, and again $a = 0$. The observed aberration of starlight demonstrates both the earth's revolution and the finite speed of light.

It must be understood that any motion of the earth displaces a star apparently in the direction of the motion. Thus the earth's rotation causes the stars to appear to be slightly east of their true positions. This *diurnal aberration* is $0''.3$, at the most.

2.11. The Finite Speed of Light.

Effects of the relatively slow speed of sound are observed by everyone. The rumble of thunder follows the lightning flash; the distant band appears to be out of step with its own music. Light seems to come to us instantly, at least its

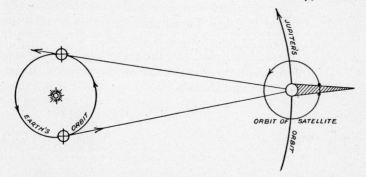

FIG. 2.11. Intervals Between Successive Eclipses of a Satellite of Jupiter. The observed intervals between successive disappearances or reappearances of the satellite are shorter when the earth is approaching Jupiter, and longer when it is receding.

speed is too great to be determined by methods usually employed for sound.

The finite speed of light was first demonstrated, in 1675, by Roemer's observations of the eclipses of Jupiter's satellites. It is one of many instances in which the celestial laboratory has offered wider opportunity than the terrestrial one for the study of physical phenomena. But Roemer's important contribution was discredited, until his conclusion was confirmed by Bradley's discovery of aberration 52 years later.

Three or four of the satellites of the planet Jupiter revolve in such a way (5.30) that they must pass through its shadow at regular intervals, neglecting the disturbing effects of their interactions. During eclipses the satellites are invisible to us. Roemer observed that the intervals between disappearances or reappearances of a satellite are not regular; they increase or decrease, depending on the earth's motion relative to Jupiter. The intervals are smaller when the earth is approaching this planet, and greater when it is receding from it.

As an illustration, consider the predicted times of disappearances of Jupiter's third satellite, as seen from the earth at different seasons; they are Greenwich civil times.

Disappearance of Jupiter's Satellite III

Earth receding from Jupiter					Earth approaching Jupiter			
1930	Feb.	21^d	12^h	58^m	0^s	Oct.	8^d 20^h 41^m 54^s
	Feb.	28	16	58	24	Oct.	16	0 40 30
Interval		7	4	0	24		7 3 58 36

When the earth is receding from Jupiter, there is greater delay between the actual disappearance and its observation at the later date than at the earlier one; when the earth is approaching, the observation of the second disappearance is less delayed. The agreement between the observed and predicted times in such cases as these gives evidence of the finite speed of light. It is to be noticed that the results in themselves do not constitute proof of the earth's revolution; the same thing would happen if Jupiter were approaching and receding from a stationary earth, as the early astronomers supposed.

2.12. The Velocity of Light. Light travels 50 miles in less than three ten-thousandths of a second. To measure its speed, long distances and highly refined methods are required. Astronomical observations of aberration and the eclipses of Jupiter's satellites give only approximate values. The first direct determination of the velocity of light was made in 1849 by the French physicist Fizeau, who employed a rotating toothed wheel. Foucault, in 1862, made use of a rotating mirror instead, a device which found favor with later investigators.

Michelson's determination of the velocity of light, in 1925–26, was effected by a modification of Foucault's method. A strong beam of light was flashed by a rotating mirror on Mount Wilson, in California, to Mount San Antonio 22 miles away, where a fixed mirror reflected the light back to the moving mirror. The experiment consisted in rotating the mirror faster and faster until the beam was returned to its original direction. In order to accomplish this result a simple mirror must rotate completely while the light is making the round trip of 44 miles. It would amount to 4224 rotations a second — an excessive rate. Thus 44 multiplied by 4224 equals about 186,-000, roughly, the speed of light in one second.

To reduce the rate of rotation from 8 to 16 times, Michelson substituted for a single mirror small short regular prisms of glass or steel having from 8 to 16 faces which served as mirrors. Even then, one of the glass prisms burst because it had to be turned so rapidly. From many separate measurements Michelson concludes that the

$$\text{velocity of light} = \begin{cases} 299,796 \text{ km./sec.} \pm 3 \text{ km./sec.} \\ 186,284 \text{ miles a second} \end{cases}$$

This is the velocity *in a vacuum*. Starlight, regardless of its color, comes to us at this rate through empty space, but its speed is reduced in the earth's atmosphere. In general, the denser the medium the greater is the reduction, and blue light is affected more than red light. While the velocity may become less, it is supposed that it can never exceed the value in a vacuum, even when the observer rapidly approaches the source of the light. This maximum velocity of light is accordingly a constant of nature.

2.13. Significance of the Probable Error. The *probable error*, ± 3 km./sec., following the value of the velocity of light, does *not* mean that the true velocity certainly lies between 299,793 and 299,799. It signifies the even chance that the error is less or greater than 3, and thus informs us of the degree of accuracy of the result.

All measurements are inaccurate, if they are recorded in units sufficiently small. The length of a room may come out the same in even yards, however often it is

FIG. 2.12. Twelve-Faced Mirror Used in Determining the Velocity of Light. (By courtesy of the Sperry Gyroscope Company)

measured, but when this length is needed to a thousandth of an inch, perhaps no two of ten determinations agree exactly. If the measures seem to be equally reliable, the best that can be done is to accept the average of the ten as the final result; if they are thought to be of unequal reliability, a weighted mean is adopted. The differences between the mean and the separate measures are the residuals, from which the probable error can be calculated by a simple formula.

In this way the degree of precision of the determination is indicated, if the errors in the separate measures are *accidental*, so that any measure is as likely to be too large as too small. But the probable error becomes misleading, if the measures include *systematic errors* which are the same in amount and direction for them all; if, for instance, some peculiarity in the apparatus or observer had made all the measures of the velocity of light 100 km. too large. Great care was taken, however, to eliminate systematic errors.

In connection with the velocity of light determination, the distance between the mirrors on Mount Wilson and San Antonio Peak, about 22 miles, was measured by the United States Coast and Geodetic Survey with a probable error of only three sixteenths of an inch. According to Bowie, the length of this line has been determined with greater accuracy than that of any other line of triangulation in the world.

2.14. Form of the Earth's Orbit. The sun appears about the same size throughout the year; in fact, without the aid of a telescope no variation in its apparent diameter can be noticed, so that the sun's distance must be always nearly the same. The earth's path around the sun is therefore not much different from a circle with the sun in the center.

As the Table shows, the sun's distance is slightly variable during the year; it is 1.7 per cent less than the mean distance about January 1, and the same amount greater about July 1. Expressed in miles, the entire variation of 3.4 per cent presents a more formidable aspect, for it exceeds 3 million miles. The apparent diameter of the sun varies inversely as the distance; it is 3.4 per cent, or a little more than one minute of arc, greater in January than in July.

TABLE 2.I. VARIATIONS IN THE SUN'S DISTANCE AND APPARENT SIZE

	Sun's Distance (mean = 1)	Sun's Apparent Diameter		Sun's Distance (mean = 1)	Sun's Apparent Diameter
January 1	0.983	32' 36"	July 1	1.017	31' 31"
February 1	0.985	32 31	August 1	1.014	31 35
March 1	0.991	32 20	September 1	1.009	31 46
April 1	0.999	32 4	October 1	1.001	32 1
May 1	1.008	31 48	November 1	0.992	32 18
June 1	1.014	31 36	December 1	0.986	32 30

As early as 120 B.C. Hipparchus observed that the sun spends more time going from the vernal to the autumnal equinox than it does returning; the difference is a whole week. He inferred, therefore, that the earth is not *exactly* at the center of the sun's orbit. At that time, and for many centuries afterward, all celestial orbits were believed to be perfect circles. Kepler, in 1609, showed not only that the earth revolves around the sun, but also that the orbits of the planets are ellipses, instead of circles. Newton later demonstrated this fact as a consequence of his law of gravitation.

2.15. The Earth's Orbit is an Ellipse of small eccentricity with the sun at one focus. It is the path the earth follows in its revolution around the sun and it must not be confused with the ecliptic, the great circle which the sun seems to describe annually on the celestial sphere. The plane of the earth's orbit is also the plane of the ecliptic. Since the orbits of the celestial bodies are generally ellipses, the following definitions will be useful here and elsewhere.

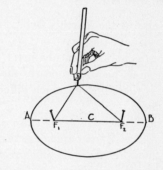

FIG. 2.15. The Ellipse. An easy way to draw an ellipse is shown. The sum of the distances from any point on the circumference to two points within, *the foci*, F_1, F_2, is always the same, and equal to the major axis, AB. The eccentricity of the ellipse is the fraction: F_1F_2/AB.

The ellipse is a plane curve such that the sum of the distances from any point on its circumference to two points within, the foci, is always constant and equal to the major axis of the ellipse (Fig. 2.15).

The eccentricity of the ellipse, e, is half the distance between the foci divided by the semi-major axis. It is the conventional way of denoting the degree of flattening of the ellipse. The eccentricity may have any value between $e = 0$, when the figure is a circle, and $e = 1$, when it becomes a parabola. The eccentricity of the earth's orbit is about .017 or 1/60.

Perihelion and *aphelion* are the two points on the earth's orbit respectively nearest the sun and farthest from it. They are the extremities of the major axis, whose extension is the *line of apsides*. The earth is at perihelion about January 1 and at aphelion about July 1. These dates fluctuate somewhat, and in addition advance, on the average of 25 minutes a year, because the line of apsides of the earth's orbit rotates eastward about 11″ yearly.

The earth's *mean distance* from the sun is the semi-major axis of its orbit, or the average between the perihelion and aphelion distances. At the extremities of the minor axis of its orbit the earth reaches its mean distance from the sun; the dates are about April 3 and October 5. The line joining the earth and sun is the *radius vector*.

TIME

For practical purposes in science and in everyday affairs we are concerned with intervals of time — their measurement and use. Time of day is the interval that has elapsed since noon or midnight.

Perfectly uniform motion or periodicity is prerequisite for the ideal time-keeper. Clocks and other artificial devices do not fulfill this requirement. Even the best clocks have variable rates. The earth's rotation, or the consequent daily rotation of the heavens, provides a natural unit of time which is not far from meeting the requirement of uniformity (2.7). The day and its arbitrary subdivisions, the hour, minute, and second, are units for measuring intervals of time. A second natural time unit, the year, is the period of the earth's revolution.

2.16. Time Reckoning. Two features of a clock are necessary for telling time, first a time reckoner, the hour hand; second, a reference line from the noon mark to the center of the dial. The angle between the hour hand and the reference line, when converted from degrees to hours and minutes, denotes the time of day. Numerals around the dial are added for convenience in reading time; and interpolating devices, the minute and second hands, add accuracy to the reading.

To observe the time from the fundamental clock in the sky, a point on the celestial sphere is chosen as the *time reckoner;* it may be regarded as the end of the hour hand which joins this point and the celestial pole, and which circles once a day westward around the pole. The *reference line* is the observer's celestial meridian.

The selected point is at *upper transit* when it crosses that half of the celestial meridian which includes the zenith; it is at *lower transit* when it crosses the opposite half below the celestial pole. Three general rules are applicable to any kind of time.

It is *noon* when the time reckoner is at upper transit; it is *mid-*

night when it is at lower transit. A *day* is the interval between two successive upper or lower transits of the time reckoner. *Time of day* is either the hour angle of the time reckoner, or it is the hour angle plus 12 hours, depending on whether it is measured from upper or lower transit.

Three time reckoners are in use, namely, the vernal equinox, the apparent sun, and the mean sun. Noon, day, and time of day for each one are defined by the above rules. The three kinds of time are sidereal time, apparent solar time, and mean solar time.

2.17. The Sidereal Day is Shorter than the Solar Day.
The sidereal day is the interval between two successive upper transits of the vernal equinox. The solar day is the interval between two successive

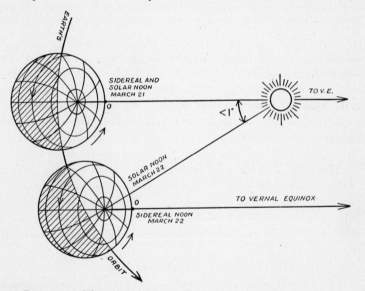

Fig. 2.17. The Sidereal Day is Shorter than the Solar Day. Owing to the earth's revolution, the meridian of the observer, at *O*, must be rotated once around to complete the sidereal day, and about one degree more to complete the solar day.

lower transits of the sun. If both time reckoners were fixed on the celestial sphere, their days would be the same in length and equal to the true period of the earth's rotation. But this is not the case. The sun's eastward motion along the ecliptic delays its return to the meridian. In one day the sun moves approximately 360°/365.25, or a little less than 1° toward the east. Since the daily rotation of the sky westward proceeds at the rate of 1° in 4 minutes, *the sidereal day is about four minutes shorter than the mean solar day.* More exactly, this difference is $3^m 55^s.909$ in mean solar time.

This is the situation as we see it. What actually occurs is shown in Fig. 2.17. The earth rotates and revolves in the same sense. The revolution alters the sun's direction, but not that of the vernal equinox on the remote celestial sphere. While a single rotation of the earth suffices to bring the observer's meridian around to the vernal equinox, a longer period is necessary to bring this meridian again under the sun.

Owing to precession of the equinoxes (2.32) the sidereal day is really shorter than the true period of the earth's rotation. The average difference is less than a hundredth of a second of time. On account of the irregularity in the motion of the equinox, the sidereal day is not strictly constant in length, but its variation is too small to be detected with certainty. For most purposes the sidereal day is regarded as constant and equal to $23^h 56^m 4^s.091$ of mean solar time.

2.18. Sidereal Time is the hour angle of the vernal equinox. It is local time, referred to the observer's meridian. The sidereal day begins at sidereal noon, at the upper transit of the vernal equinox, and is reckoned through 24 hours to the next sidereal noon.

The sidereal clock of an observatory is set to read the hour angle of the vernal equinox, and runs faster than the mean time clock. The two clocks agree about September 23. Thereafter, the sidereal clock gains $3^m 56^s$ a day, which accumulates to two hours in a month, and to a whole day in the course of a year. The specific convenience of the sidereal clock in the observatory is that it keeps star time. A star rises or transits always at the same sidereal time.

On ordinary time a star rises or crosses the meridian four minutes earlier from night to night, or two hours earlier from month to month. A star which rises at 10 o'clock in the evening on November 1 will rise at 8 o'clock on the first of December. The westward march of the constellations with the advancing seasons thus arises from the difference in length between the sidereal and the solar day.

2.19. Apparent Solar Time. Although sidereal time is suited to many activities of the observatory, it is not useful for civil purposes, because our daily affairs are governed by the sun's position in the sky, and not by the vernal equinox. Sidereal noon, for example, comes at night during a part of the year.

The *apparent sun* is the sun we see. The hour angle of its center plus 12 hours is *apparent solar time,* or simply apparent time. The apparent solar day begins at midnight and is reckoned through 24 hours continuously. Unfortunately the sun itself is not a reliable time keeper. It runs fast or slow, at times nearly half a minute in a day. The sundial is the only timepiece adapted to its erratic behavior. The lengths of apparent solar days at different times of the year, measured in mean solar time, from noon to noon by the sundial, are:

$$
\begin{array}{llrrr}
1930, & \text{January 1} & 24^{\text{h}} & 0^{\text{m}} & 28^{\text{s}}.6 \\
& \text{April 1} & 23 & 59 & 42 .0 \\
& \text{July 1} & 24 & 0 & 11 .8 \\
& \text{October 1} & 23 & 59 & 40 .6 \\
\end{array}
$$

It is interesting to notice that the longest days occur in winter, when the days are commonly said to be the shortest. Evidently the word "day" is used with more than one meaning.

Two causes contribute chiefly to the irregularity in the lengths of apparent solar days: (1) The variable revolution of the earth, owing to the eccentricity of its orbit. (2) The obliquity of the ecliptic.

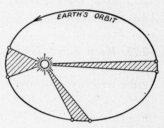

FIG. 2.20. Variable Revolution of the Earth. Since, by Kepler's law, the line joining the earth and the sun sweeps over the same area every day, the earth travels farther in a day when it is nearer the sun.

2.20. Effect of the Earth's Variable Revolution. Because of the eccentricity of the earth's orbit, the speed of the earth around the sun is not uniform. The closer it is to the sun, the faster the earth revolves. This relation is expressed precisely as a particular case of Kepler's law of areas: *The line joining the earth to the sun sweeps over equal areas in equal intervals of time.*

When the earth is near perihelion, in January, it moves farthest in a day; the sun's motion in the ecliptic is therefore the greatest, and apparent solar days would be of maximum length, if this were the only cause of the variation. When the earth is near aphelion, in July, it makes the smallest advance in its orbit in a day; the sun then suffers the least displacement, and apparent solar days would be of minimum length. Thus throughout the year, as the earth's speed varies, the sun's daily progress in the ecliptic is variable, so that the lengths of apparent solar days are not the same.

2.21. Effect of the Obliquity of the Ecliptic. Even if the sun's motion in the ecliptic were uniform, the length of the apparent solar day would remain variable, because the ecliptic is inclined to the celestial equator. It is the projection of the sun's eastward motion upon the celestial equator that determines the delay in completing the apparent solar day.

Near the equinoxes, a considerable part of the sun's motion in the ecliptic is north or south, which does not delay the sun's return. Near the solstices, where the ecliptic is parallel to the equator, the entire motion is eastward; moreover, the hour circles are closer together here. Therefore, so far as the obliquity of the ecliptic is concerned, apparent solar days would be longest at the solstices and shortest at the equinoxes. It will be noticed that both causes conspire to make the apparent day longest in winter.

2.22. Mean Solar Time; Civil Time. The *mean solar day,* as the term implies, is the *average* apparent solar day. It is therefore of the same length throughout the year, and remains practically constant over a long period of time. It is the basis of all ordinary measurements of time. The *mean sun* is an imaginary point which moves uniformly eastward in the celestial equator, completing its circuit in the same period as that of the apparent sun in the ecliptic. The interval between two successive lower transits of the mean sun is the mean solar day, or *civil day.*

Civil time is the specific reckoning of mean solar time from midnight through 24 hours continuously. It is the hour angle of the mean sun plus 12 hours. Until the beginning of 1925, astronomical mean time was reckoned from noon, and was 12 hours later than civil time. Now the two are the same. Astronomers, however, usually avoid the two 12-hour divisions of the day, and the designations A.M. and P.M. In astronomical records 6 P.M. appears as 18^h.

2.23. The Equation of Time is the difference at any instant between apparent and civil time; it is the difference between the hour angles of the apparent and mean sun. Four times a year, as the Table shows, the two agree. At other times the apparent sun is either fast or slow. In November, the sundial is more than a quarter of an hour ahead of the local civil time. The Table gives the amount of the equation of time on the first of each month in 1930, at noon at Washington. The seconds fluctuate somewhat from year to year. Accurate values are obtained from tables in the nautical almanacs.

EQUATION OF TIME
(Apparent sun fast or slow)

Jan. 1	3^m	34^s	slow	July 1	3^m	34^s	slow
Feb. 1	13	42	slow	Aug. 1	6	12	slow
Mar. 1	12	32	slow	Sept. 1	0	4	slow
Apr. 1	4	1	slow	Oct. 1	10	12	fast
May 1	2	57	fast	Nov. 1	16	20	fast
June 1	2	26	fast	Dec. 1	11	0	fast

The rapid change in the equation of time near the winter solstice noticeably affects the times of sunrise and sunset. At this time the apparent sun is going slow *fastest*. As the sun begins to move north after passing the solstice, it might be expected to rise earlier and set later. But the change in the equation of time from day to day delays both the rising and setting. For this reason the sun continues to rise later each day for about two weeks after December 22; similarly, the earliest sunsets occur about two weeks before the winter solstice.

2.24. Difference of Time Equals Difference of Longitude.
In any one of the three kinds of time, a day of 24 hours is completed when the earth has made one rotation, through 360°, relative to the point in the sky that serves as the time reckoner. Thus 24 hours of time equal 360°, or 24 hours of longitude on the earth; and a difference of one hour between the local times of two places means that their longitudes differ by 15° or one hour.

When the local time of one place is known, and the corresponding time at another place is required, *add the difference of longitude, if the second place is east of the first; subtract, if it is west.*

When the sundial at Columbia University (longitude 4^h 56^m west of Greenwich) reads noon, what is the time by the sundial at the University of California (longitude 8^h 9^m west)? If the date is November 1, what is the local civil time at the second place?

Since the difference between the two longitudes must be subtracted in this case, the required apparent time is $12^h\ 0^m - 3^h\ 13^m = 8^h\ 47^m$. From the table in the preceding Section the apparent sun is 16^m fast on November 1. The local civil time is therefore $8^h\ 31^m$, or 8:31 A.M.

Conversely, *difference of longitude equals difference of time*. This is the fundamental rule for astronomical determinations of longitude. Since longitudes are measured from the meridian of Greenwich, it is necessary to have

FIG. 2.24. The Royal Observatory, Greenwich. Longitude is measured from the meridian passing through the meridian circle of this observatory.

at the same instant the local time and the corresponding Greenwich time. Their difference is the longitude of the place. It is evident that the time of any other meridian will serve equally well, if the longitude of that meridian is known. Before the days of accurate time signals by wire and radio, it was not the easiest matter to get the Greenwich time accurately.

2.25. Standard Time.

Local time varies as we go east or west, at the rate of 8 minutes in a hundred miles, in latitude 40°. In the early days when traveling was arduous and infrequent, the keeping of local time in each community caused no inconvenience. But with the development of railroads it became necessary to keep the same time over greater areas of the country. At first, the absence of a uniform rule in these consolidations resulted in much confusion. In 1884, an international conference at Washington proposed the plan of standard time.

Standard meridians are marked off at intervals of 15° or one hour east and west of the meridian of Greenwich. The local civil time of each standard meridian becomes the standard time of the entire belt through which the meridian runs centrally. The ideal standard time at any place would be the local civil time of the standard meridian nearest the place; but the meridian actually chosen is often not the nearest, especially in regions about midway between standard me-

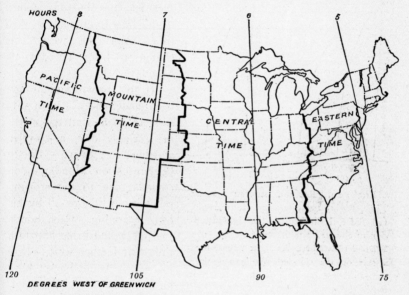

FIG. 2.25. Standard Time in the United States. Eastern standard time is the local civil time at the meridian 5 hours west of Greenwich; it is there-fore 5 hours earlier than Greenwich civil time. Central, Mountain, and Pacific times are respectively 6, 7, and 8 hours earlier than Greenwich civil time.

ridians. Thus the earth is divided into belts whose times differ by even hours from Greenwich time. In practice the scheme is far from uniform, and its adoption is not universal.

Five standard times are used in the United States and Canada, namely, Atlantic, Eastern, Central, Mountain, and Pacific. They are respectively the local times of the meridians 60°, 75°, 90°, 105°, and 120° west of Greenwich; they are therefore 4, 5, 6, 7, and 8 hours slow compared with Greenwich civil time, the minutes and seconds being the same.

"Daylight saving time," or summer time, is the usual standard time increased by one hour; or it is the standard time of the belt adjoining to the east. It has been used since 1916 during a part of the year in some sections of America and Europe.

2.26. Where the Day Changes. The "date-line" coincides as nearly as possible with the meridian 180° from Greenwich, which lies for the most part in the Pacific Ocean. Whenever this line is crossed, the date is set ahead or back a full day. If the line is crossed from the east on Monday noon, it then becomes Tuesday noon; if the line is crossed at this time from the west, the change is from Tuesday to Monday.

If this provision had not been made, and if it were possible to go around the world in a single day, a traveler starting westward from Greenwich on Monday noon could return to the starting point in no time at all by his own reckoning. Each hour's journey would bring him to a time belt farther west, where his watch would be set back an hour.

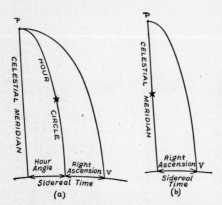

FIG. 2.27. Relation between Sidereal Time, Right Ascension, and Hour Angle. (*a*) Sidereal time equals the right ascension of the star plus its hour angle. (*b*) Sidereal time equals the right ascension of a star on the celestial meridian (upper transit); here the hour angle is zero. *V* marks the vernal equinox.

2.27. Determining the Time. Civil time of day, either local or standard, can not be determined by direct observation. It is calculated from either the apparent time or the sidereal time. When the apparent time, or hour angle of the apparent sun, is observed, it is converted to local civil time by applying the equation of time. Then the addition or subtraction of the difference between the observer's longitude and that of his standard meridian gives the local civil time of that meridian, which is the desired standard time.

At what standard time does the sundial read noon on November 1 in a place whose longitude is $4^h 56^m$ west?

Apparent solar time	12^h	0^m
Equation of time		-16
Local civil time	11	44
Difference of longitude		-4
Eastern standard time	11	40

The sundial reads noon at 11:40 A.M.

Standard time is determined more accurately from the sidereal time which is obtained by observing the transits of stars across the celestial meridian. This is the usual way of correcting the clocks in observatories. The fundamental rule for determining sidereal time follows:

The sidereal time equals the right ascension of a star when the star is on the celestial meridian at upper transit.

To calculate approximately the local civil time at a given sidereal time, we have to remember that the two times are the same about September 21 and that thereafter the sidereal clock gains 3^m 56^s daily.

The star α Pegasi (right ascension 23^h 1^m) is observed at upper transit on November 1 at a place whose longitude is 4^h 56^m west. What is the standard time?

Sidereal time	23^h	1^m
Gain of sidereal time in 41 days	2	41
Local civil time	20	20
Correction to standard meridian		−4
Eastern standard time	20	16 or 8:16 P.M.

FIG. 2.27A. Transmitting Clock and Switchboard at the Naval Observatory. The time signals which are sent out from the Naval radio stations at Arlington and Annapolis are the beats of this clock.

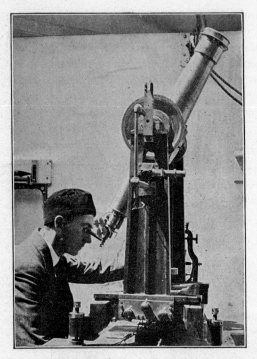

FIG. 2.28. Transit Instrument of the Naval Observatory, Washington. This is one of the transit instruments employed in making observations for determining the corrections to the master clock of the Naval Observatory.

A more accurate calculation is easily performed with the aid of tables in the *Nautical Almanac*.

The precision with which the clock may be set or corrected by observations of star transits depends on the ability to determine the instant when the star is on the celestial meridian. This is accomplished with the astronomical transit instrument.

2.28. The Transit Instrument

is a rather small telescope mounted on a single horizontal axis which is set east and west. The telescope may be pointed anywhere along the celestial meridian, but nowhere else. Its purpose is to determine the instant when a star is crossing the meridian.

With the aid of the graduated circle on the axis the telescope is directed toward the point of the celestial meridian where the star will soon cross. Looking into the eyepiece, the observer finds the star perhaps near the edge of the field of view, and moving toward the middle. A vertical *wire* — often a spider thread — in the middle of the field marks the meridian. At the instant of the star's bisection by the wire, the reading of the sidereal clock is recorded. Suppose that the clock reading is $6^h 40^m 17^s.22$, and that the star's right ascension, taken from a table, is $6^h 40^m 15^s.71$. The clock is therefore $1^s.51$ fast, because at

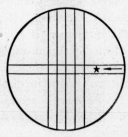

FIG. 2.28A. Field of a Transit Instrument.

the instant of its transit the star's right ascension is the correct sidereal time.

It must be understood that the correction of a clock to a hundredth of a second is not obtained as easily as this. The details and technique of the transit instrument are treated in books on practical astronomy.

PRECESSION

2.29. Conical Motion of the Earth's Axis. The axis of a spinning top describes a cone around a line perpendicular to the floor. When it stops spinning, the top falls over. But while it is spinning, the force of gravity, instead of tipping the axis, causes the conical motion that we observe. This is the precession of the top.

Just as the axis of the top leans away from the vertical, so the earth's axis is inclined 23½° from the perpendicular to the plane of its orbit. If the earth did not rotate, the attractions of the moon and sun, both nearly in the plane of the ecliptic, on the earth's equatorial bulge (3.2) would bring the equator into the ecliptic plane. Owing to the earth's rotation, however, the inclination is not much affected. Again as in the

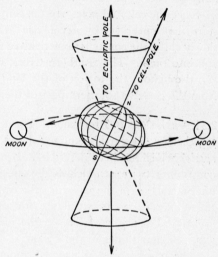

FIG. 2.29. The Earth's Precessional Motion. The effort of the moon to bring the earth's equator into the plane of the moon's orbit (on the average, the ecliptic plane), combined with the earth's rotation, gives the earth's axis a slow conical motion around the line joining the ecliptic poles.

case of the top, these attractions produce a conical motion of the axis, but in the opposite direction with respect to the rotation.

The earth's precessional motion is the slow conical movement of the earth's axis westward around a line joining the ecliptic poles, having a period of about 26,000 years.

2.30. Precessional Paths of the Celestial Poles. The conical motion of the earth's axis causes the celestial poles, toward which the axis is directed, to slowly describe circles around the ecliptic poles; the radii of the two circles are the same and equal to 23° 27′. This is a movement of the poles with reference to the constellations.

As one faces north, the precessional motion of the celestial pole is counterclockwise. This pole is now 1° 4′ from the star Polaris, which it will continue to approach until the minimum distance of 28′ is reached, about the year 2100. Thereafter, the diurnal circle of Polaris will grow larger. For those who live in the year 7500, α Cephei will be the nearly invariable pole star, and Polaris will circle daily around it, 28° away.

Since the celestial poles are the centers of the circumpolar caps of stars that never set or never rise (1.13), the precessional motion slowly shifts the constellations relative to these regions — out of them and into them. The Southern Cross, which rose and set 6000 years ago throughout the region of the United States, is now visible only from the extreme southern part of the country.

2.31. Variations in Precession. The attractions of the sun and moon together on the earth's equatorial bulge result in the *luni-solar precession* which has been described. Because it is the nearer, the moon contributes twice as much as the sun does to this effect. While the total attraction of the moon for the earth is less than that of the sun, the difference in its attraction for different parts of the earth is greater. For the same reason the moon is more effective than the sun in forming tides in the ocean.

The moon's orbit is inclined about 5° to the ecliptic; moreover, the two points of the intersection move rapidly around the ecliptic (3.32), completing the circuit in a little less than 19 years. On this account, the inclination of the moon's orbit to the equator varies in this period from 18½° to 28½°, which produces a corresponding variation in the precession.

Once in 19 years, therefore, the celestial pole completes a little ellipse around its mean position on the circular precessional path. The semi-major axis of the ellipse in the direction of the ecliptic pole is 9″.2. This is the chief term in *nutation*, the nodding of the pole. Thus the precessional path breaks into many little waves.

Nor is the ecliptic pole stationary. *Planetary precession* is the effect of the planets on the plane of the earth's orbit, which swings around very slowly (0″.11 a year) toward the east. At the same time, the obliquity of the ecliptic fluctuates between 21° 59′ and 24° 36′ over a long period of time, introducing another variation in precession. The movement of the celestial pole is therefore complicated; it is not exactly circular and it is not the same with reference to the constellations from one cycle to the next.

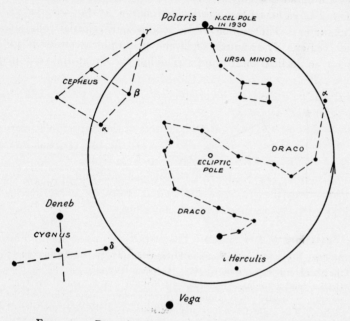

FIG. 2.30. Precessional Path of the North Celestial Pole. The celestial pole describes a circle among the constellations, having a radius of $23\frac{1}{2}°$ and the ecliptic pole at its center. Alpha Draconis was the pole star about 3000 B.C. In the year 7500 A.D. α Cephei will be the pole star, and in 14,000 A.D. Vega (α Lyrae) will have this distinction.

2.32. Precession of the Equinoxes.

Precession has been defined as the conical motion of the earth's axis. It might equally well be considered to be the motion of the equator. The equator swings slowly westward, maintaining very nearly the same inclination with reference to the plane of the earth's orbit. The celestial equator, of course, performs the same gyration relative to the ecliptic, so that the points of their intersection, the equinoxes, slide westward along the ecliptic. This is precession of the equinoxes.

General precession is the motion described. It is the luni-solar precession of the equinoxes on the ecliptic, combined with planetary precession, the backward trend of the ecliptic itself. This motion proceeds at the rate of 50".26 a year.

Since the vernal equinox is a fundamental point of reference on the celestial sphere, the westward precession of this equinox introduces a number of complications.

(1) *The right ascensions and declinations of the celestial bodies are changing.* The motion of the equinox in celestial longitude is $50''.26$ yearly. The annual displacement in right ascension is $46''.09$ or $3^s.07$; in declination it is $20''.04$. Thus the equatorial coordinates

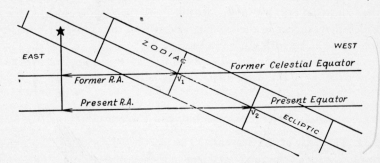

FIG. 2.32. Precession of the Equinoxes. The westward motion of the vernal equinox, from V_1 to V_2 causes the signs of the zodiac (the twelve equal divisions of the zodiac marked off from the vernal equinox) to slide westward away from the corresponding constellations of the zodiac. The right ascensions and declinations of the stars are altered also.

of a star, which are measured from the vernal equinox, change continually. Accurate catalogues give the positions of stars at a stated time, and their annual variations, so that the positions at any other time may be calculated.

(2) *The sidereal day (2.17) is slightly shorter than the true period of the earth's rotation.* The difference is found by dividing the annual displacement of the equinox in right ascension, $3^s.07$, by 365.25; it is eight thousandths of a second of time. The length of the sidereal day is $23^h\ 56^m\ 4^s.091$ of mean solar time. The true period of the earth's rotation is $23^h\ 56^m\ 4^s.099$.

(3) *The tropical year (year of the seasons) is shorter than the true period of the earth's revolution (2.33),* because the vernal equinox moves westward to meet the sun in its annual circuit of the ecliptic. The year of the seasons is shortened by the fraction $50''.26/360°$ of 365.25 days, a little more than twenty minutes.

From this effect the precession of the equinoxes was discovered by Hipparchus about 125 B.C. Comparing his own observations with the records of earlier astronomers, he noticed that the dates of the heliacal risings and settings of the stars were advancing with respect to the date of the equinox. The *heliacal setting* of a star occurs on the latest date the star is visible in the west after sunset; it is setting just as the sky becomes dark enough to make it visible. This date for any star advances on the average of one day in 70 years. Thus the constellations we now identify with certain seasons, during which they appear in the evening sky, will in the course of time become associated with other seasons.

(4) *The signs of the zodiac no longer agree in position with the constellations of the same name* (1.19).

THE SEASONS AND THE CALENDAR

2.33. The Year of the Seasons. The year is the period of the earth's revolution, or of the sun's apparent motion in the ecliptic. The kind of year depends on the point of reference to which the motion is referred, whether it is fixed or is itself in motion. Just as the day in common use is not the true period of the earth's rotation, so the ordinary year is not the true period of its revolution. Two kinds of year have the greatest use.

The *sidereal year* is the interval of time in which the sun apparently performs a complete revolution with reference to the stars. Its length is 365^d 6^h 9^m $9^s.5$ ($365^d.25636$) of mean solar time, which is now increasing at the rate of $0^s.01$ a century, in addition to any change caused by variations of the earth's rotation. The sidereal year is the true period of the earth's revolution.

The *tropical year* is the interval between two successive returns of the sun to the vernal equinox. Its length is 365^d 5^h 48^m $46^s.0$ ($365^d.24220$) of mean solar time, and it is now diminishing at the rate of $0^s.53$ a century. It is the year of the seasons, the ordinary year to which the calendar must conform. Owing to the westward precession of the equinox, the tropical year is twenty minutes shorter than the sidereal year.

2.34. Cause of the Seasons. Since the earth's equator is inclined to the plane of its orbit, and since it maintains nearly the same direction in space during a complete revolution, each pole is presented to the sun for part of the year, and turned away from it for the remainder. This is the cause of the changing seasons. The amount of the inclination determines the boundaries of the climatic zones. The *frigid zones* are the regions within 23½° from the poles, in which the sun becomes circumpolar, and where the seasons are accordingly extreme. The *torrid zone* has as its boundaries the tropics of Cancer and Capricorn, 23½° from the equator. Here the sun may be over-

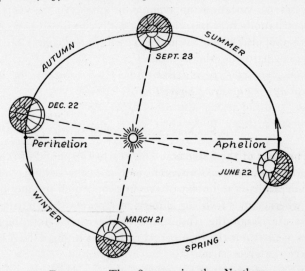

FIG. 2.34. The Seasons in the Northern Hemisphere. This hemisphere is tipped farthest toward the sun at the summer solstice (June 22), and farthest away at the winter solstice (December 22). Soon after the time of the winter solstice the earth arrives at perihelion, about the first of January.

head at noon; the durations of sunlight and darkness never differ greatly, and temperature changes during the year are not marked. In the *temperate zones* the sun never appears in the zenith, nor does it become circumpolar.

The inclined direction of the axis brings about the sun's annual migration in declination. When the sun is farthest north, at the summer solstice, its average altitude in the daytime is the greatest for our region of the world, and the duration of sunlight is the longest. At the winter solstice we have the other extreme, namely, the lowest sun and the shortest duration of sunlight.

2.35. Seasonal Changes in Temperature arise from progressive variations in the *insolation,* or exposure to sunshine, of a region of the earth's surface. The daily amount of the insolation depends on its intensity and duration. The intensity of the sunshine depends on the sun's altitude, aside from the effects of the sun's varying distance, which will be discussed later, and of variations in the output of its radiation and in the state of the intervening atmosphere.

When the sun's rays strike the ground obliquely, a given amount of radiation spreads over more territory than when the sun is at the zenith, and is therefore less effective in heating any part of it. Moreover,

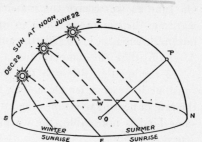

FIG. 2.35. Diurnal Circles of the Sun in Different Seasons. The daily duration of sunlight is longer in the summer, and the sun is higher at noon.

when the sun is low, its rays have to penetrate a greater thickness of air before they reach the ground; they are subject to more absorption and scattering. Summer is a warmer season than winter with us in the northern hemisphere because the two factors conspire together to produce higher temperatures; the sun's altitude is greater and the daily duration of sunlight is longer.

At the time of the summer solstice the sun is higher at noon in the latitude of New York than it is at the equator, and it is visible for a longer time, so that the amount of heat delivered is fully 25 per cent greater. Even at the north pole at that time the daily insolation at the surface is nearly the same as that at the equator. The uninterrupted radiation from the midnight sun compensates its lower altitude; but the temperature is lower there because much of the heat is taken up in the melting of the ice.

2.36. Lag of the Seasons. If the temperatures depended on insolation alone, the warmest days in the northern hemisphere should come around June 22, and the coldest part of the winter about December 22. But the records show that the highest temperatures, on the average, are delayed until August 1, and the lowest until February 1. Thus the seasons lag. The reason is found in the conservation of heat by the atmosphere.

The air serves as a great blanket around the earth preventing the rapid dissipation of its heat. It is the balance of heat on hand at any time that determines the temperature. As with one's bank balance, the quantity increases as long as the deposits exceed the withdrawals. On June 22 we receive the maximum amount of radiation. Afterwards, as the sun moves south again, the quantity received grows less, but until August 1 it exceeds the amount the earth returns into space. After this date the temperature falls.

In the winter, although the sun's altitude and the duration of sunshine increase after December 22, it is not until February 1 that the rate of heating overtakes the rate of cooling. A diurnal lag of the same kind is noticeable; the warmest part of the day comes in the afternoon.

2.37. The Seasons in the Southern Hemisphere differ from ours, of course, in that the same season occurs at the opposite time of the year. Another difference is introduced by the eccentricity of the earth's orbit. Since the earth arrives at perihelion soon after the winter solstice, southern summers are warmer and shorter than the northern ones; and the winters are colder and longer than ours, because the earth is then near aphelion. The greatest distance from the sun, however, is only three per cent more than the distance at perihelion; for this reason, and because of the greater amount of water in the southern hemisphere, temperatures do not differ greatly in the two hemispheres during corresponding seasons.

It is interesting to notice that the conditions which produce the difference between the seasons of the northern and southern hemispheres are nearly repeated in the case of the planet Mars, and that the effect is made more noticeable (5.16) by the greater eccentricity of that planet's orbit.

2.38. The Calendar. The difficulty in the construction of calendars arises from the incommensurability of the natural divisions of time. The periods of the earth's rotation, the moon's revolution, and the earth's revolution can not be compromised into a convenient chronological scheme that will keep step with these astronomical occurrences without frequent arbitrary adjustment. Leap year is an example.

Our calendar is inherited, much modified, from the Romans who first divided the year into ten months beginning with March. Four of their number months, September to December, survive, but without the original significance. January and February were added later to make 12 months in all, each one equal as nearly as possible to the period of the moon's phases, about 29.5 days. Since the calendar year contained only 355 days, an extra month was intercalated from time to time at the discretion of those in authority.

At the time of Julius Caesar the calendar had been managed so unwisely that the vernal equinox was coming in December. With the advice of an astronomer, Caesar instituted a drastic reform. He increased the lengths of the months, disregarding the moon, and thus abolished the intercalary month. The "last year of confusion," 46 B.C., was made 445 days in length in order to bring the vernal equinox to March 25.

2.39. The Julian Calendar. The chief feature of the Julian reform was the adoption of 365¼ days as the length of the calendar year, beginning January 1, 45 B.C. Here leap year enters. Three common years of 365 days are followed by a fourth containing 366 days — the bissextile year, so called because the extra day was then introduced by repeating the sixth day before March 1. Leap year in the Julian calendar occurs whenever the number of the year is evenly divisible by 4; the years ending in 00, 04, 08, 12, and so on are leap years.

This calendar year of 365^d 6^h is 11^m 14^s longer than the tropical year (365^d 5^h 48^m 46^s), the year of the seasons. The difference accumulates to 3 days in about 400 years. At this rate the date of the vernal equinox falls back on the calendar.

When the Council of Nice convened in A.D. 325, the vernal equinox came on March 21, the leap year scheme accounting for the extra day. At this important meeting of churchmen the rule was adopted for fixing the date of Easter — the first Sunday after the 14th day of the moon (nearly full moon) which occurs on or immediately after March 21.

As the date of the vernal equinox falls back in the calendar, March 21 and anniversaries such as Easter, which are reckoned from it, advance in relation to the seasons. At the end of the sixteenth century the vernal equinox had fallen back to March 11. Another reform was demanded.

2.40. The Gregorian Calendar. In 1582 Pope Gregory XIII, with the advice of the astronomer Clavius, advocated the suppression of 10 days in the calendar of that year, in order to bring the vernal equinox back to March 21. On this plan the day following October 4, 1582, became the 15th of that month.

To make the average calendar year more nearly equal to the tropical year it was necessary to omit three days in 400 years, by which the Julian calendar is too long. This was accomplished by making the even century years common years, unless the number is evenly divisible by 400. Thus the years 1700, 1800, and 1900 became common years of 365 days, while 2000 is a leap year as before.

The Gregorian calendar was eventually adopted by Christian nations generally. When Russia, in 1918, and Rumania in the following year finally discarded the Julian calendar, the difference between the two calendars had increased to 13 days.

The average length of the year in the Gregorian calendar is

$$\frac{365.25 \times 400 - 3}{400} = 365.24250 \text{ days, or}$$

$365^{\mathrm{d}}\ 5^{\mathrm{h}}\ 49^{\mathrm{m}}\ 12^{\mathrm{s}}$ of mean solar time, which exceeds the tropical year by only 26 seconds. In its close accordance with the year of the seasons the present calendar is satisfactory. Agitation for further calendar reform arises from other considerations of uniformity, namely, the inequality in the lengths of the months and the absence of fixed relations between the days of the month and of the week. On what day of the week, for example, does July 4 fall in 1986?

One of the proposed reforms fixes the length of the calendar month at 28 days, or exactly 4 weeks. On this plan 13 months are needed. But 13×28 days = 364 days. The extra day required to round out the year must be no day of the week at all; and a similar provision must be made for the intercalary day of leap year. All months conform to the same pattern. If they begin on Sunday, the fourth of the month falls on Wednesday. The simplicity and permanence of this scheme is urged by its proponents.

The *Julian day* is the number of days that have elapsed since noon on January 1, 4713 B.C. This zero day is merely a convenient beginning of the "Julian era." It is much used in astronomical records. When the number of days between two events is required, especially if the dates are widely separated, it is easier to set down the dates in Julian days and simply take the difference between them. The *Nautical Almanac* contains a table from which the Julian day number of any date is readily obtained. January 1, 1930 is J. D. 2,425,978.

REFERENCES

Nautical almanacs are published by various governments for each year, about two years in advance. They contain data indispensable for many astronomical observations and calculations, and for purposes of navigation and geodesy, such as the apparent places of the sun, moon, planets, and brighter stars at suitable intervals during the year. The circumstances of solar and lunar eclipses, occultations, and various phenomena of the planets and their satellites are among the predicted data. The principal almanacs are:

The American Ephemeris and Nautical Almanac (Government Printing Office, Washington, price $1.75 a volume).

The Nautical Almanac (London).

Connaissance des Temps (Paris).

Berliner Astronomisches Jahrbuch.

Among the many treatises on practical astronomy and its special applications to astronomical, nautical, and geodetic problems are:

William Chauvenet, *A Manual of Spherical and Practical Astronomy* (Lippincott), in two volumes.

J. J. Nassau, *A Textbook of Practical Astronomy* (McGraw-Hill, 1932).

W. M. Smart, *Text-Book on Spherical Astronomy* (Cambridge University Press, 1931).

William Bowie, *Determination of Time, Longitude, Latitude, and Azimuth* (U. S. Coast and Geodetic Survey, Special Publication, No. 14, 1913).

Simon Newcomb, *A Compendium of Spherical Astronomy* (Macmillan).

Nathaniel Bowditch, *American Practical Navigator* (Government Printing Office, Washington).

Lick Observatory, Mount Hamilton, California.

CHAPTER III

THE EARTH AND THE MOON

THE EARTH — THE EARTH'S ATMOSPHERE — MOTIONS OF THE MOON —
THE MOON'S PHYSICAL FEATURES — ECLIPSES OF THE MOON AND SUN

THE EARTH

3.1. The Earth's Globular Form. The ordinary proofs that the
earth is a great ball are so familiar and acceptable to almost everyone that they need not detain us. Repeated observations in many
parts of the world, that the superstructure of a ship appears above the
horizon before the hull comes into view, indicate the downward curvature of the ocean's surface everywhere. By this and other evidence
we are convinced that the form of the earth is *approximately* spherical. More refined observations are needed to show what regular
solid the earth most nearly resembles.

If the earth is a perfect sphere, after the mountains and depressions are smoothed, all meridians must be circles, so that a degree of
latitude will have the same length in miles wherever the degree is
measured. Since the latitude equals the altitude of the celestial pole,
the length of one degree is the distance one must go along the meridian in order to have the pole rise or drop exactly 1°; this distance
is then measured by the appropriate method of surveying. Many
such measurements, usually over longer arcs of a meridian, show that
a degree of latitude is everywhere nearly equal to 69 miles. The
results are:

At the equator, latitude 0°, 1° of latitude = 68.7 miles
$$20° \qquad\qquad\qquad = 68.8$$
$$40° \qquad\qquad\qquad = 69.0$$
$$60° \qquad\qquad\qquad = 69.2$$
At the poles, latitude 90°, 1° of latitude = 69.4 miles.

3.2. The Earth is an Oblate Spheroid. Although the length of one
degree of latitude is nowhere far from 69 miles, the steady increase
in its value from the equator to the poles is significant. It must be

understood that the length at the poles is not the result of measurements in those regions, but is an extrapolation from the observed increase in lower latitudes. The greater length of one degree of latitude at the poles shows that the meridians curve less rapidly there than at the equator. The meridians are therefore not circles, but ellipses; and the earth is not a sphere, but an *oblate spheroid* — flattened at the poles and bulging at the equator. This figure is also an *ellipsoid of revolution,* generated by rotating an ellipse around its minor axis, or in this case by the rotation of a meridian around the earth's axis.

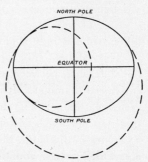

FIG. 3.2. Curvature of a Meridian at the Pole and Equator. The greater length of a degree of latitude at the pole shows that the meridian is there part of a larger circle.

The conclusion that the earth is flattened at the poles, which results from the measurements of distances on its surface, is verified by observations with the pendulum of the varying acceleration of gravity in different latitudes (3.5), by the earth's precessional motion, and in other ways.

3.3. Dimensions of the Earth; its Oblateness. If the earth were exactly spherical, the determination of its size would be an easy matter; for the number of miles in one degree of latitude multiplied by 360 would give the circumference. This simple procedure was employed as early as 250 B.C. by Eratosthenes of Alexandria. If the earth had any other regular geometrical figure, the determination of its size from measurements at the surface would present no difficulties. It is the irregularity of the surface that complicates the problem. The *dimensions of the earth* are the dimensions of the regular spheroid whose surface nearly fits the earth's surface.

The "Hayford spheroid" was calculated in 1909 from the measurements of the United States Coast and Geodetic Survey. Its dimensions are:

Equatorial diameter = 7926.68 miles, or 12756.78 km.
Polar diameter   = 7899.98 miles, or 12713.82 km.
Difference   =   26.70 miles.

$$\text{Oblateness of the earth} = \frac{26.70}{7926.68} = \frac{1}{297}$$

The accuracy of this determination of the equatorial diameter is indicated by its probable error of about 400 feet. The present standard figure of the earth for geodetic purposes is the "international ellipsoid of reference" which is based on the Hayford spheroid, and differs from it only slightly.

The *oblateness,* or *ellipticity,* of a spheroid is found by dividing the difference between the equatorial and polar diameters by the equatorial diameter. It is the conventional way of denoting the degree of flattening. The small value of this fraction for the earth shows that it is not much flattened. If the earth is represented by a globe 18 inches in diameter, the radius at the pole is $\frac{1}{32}$ inch less than the equatorial radius, and the highest mountain is only $\frac{1}{75}$ inch above the sea level. It has been said that the earth is rounder and smoother than most of the balls in a bowling alley.

3.4. The Cause of the Oblateness.

The effort of a stone to fly away, when it is whirled around at the end of a string, is an example of *centrifugal force.* Similarly, all parts of the earth, owing to its rotation, are subject to a centrifugal force directed away from the axis; this outward acceleration amounts to 1⅓ inches a second (3.3917 cm./sec.²) at the equator, and diminishes to zero at the poles. The effect at any point may be resolved into two accelerations at right angles, one, perpendicular to the earth's surface, diminishes gravity and therefore the weight of an object to that point; the other is directed along the surface toward the equator. Newton cited as a proof of the earth's oblateness the fact that things which are free to move, the water of the oceans for example, have not assembled around the equator. The material of the earth has adjusted itself to compensate this sliding effect.

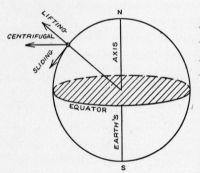

FIG. 3.4. Effect of the Earth's Rotation on a Body at its Surface. The centrifugal force directed away from the earth's axis is resolved into two forces at right angles. One diminishes the weight of the body; the other urges it toward the equator.

The amount of the oblateness depends on the ratio of the centrifugal force to the acceleration of gravity at the equator. For the earth this ratio,

m, is $1\frac{1}{3}$ inches/32.2 feet, or 1/289. The oblateness, ϵ, depends also on the distribution of the material within the earth. Theoretically $\epsilon = 1.25\ m$, if the density is the same throughout, and 0.50 m, if the material is mostly collected at the center. In the case of the earth the oblateness is 1/297, or 0.97 m, which suggests a considerable increase of density from the surface to the center.

3.5. Gravity at the Earth's Surface.

As we have seen, the earth's rotation lifts objects on its surface so that they weigh less at the equator than at the pole by 1 pound in 290. *Gravity is the resultant of the earth's attraction (gravitation) and the outward component of the centrifugal force.* The acceleration of gravity, g, is the rate at which a falling body picks up speed; its value at sea level increases with the latitude.

At the equator $g = 978.039$ cm./sec.^{2} = 32.09 feet/sec.^{2}
At the poles $\quad g = 983.217$ cm./sec.^{2} = 32.26 feet/sec.^{2},

according to Bowie. Therefore, the weight of an object, which is its mass times g, is actually less at the equator than at the poles by 1 pound in 190, which leaves 1 pound in 550 unaccounted for by centrifugal force. The difference is caused by the earth's oblateness. An object at the equator weighs less also, because it is farther away from the center of attraction.

Differences in the acceleration of gravity at different places are accurately determined by swinging a pendulum. For the simple pendulum $g = 4\pi^2 l/t^2$, where l is the length of the pendulum, and t is the time in seconds of a complete oscillation. This is one of the best methods for determining the amount of the oblateness.

3.6. Astronomical and Geographical Latitude.

Astronomical latitude has been defined as the angle between the direction of gravity and the equator plane; it equals the altitude of the celestial pole (1.10). Since the direction of gravity is altered by irregularities in the form and density of the earth, the astronomical latitude of any place is generally different from the value it would have if the earth were a smooth homogeneous spheroid. The difference is the *station error* which rarely exceeds 30″, and is usually very much smaller.

Geographical, or *topographical,* latitude is the angle between the line perpendicular to the surface of the standard spheroid and the equator plane. It is the astronomical latitude corrected for station error, and is used in the making of accurate maps.

Geocentric latitude is the angle that the line from the station to the center of the earth makes with the equator plane. It is the same as geographical latitude only at the equator and the poles; elsewhere the two are different because the earth is not a sphere, and the greatest difference, in latitude 45°, is 11½′.

The methods that are used for determining the longitude and latitude for a point on the earth's surface are to be found in treatises on spherical and practical astronomy.

3.7. The Law of Gravitation; Mass. That objects near the earth's surface fall toward it is an example of a characteristic of matter everywhere, which is stated in Newton's law of gravitation:

Every particle of matter in the universe attracts every other particle with a force which is proportional to the product of their masses, and which varies inversely as the square of the distance between them.

The mass of a body is therefore an important consideration. When its value is known, the effects on the motions of all other bodies may be calculated. Conversely, the mass itself is determined by these effects. From the law of gravitation we have for the acceleration, a, of a body in the direction of another, whose mass is m and distance d, the relation (4.14):

$$\text{Acceleration} = Gm/d^2,$$

where G is a universal constant best determined in the physical laboratory.

Mass is conveniently described as the quantity of matter a body contains. The relative masses of two bodies can be found by weighing them at *the same place*. *Weight* is the product of the mass times the acceleration of gravity, and may not be the same at different places. *Density* is defined as the mass of a body divided by its volume; it expresses the degree of concentration of the material, and is often stated in terms of water as the standard.

3.8. The Earth's Mass. The process of evaluating the constant G (4.14) in the statement of the law of gravitation is sometimes called "weighing the earth," because, when the constant is known, it is easy to calculate the mass of the earth from this law. Only two additional data are needed, namely, the acceleration of a falling body at some point on the surface, with allowance for the centrifugal effect of the earth's rotation, and the distance of that point from the center of attraction. By the law of gravitation, the mass is ad^2/G. When these quantities are known, the mass can be calculated; and the density is found by dividing the mass by the volume.

The earth's mass is 5.98×10^{27} grams, or 6.6×10^{21} tons.
The volume is 1.083×10^{27} cm.^{3}
The density is 5.52 times that of water.

In other words, the earth has 5½ times the mass of an equal volume of water.

The earliest attempts to weigh the earth followed a different plan. They consisted in observing the effect of a mountain on the direction of gravity at a nearby station (the station error). The deflection of the plumb line toward the mountain gives the ratio between the mass of the mountain and that of the earth. If the former can be estimated, the earth's mass becomes known. This method was first tried by Bouguer, in 1740, on Mount Chimborazo in Peru. It makes an appeal to the imagination, this mighty balance with the earth in one pan and the mountain in the other; but the mountain method is not an accurate one.

Formerly a mountain was regarded as something extra that was piled above the normal surface of the earth. The present view holds that there is a deficit of material under a mountain and an excess under an ocean bed, so that the surface irregularities are everywhere compensated, when a depth of 60 miles is reached. All vertical columns of the earth of the same cross section are equally massive. This is the theory of compensation, or isostasy.

3.9. The Interior of the Earth.

The deepest borings have penetrated to a depth of scarcely more than two miles. What lies below is as inaccessible to direct observation as the interior of a remote star. The evidence we have concerning the earth's interior comes indirectly from astronomical and geophysical sources.

The earth's interior is denser than the surface layers. This is certain, because the earth as a whole is 5.5 times as dense as water, while the surface rocks average only 2.7. Moreover, the ellipticity is less and the precessional motion is faster than they would be if the density were uniform. It was formerly supposed that increasing density with increasing depth is caused entirely by the added pressure. At the center of the earth, the pressure of the overlying rocks exceeds three million atmospheres. But high compression alone is not sufficient explanation.

The interior is composed of heavier materials. According to Adams and Williamson (1923) of the Geophysical Laboratory at Washington, the arrangement of material within the earth is something like the following:

	Lowest depth in miles	Density (times water)	Composition
outer layer	35	2.7–3.3	granites; silicates
basic layer	1000	3.3–4.4	iron-magnesium silicates
pallasite layer	2000	4.4–9.5	silicates; iron
central core	center	9.5–10	nickel-iron

The idea that the earth may have an iron core was considered as early as 1873 by Dana. Revived by Wiechert in 1897, the theory has found favor, because it interprets fairly well the velocities with which earthquake shocks are transmitted through the earth. The density of the core is about the same as that of the nickel-iron meteorites (6.30), if they were similarly compressed. If this view of the interior is the correct one, the chief constituents of the earth are the elements: iron, magnesium, silicon, and oxygen.

There is considerable difference of opinion regarding the internal constitution. So far as borings go, the temperature of the rocks rises about 1° C. for every 100 feet increase in depth. *If the rule persists* at greater depths, the temperature 60 miles below the surface must exceed the ordinary melting points of the rocks; but accompanying increase in pressure may well maintain the solid form all the way to the earth's center.

The interior of the earth is more rigid than steel. This fact is demonstrated by the speed with which earthquake waves are transmitted through the earth to distant seismographs, and by the height of the tides in the earth itself (4.38).

THE EARTH'S ATMOSPHERE

As the medium through which the heavens are viewed, the atmosphere is of interest in astronomy. Whatever effect it has on the light of the celestial bodies, that alters their directions or appearance, must be understood and allowed for. A number of phenomena within the atmosphere have important astronomical connections; "shooting stars" are an example. Cyclones have their counterparts in the sun, and auroras have the same frequency as sun-spots. Moreover, the telescopic views of other planets having atmospheres can be best interpreted on the basis of a knowledge of our own atmosphere.

3.10. Its Arrangement and Composition. The earth's atmosphere is a mixture of gases of different kinds under the influence of gravity. If it were left to itself, the air would assume an *isothermal* arrangement, that is to say, it would have a uniform temperature and decreasing density upward, with the heavy gases at the bottom and the light ones at the top. But the air is heated from above by the sun and from below by the earth's radiation, and it passes the heat along slowly. Moreover, at the bottom it is continually agitated by currents and storms. The lower and the upper layers of the atmosphere are therefore different in arrangement and receive different names.

(1) The *troposphere,* or *convection region,* extends from the earth's surface to a height of seven miles, or a little more. It is the region of vigorous convection — ascending and descending currents

— and of clouds. Since the density of the air diminishes rapidly with increasing elevation, this shallow layer contains 80 per cent of the mass of the entire atmosphere. The mean temperature drops as we ascend, at the rate of 9°.4 C. a mile, from 11° C. at the earth's surface to −55° C. at the top of the troposphere.

(2) The *stratosphere,* or *isothermal region,* has its base at the elevation of about seven miles and rises to a height of several hundred miles. At least to an elevation of 22 miles, the maximum attained by sounding balloons, the average temperature of this region remains the same, about −55° C., or 67° below zero Fahrenheit.

The principal gases of the atmosphere at the earth's surface by volume in dry air, according to Humphreys, are: nitrogen 78 per cent, oxygen 21 per cent, argon 1 per cent, and much smaller amounts of carbon dioxide, neon, hydrogen, and helium. Dust is present in variable amounts and water vapor averages 1.2 per cent of the whole volume. These proportions of the gases remain the same to the base of the stratosphere, except that the water vapor is practically all condensed into clouds before this level is reached.

In the stratosphere the gases are distributed according to their molecular weights. At the height of 75 miles not much remains except the lightest element, hydrogen, and a trace of helium. Some authorities have questioned the presence of hydrogen in the atmosphere in any appreciable amount; they suggest that helium predominates at very high levels.

The mass of the atmosphere, according to Humphreys, is 5.11×10^{21} grams, or 5.1×10^{15} tons, which is somewhat less than one millionth of the mass of the solid earth. In order to weigh the atmosphere, we have merely to multiply the average air pressure at the earth's surface (1002 grams/cm.^{2}, or 14.3 pounds to the square inch) by the area of the surface (51×10^{17} cm.^{2}); for the pressure on any area of the surface is the weight of the column of air above it, and the weight, after slight corrections have been made, gives the mass.

3.11. Sounding the Atmosphere.

Mountains make it possible to study the atmosphere thoroughly to a height of more than four miles. Airplanes and manned balloons have ascended into the stratosphere. Sounding balloons have carried self-registering instruments as far as 22 miles aloft. Up to this level, the characteristics of the atmosphere are fairly well known. Conditions above this level are arrived at by inference from the known region below, and from observations of three phenomena which occur in the upper regions.

The observed duration of twilight (3.20) shows that the air is sufficiently dense up to an elevation of 45 miles to reflect a considerable amount of sunlight.

Meteors become luminous at heights averaging around 75 miles. They are bits of stone and metal which plunge into the atmosphere and are heated to incandescence by friction with it. With allowance for the flight through the air before the meteors become hot enough to glow, observations of meteor trails (6.19) indicate the presence of air at a height exceeding 100 miles.

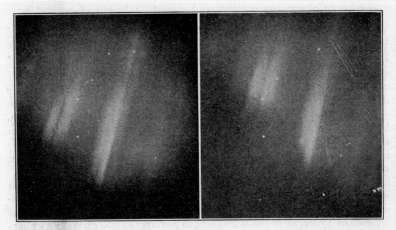

FIG. 3.11. Auroral Streamers Photographed Simultaneously at Two Stations. The difference in direction of the streamers on the two photographs can be seen with reference to the stars of the Dipper. By this parallax effect (4.21) the height of the streamers was determined. (From photographs by Carl Störmer in Norway)

Auroral streamers (3.21) have been observed by Störmer as high as 500 miles above the earth's surface. If the earth is represented by a globe 18 inches in diameter, this observed height is a little more than an inch above the surface of the globe. It seems probable that the atmosphere extends, highly rarified, to still greater altitudes.

3.12. Clouds. Aside from the obvious fact that we cannot observe the celestial bodies when the sky is cloudy, this subject may seem to have no connection with them. But other planets, Venus, Mars, Jupiter, and Saturn, have atmospheres and clouds too, which partly or entirely obscure their surfaces. Some attention to our own clouds may well be of service for the interpretation of the restricted " upside-down " view we have of weather conditions on the other planets.

Rising air is the principal source of clouds. Diminishing pressure as the altitude increases allows the air to expand; thereby it is cooled and the water vapor it contains is condensed, as on a cold window pane. Descending air is becoming warmer by compression and is therefore unfavorable for cloud formation. Thus the sky is more likely to be cloudy in regions of low pressure where the air is rising, and clear in the " highs " where it is descending. Clouds are classified with regard to appearance and altitude into four primary types:

Fig. 3.12. Cirrus Clouds. (From a photograph by F. Ellerman, Mount Wilson Observatory)

Cirrus clouds are the fibrous and feathery clouds of fair weather. They are the highest clouds, attaining altitudes of seven miles or more, where temperatures are far below freezing; they are therefore composed entirely of ice needles and snowflakes. As a storm approaches, they thicken into the more uniform but still fibrous and icy cirro-stratus clouds at altitudes of five miles or more, which are accountable for the finest halos around the sun and moon.

Cumulus clouds, or " woolpack " clouds, are the most spectacular. Their flat bases are about a mile above the earth's surface, and their spreading tops are much higher. Cirro-cumulus clouds have altitudes averaging four miles; they produce the " mackerel sky." There are other interesting varieties.

Stratus clouds, or layer clouds, occur in various combinations at widely different altitudes, from the high cirro-stratus to the fog-like stratus proper, whose average altitude is one-half mile, and to the surface fog itself. *Nimbus clouds* are the formless clouds from which rain is falling.

3.13. Kinetic Theory of Gases. It is supposed that the molecules of which a gas is composed are in continual motion, and that their speeds become greater as the temperature of the gas is raised. This theory transforms the apparently still air of a room into a very lively scene. Innumerable molecules are speeding in all directions, incessantly colliding with one another and with the walls, and bounding back. By virtue of the collisions, any one of the molecules may be brought momentarily almost to rest, or else impelled to a speed far exceeding the average.

The absolute temperature of the air is proportional to the average kinetic energy of its molecules (the mass of each one times the square of its velocity), or the average mv^2. Therefore v^2 is proportional to $T/\overline{m}$. *The average squared velocity of the molecules varies directly as the temperature of the gases, and inversely as their mean molecular weight.* For some of the constituents of the air the molecular velocities at 0° C. are as follows:

Hydrogen	1.84 km./sec.	Nitrogen	0.49 km./sec.
Helium	1.31	Oxygen	0.46
Water vapor	0.61	Carbon dioxide	0.39

At 100° C. these velocities are increased 17 per cent; at −100° C. they are diminished 20 per cent. The velocities of the molecules in the air at ordinary room temperatures are around one third of a mile a second. The kinetic theory of gases is an important consideration in its relation to the atmospheres of the earth and of the celestial bodies, and indeed wherever we are concerned with aggregations of gas, as for example in theories of cosmic development.

3.14. Loss of Atmosphere; the Velocity of Escape. The ability of any planet to retain an atmosphere of gases around it depends on the *velocity of escape* at the planet's surface, that is to say, the speed an object must acquire in order to escape from the planet. If a ball is thrown upward, it is soon brought down by the earth's attraction; if it is now given a greater initial speed, the ball goes higher, but again it returns to the ground. The problem is to calculate the initial speed that is just enough to overcome the downward pull of gravity, so that the ball will continue upward and become an independent celestial body.

If the planet's mass, m, and radius, r, are known, the calculation is easily performed; for it can be shown that the velocity of escape squared, v^2, is $2\,G\,m/r$, where G is the known constant of gravitation. Thus the velocity of escape at the earth's surface is 11.2 km./sec., or about seven miles a second. Now a molecule having this speed near the earth's surface would be trapped by surrounding molecules and could not escape; but in the rarified upper air it might well succeed in doing so. Jeans has calculated that the time required for the entire isothermal region of the planet's atmosphere to stream away is only a thousand years, if the mean velocity of the molecules is one fourth the velocity of escape; but the time rises to a billion years, if the fraction is one fifth.

Planet	Velocity of escape	Mean velocities of the molecules at which the entire *upper* atmosphere will escape in		
	km./sec.	1 thousand km./sec.	1 million km./sec.	1 billion years km./sec.
Jupiter	60	15	13.5	12
Earth	11.2	2.8	2.5	2.2
Mars	5.0	1.2	1.1	1.0
Mercury	3.6	0.9	0.8	0.7
The Moon	2.4	0.6	0.5	0.5

It is interesting to compare the accompanying table with the actual mean velocities of the molecules given in the preceding section. The planet Jupiter ought to have an extensive atmosphere; and this applies equally well to the outer planets Saturn, Uranus, and Neptune, whose velocities of escape are respectively 36, 21, and 23 km./sec. The earth should retain all gases except perhaps hydrogen; the same is true of Venus, for which the velocity of escape is 10.2 km./sec. In the case of Mars, helium becomes doubtful, but water vapor and the heavier gases should remain. For Mercury the retention of water vapor, nitrogen, and oxygen in any considerable amounts seems improbable, owing to the proximity of this planet to the sun and the consequently high temperature of its surface. It appears almost certain that the moon has been unable to keep any of these gases.

The conclusion is that all the principal planets, except Mercury, may have atmospheres, and that celestial bodies no larger than the moon have none, because their attractions are too weak.

3.15. Refraction of Light.

The wave theory of light asserts that light is produced by waves which are propagated in all directions from a source of light, and are analogous to the waves that spread over the surface of a pond, when a stone is thrown in. Waves of different lengths, from crest to crest, give rise to the different colors of the spectrum, varying from 1/35,000 inch for the reddest light to 1/70,000 inch for the violet; this is the range of wave-length to which the eye is sensitive. All waves have the same speed in a vacuum (2.12). They move less rapidly through a medium such as air, glass, or water,

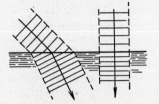

FIG. 3.15. Refraction of Light. A ray of light passing from a rarer into a denser medium is refracted toward the perpendicular.

depending on the density of the medium; and the retardation is greater for the shorter waves than for the longer ones.

A *" ray of light "* denotes the direction in which any portion of the wave system is moving. For certain purposes it is convenient to picture rays of light as radiating in all directions from the source and continuing always in straight lines, as long as they remain in the same homogeneous medium. Thus light is said to travel in straight lines.

When a ray of light passes from one medium into another, as from air into water, part of the light is turned back, or *reflected* at the boundary; the remainder goes on through the water with reduced speed in this denser medium. If the ray falls obliquely, the part of each wave crest on one side of the " ray " enters the water and has its speed reduced before the part on the other side enters. The crest is therefore swung around, and the ray changes direction (Fig. 3.15).

Refraction of light is the change in the direction of a ray of light when it passes from one medium into another of different density. The change is generally *toward the perpendicular to the boundary, if the second medium is the denser, and away from the perpendicular, if it is less dense.* When the light enters the second medium at right angles to the boundary, there is no refraction; for all parts of the wave crest enter and are retarded at the same instant.

When a ray of white light passes obliquely into another medium, it is *dispersed* into the colors of the rainbow, because *the amount of refraction increases as the wave-length decreases;* the change in direction is greater for violet than for red light. Refraction of light is thus accompanied by its dispersion into the spectrum having the red and the violet at the ends, and the other colors in between.

3.16. Refraction Increases the Altitude of a Star.

As a ray of starlight enters the atmosphere, it is refracted downward according to the rule just given; and the bending continues until the earth's surface is reached, because the density of the air increases downward. The point in the sky from which the light appears to come is therefore above the star's true direction. Atmospheric refraction elevates the celestial bodies by amounts which depend on the distance from the zenith.

Zenith distance	Refraction	Zenith distance	Refraction
0°	0′ 00″	85°	9′ 45″
20	0 21	86	11 37
40	0 48	87	14 13
60	1 40	88	18 06
70	2 37	89	24 22
80	5 16	90	34 50

These values for average conditions are somewhat altered by variations in the temperature and pressure of the air.

A star directly overhead is not displaced by refraction, because its rays are perpendicular to the atmospheric layers. The amount of the refraction increases as the distance from the zenith increases, but so slowly at first that for considerably more than halfway to the horizon the effect on a star's direction is appreciable only with the telescope. As the horizon is approached, the effect becomes rapidly more noticeable. A star at the horizon is raised by refraction more than half a degree, or slightly more than the apparent diameter of the sun, or moon.

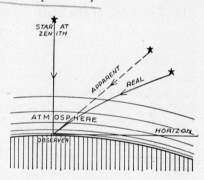

FIG. 3.16. Atmospheric Refraction Increases the Star's Altitude. Since the starlight is bent down in passing through the air, the star is apparently elevated. A star in the zenith is not displaced by refraction.

3.17. Refraction Effects near the Horizon. Owing to refraction the sun comes fully into view in the morning before any part of it is really above the horizon, and in the evening it is still visible when it has really passed below the horizon. Thus *refraction lengthens the daily duration of sunshine;* in latitude 40° three or four minutes are added at both ends. The times of sunrise and sunset (also moonrise and moonset) are given in the *Nautical Almanac*. They are the times when the upper limb appears on the horizon; the center is really 50′ below, of which 34′ is due to refraction, and 16′ is the sun's semi-diameter.

Similarly, the rising of a star is hastened, and its setting is delayed. Refraction also increases by more than half a degree the radius of the region around the north celestial pole whose stars never set (1.13), and diminishes by the same amount the southern cap of the sky that never rises.

Since refraction increases with the distance from the zenith, the bottom of the sun's disk is raised more than the top. This apparent vertical contraction of the sun is more noticeable near the horizon, because it is there that the amount of the refraction becomes greater most rapidly as the zenith distance increases. Sometimes the sun appears so decidedly flattened, when it is near the horizon, that even the casual observer remarks on its resemblance to a football.

3.18. Twinkling of the Stars. The twinkling, or scintillation, of the stars, that is to say, their rapid changes in brightness and sometimes in color also, is an effect of the continual turmoil in the atmosphere near the earth's surface. Vertical currents and the horizontal movements of layers differing in temperature and in water content produce varying irregularities in the density of the air through which the rays of starlight pass. Two factors contribute to the twinkling, first, the *variable refraction of the rays;* at any point they may be focused for an instant and spread out at the next. The second factor is *interference* of the light, which results either in the reinforcement, or else in the mutual destruction of the rays so focused. Thus starlight comes to us non-uniformly, just as sunlight gathers into dancing patches at the bottom of a brook.

Stars near the horizon twinkle most noticeably, because their rays describe longer paths through the atmosphere. Here, too, the bright stars change color as they twinkle. Dispersion, which always accompanies refraction of light, elongates the stars into very short spectra whose colors twinkle separately. Sirius, the Dog Star, is remarkable in this respect, owing to its great brilliancy; near the horizon it flashes the whole gamut of prismatic colors.

Ordinarily the large planets do not twinkle perceptibly. Their steady light readily distinguishes them from the neighboring stars.

Similarly the moon does not twinkle, nor does a street light that is close at hand. The planets, like the moon, are luminous disks, although the telescope is required to show them as such. Each point of the disk twinkles, but the effects are not synchronized; for the rays from different points take slightly different paths through the air, and do not encounter the same irregularities. Thus the planet's light maintains a fairly steady average brightness.

3.19. Lunar and Solar Halos.

The luminous rings often seen around the moon are formed by the refraction of moonlight through the ice

FIG. 3.19. A Solar Halo. Halo of 22° radius observed at St. Moritz, Switzerland, October 8, 1928. (From a photograph by F. Quénisset)

needles and snowflakes which constitute the cirrus and cirro-stratus clouds. These crystals are six-sided, with flat bases, like the ones that fall in winter. Since they are turned in all directions in the clouds, the light takes different paths through them, and many effects are possible. Most common of the halo formations is the ring of 22° radius. It has often the colors of the rainbow, with the red inside and most prominent. Within this ring the sky is always darker than it is outside. When many crystals float with their bases horizontal, two "moon dogs" appear on the ring to the right and left of the

CARL A. RUDISILL
LIBRARY
LENOIR RHYNE COLLEGE

CARL A. RUDI...
LIBRARY
LENOIR RHYNE

moon. A second ring having a radius of 46° and other effects are observed less frequently.

Solar halos and " sun dogs " are produced in the same way and have the same characteristics. The popular belief that halos are warnings of approaching storms has scientific foundation in the fact that cirro-stratus clouds themselves are forerunners of storms.

3.20. Twilight. Daylight is not abruptly followed by darkness after sunset, because the air overhead is still in sunlight, and *reflects* and scatters it down to us. Night comes on gradually, as the sun sinks farther below the horizon, and as the dull blue *twilight arch* of the earth's shadow rises in the east and overspreads the sky. *Civil twilight* lasts about 30 minutes in latitude 40°, until the sun's center is 6° below the horizon, when the light has become too dim for outdoor activities of the daytime, although it is still twenty times brighter than the light of the full moon. *Astronomical twilight* ends when the sun's center is 18° below the horizon. The sky is then so dark that the faintest stars have come out overhead.

The duration of twilight is shortest at the equator (about $1^h 10^m$), because the sun's diurnal motion is there perpendicular to the horizon (1.12) so that the sun descends most rapidly. In the latitude of New York the duration varies from $1^h 30^m$ at the times of the equinoxes to two hours in June. On June 22, astronomical twilight persists all night north of latitude 48½°, civil twilight north of 60½°, up to about 66° where the midnight sun is seen.

Since twilight is an effect of the atmosphere, the appearance of a twilight zone between the day and night sides of the planet Mars shows that it has an atmosphere; the absence of such a zone on the moon indicates lack of atmosphere there.

3.21. The Aurora Borealis, or " northern lights," is a familiar occasional phenomenon of the upper atmosphere. Characteristic of many auroras is the luminous arch in the northern sky, having its apex in the direction of the magnetic pole. Rays like searchlight beams spread upward from the arch, while bright patches, streamers, and draperies sometimes extend to all parts of the sky. Many auroras are white, but green, yellow, and red ones are not uncommon. At times their light is fairly steady; at other times the features change in brightness and position with surprising rapidity. Auroral displays are more frequent in the northern parts of the United States than in the southern parts, and are still oftener seen in Canada. The aurora australis is the same phenomenon observed in high latitudes of the southern hemisphere.

While the cause of the aurora is imperfectly understood, it is generally agreed that the glow is produced by something coming from outside. Störmer and others have advanced the theory that it is caused by electrified particles emitted from the sun. Hulbert suggests that atoms in the upper atmosphere, after being disrupted by the sun's ultra-violet rays, may drift toward the magnetic poles and recombine with the emission of auroral light.

Auroras are more frequent when sun-spots are numerous. They are always accompanied by unusual activity of the compass needle

FIG. 3.21. The Aurora Borealis. The V-shaped head of Draco appears near the upper extremity of the long streamers. (From a photograph by Carl Störmer, Oslo, Norway)

(magnetic storms) and sometimes by serious interference with telegraph and radio service. Auroral light is diffused over the sky at all times, whether or not definite streamers are visible.

3.22. Effects of the Atmosphere on Radiation of Different Kinds.
The effects of the atmosphere on the radiations that it receives from the sun and earth differ in a remarkable way, depending on the wavelength (color) of the radiation.

(1) *The air scatters the short waves (ultra-violet, violet, and blue light).* The molecules of the air are too small to reflect light waves as a mirror does; instead they serve as impediments to the shorter waves chiefly, and scatter them in all directions. This splashing of the short waves of the sunlight accounts for the blue color of the sky, and for its brightness which prevents the stars from being seen in the daytime. Since the maximum scattering is outward, the extreme

ultra-violet light, that is destructive to life, is fortunately unable to penetrate to the surface of the earth. Scattering accounts also for the reddening of the sun when it is near the horizon.

(2) *The air transmits longer waves (especially yellow, orange, and red light)* to the earth's surface. Part of the sunlight is at once reflected back again; part is absorbed by the surface and more slowly returned by reradiation. This radiation from the earth is, almost entirely, of wave-length greater than that of the reddest light.

(3) *The air absorbs the still longer waves which the earth radiates*, and is warmed thereby. It returns some of the heat to the earth, and passes the rest on outward very slowly, thus serving as a great blanket around the earth, protecting it against the rapid dissipation of its heat. Like the glass roof of the greenhouse the atmosphere allows the sun's radiation to enter freely, and hinders the escape of the heat it produces. The water vapor is very effective in this respect.

These properties of the atmosphere relative to radiation have an important bearing on climate and on life. They are also of interest in connection with studies of other planets having atmospheres. The clearest views of details in a planet's atmosphere ought to be obtained by photographing it through ultra-violet filters, while the surface details of the planet should be best delineated on plates exposed behind red filters. We shall see, in Chapter V, that this is indeed the case.

MOTIONS OF THE MOON

3.23. The Earth-Moon System. The earth is accompanied in its annual circuit of the sun by its single satellite, the moon, whose diameter, 2160 miles, is a little more than one fourth of the earth's diameter. Small as compared with the general run of the visible celestial bodies, the moon nevertheless ranks sixth in size among all the satellites of the solar system. Moreover, it is larger and more massive in comparison with the earth than any other satellite is with respect to its primary. This is the outstanding feature of the earth-moon system; on this account it has more nearly the characteristic of a *double planet,* and it may have developed in a different manner than other planet-satellite systems.

Viewed from the earth, the satellites of the other planets are telescopic objects; but the earth-moon system as seen from one of the nearer planets would have the appearance of a brilliant double star plainly visible to the unaided eye. From Venus, for example, the earth would appear much brighter than this planet ever does to us, while the moon would be as bright as Jupiter, and their separation would be at times as much as half a degree. It seems probable that the contrasting blue color of the earth and the yellowish hue of the moon would add much to the beauty of this spectacle in the skies of Venus.

In our own skies the moon is, next to the sun, the most conspicuous of the celestial bodies, owing to its small distance from the earth; in fact, near perigee the moon is apparently a little larger than the sun, although its average geocentric angular diameter (31' 5") is slightly less. These relations have an important bearing on the character of solar eclipses. The approximate equality in apparent size arises from the remarkable circumstance that the sun, while it is nearly 400 times larger than the moon, is about this many times farther away.

3.24. Revolution of the Earth-Moon System around the Sun.
We have hitherto described the earth's annual revolution without refer-

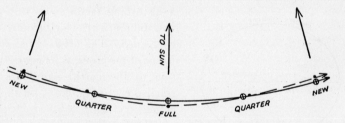

Fig. 3.24. Orbits of the Earth and Moon Around the Sun.

ence to the moon. Since these two bodies are making the circuit together, not side by side, but mutually revolving meanwhile in the period of 27⅓ days, the orbit of each one relative to the sun has a wavy character. What has been called the earth's orbit is strictly the orbit of the center of mass (4.17) of the earth-moon system, with respect to which the two bodies revolve. Imagine them joined by a stout rod. The center of mass is the point of support at which they balance.

If the masses of the earth and moon were equal, the center of mass would be halfway between their centers, and their orbits around the sun would be identical, except that the waves would differ in phase by 180°, so that the two bodies would be alternately within and without the elliptical orbit of the center of mass. The moon's mass is in fact 1/81.56 of the earth's mass. The center of mass is therefore only 1/82.56 of the way, or about 2900 miles, from the earth's center toward the moon, and so is within the earth.

The problem of determining the moon's mass is solved when the position of the center of mass becomes known. This is found by observing the extent of the earth's monthly revolution as it slightly affects the directions of the sun and nearer planets. An excellent way also of finding the moon's mass is by calculations from the rate of the earth's precessional motion.

It is not an easy matter to show by means of a diagram (Fig. 3.24) the paths of the earth and the moon around the sun. If the distance between the earth and the sun is put equal to the length of this printed page, the distance between the earth and moon on the same scale scarcely exceeds the diameter of one of the periods on the page. The reader is urged to be on guard against being misled concerning the relative sizes and distances of astronomical bodies by the limitations of the diagrams. A drawing exactly to scale would show that *the paths of both the earth and moon are always concave to the sun.*

3.25. Moon's Orbit Relative to the Earth.
The mutual revolution of the earth-moon system is unaffected by its common motion around the sun, and may be considered independent of it, although the sun is a disturbing factor; it is this relative motion with which we are now concerned. The *orbit of the moon,* for most purposes, is its course relative to the earth — an ellipse of small eccentricity, 0.055 on the average.

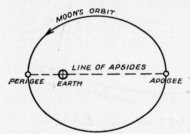

FIG. 3.25. Moon's Orbit Relative to the Earth. The orbit is an ellipse of small eccentricity (much exaggerated in the Figure) with the earth at one focus.

The mean distance between the centers of the earth and moon is 238,857 miles, or 384,403 km., about 60¼ times the earth's equatorial radius. At *perigee,* when the moon is nearest the earth, the distance is 221,463 miles; at *apogee,* when it is most remote, the distance has increased to 252,710 miles. The major axis, or *line of apsides,* revolves eastward once in 8.85 years. This is only one of many variations in the moon's orbit, which arise from the difference in the sun's attraction for the moon and earth in the course of their mutual revolution. Our present ability to foretell the positions of the moon with considerable accuracy, despite the complexity of its movements, is made possible by the thorough treatment of the disturbing factors. The work of E. W. Brown of Yale University on the lunar theory is the most recent authority in these matters.

3.26. Configurations of the Moon.

The elongation of the moon is its angular distance from the sun. *Elongation in longitude* is the difference between the celestial longitudes of the moon and sun, measured east or west from the sun through 180°. Special values of the elongation receive distinctive names, and all together are the *configurations* of the moon.

The moon is in *conjunction* with the sun when these two bodies have the same celestial longitude; it is in *quadrature* when the difference in longitude is 90°, and in *opposition* when the difference is 180°. For the conjunctions of the planets with the moon and with each other the predicted times in the *Nautical Almanac* are the instants when the two bodies have the same right ascension.

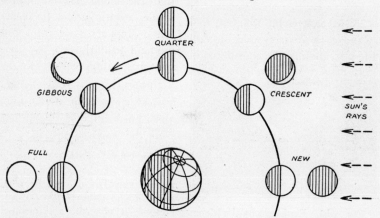

FIG. 3.27. The Phases of the Moon. The outer figures show the phases as seen from the earth.

3.27. The Moon's Phases.

The changing figures of the waxing and waning moon are among the most conspicuous of celestial phenomena, and were among the first to be understood. Like the earth, the moon is a dark globe shining only by reflected light. As the moon revolves around the earth, the sunlit hemisphere is presented to us in varying amounts. This is the cause of the phases.

At conjunction, when the moon is between the earth and the sun, the dark side is toward us and the phase is *new*. With increasing eastern elongation the illuminated hemisphere gradually comes into view; the phases are successively *crescent, first quarter,* near quadrature, *gibbous,* and finally *full,* when the moon arrives at opposition and the bright side faces fully toward us. The phases are then repeated in the reverse order with the same designations except that the phase near western quadrature is *last quarter.* The moon's *age* is the interval at any time since the preceding new moon.

The *terminator* is the line between the bright and dark sides of the moon; it is the sunrise line that we see before full moon, and the sunset line thereafter. Aside from irregularities in its course, which arise from the mountainous character of the lunar surface and which are often noticed without the telescope, the terminator is elliptical, because it is a circle seen in projection. The full circle coincides with the limb of the moon at the full phase, while at the quarter phases it is turned edgewise, appearing as a straight line. The sharp delineation of the terminator is to be noticed as one of the many indications that the moon has no appreciable atmosphere. It seems but a step across it from full daylight to darkness. No twilight band intervenes.

The horns, or *cusps,* of the crescent moon point always away from the sun, whose direction is denoted by the perpendicular to the line joining the horns at its middle point. This is also nearly the course of the ecliptic in the moon's vicinity. It will be seen, therefore, that the position of the crescent at moonrise and moonset depends on the angle between the ecliptic and horizon at those times (1.20). It is left to the reader to show that the horns of the crescent moon are most nearly vertical after sunset in the spring, and before sunrise in the autumn.

Fig. 3.28. Earthlight on the Moon at the Crescent Phase. The bright crescent is lighted directly by the sun. The remainder of the moon's disk is dimly illuminated by sunlight reflected from the earth. (From a photograph by E. E. Barnard, Yerkes Observatory)

3.28. Earthlight on the Moon. The earth as viewed from the moon exhibits the whole cycle of phases also, and these are supplementary to the moon's phases. " Full earth " occurs at the time of new moon. Thus moonlight with us has its counterpart in earthlight on the moon. At the crescent phases the part of the lunar disk that is not in direct sunlight is made plainly visible by the sunlight reflected from the earth. Full earthlight on the moon is something like 40 times brighter than the light of the full moon on the earth; for the earth is not only a larger mirror, but it is also a better one, since it reflects nearly one half of the light it receives from the sun.

The bright crescent, because of its greater brightness, appears to have a larger diameter than the earthlit part of the disk, and so to be wrapped around it. This illusion of the difference in scale of the two parts becomes more striking as the quarter phase is approached, although at this phase the earthlight has faded almost to invisibility.

Spectroscopic observations and photographs in different colors show that earthlight contains a greater percentage of blue light than there is in direct sunlight. This result is not surprising, for a considerable part of the light is selectively reflected by the earth's atmosphere, and in this light the blue of the sky predominates.

3.29. Sidereal and Synodic Months. Astronomically, the month is the period of the moon's revolution. As in the cases of the day and year the different kinds of month arise from the different points to which the motion is referred. The *sidereal month* is the true period of the moon's revolution; it is the interval between successive conjunctions with the same star, as seen from the center of the earth. Its average length is 27^d 7^h 43^m 11^s.5, or nearly 27⅓ days, but it varies as much as seven hours owing to perturbations.

The *synodic month* is the interval between successive conjunctions of the moon and sun, from new moon to new moon

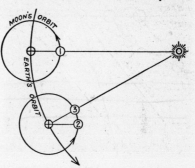

FIG. 3.29. The Synodic Month Longer than the Sidereal Month. Between positions 1 and 2 the moon has made one revolution, completing the sidereal month. The synodic month does not end until the moon has reached position 3.

again. This *month of the phases* is the period in which the moon gains a lap on the slower moving sun, and is therefore longer than the sidereal month. The average length of the synodic month is 29^d 12^h 44^m 2^s.8, or a little more than 29½ days; it varies, however, more than half a day.

Between the sidereal month M, the synodic month S, and the sidereal year E there is the simple relation: $1/M - 1/E = 1/S$. These reciprocals are mean daily motions. Thus the moon moves eastward among the constellations $360°/M$, or $13°.2$ daily; it gains on the sun $360°/S$, or $12°.2$ a day. In one hour it moves a little more than half a degree, or slightly more than its own diameter — a useful fact to remember.

3.30. Daily Retardation of Moonrise. The moon has two conspicuous movements in the sky. Owing to the earth's rotation, it rises and sets with the rest of the celestial scenery, progressing steadily westward. In addition, it is always moving eastward among the constellations, because of its revolution around the earth; this motion delays its transits, risings, and settings from day to day. Just as the solar day is longer than the sidereal day because of the sun's eastward displacement, so the interval between successive transits of the moon, which might be termed the lunar day, is longer than the solar day, because the moon's eastward movement is more rapid than that of the sun.

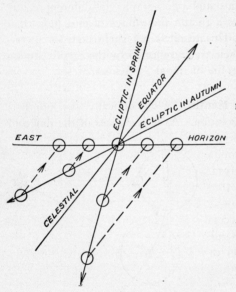

FIG. 3.31. Explanation of the Harvest Moon. Owing to the eastward motion along its path nearly coinciding with the ecliptic, the moon rises later from night to night. For the nearly full moon, the delay is the least around September 23, in northern latitudes, because the ecliptic is the least inclined to the horizon at moonrise.

When the eastward motion is considered, the moon gains a lap on the sun in one synodic month; but with respect to the diurnal motion it loses a day in this period, so that 28.5 lunar days are equal to 29.5 solar days. The interval between transits of the moon is therefore 29.5/28.5 times 24 hours, or $24^h\ 50^m.5$ — twice the interval between high tides. Thus the moon transits 50½ minutes later from day to day *on the average*. It departs from this average as much as 15 minutes, however, mainly for the same reasons that apparent solar days vary in length (2.19), namely, because its orbit is eccentric, and because its path is inclined to the celestial equator.

The daily retardation of moonrise averages 50½ minutes also, but the observed retardation at any time may depart greatly from this value, especially in high latitudes. In the latitude of New York, the greatest possible delay exceeds the least by more than an hour. It depends on the angle between the moon's path, which nearly coincides with the ecliptic, and the horizon; the smaller the angle at moonrise, the less is the retardation.

As we have already noticed (1.20), the ecliptic is least inclined to the eastern horizon (in north latitudes) when the vernal equinox rises, and most inclined when the autumnal equinox rises. In the vicinity of these two points in its monthly circuit of the heavens the moon is the least and the most delayed in its time of rising. The unusually small retardation is especially conspicuous when the moon is also near the full phase — at the times of the harvest moon and the hunter's moon.

3.31. The Harvest Moon is the full moon that occurs nearest the *time* of the autumnal equinox (September 23). Since the sun is then near the autumnal equinox, the full moon is near the vernal equinox, and is therefore in that part of its path which is the least inclined to the horizon as it rises. The peculiarity of the harvest moon, that distinguishes it from other moons near the full phase, is its minimum delay in rising from night to night, so that there is moonlight early in the evening for an unusual number of evenings. This is true only in the northern hemisphere; in southern latitudes the retardation is, in fact, the maximum at this time.

In latitude 40° north the delay may be as small as 13 minutes, while farther north it becomes even less. The small angle between the moon's path and the horizon is made further evident by the rapidity with which the rising point moves along the horizon toward the north.

The hunter's moon is the full moon following. Since it is not far from the vernal equinox, the retardation is still considerably less than average. The full moon nearest March 21 is the other extreme. In latitude 40° it may rise as much as $1^h 20^m$ later from night to night, and it therefore speedily withdraws from the early evening sky. It is at this season, however, that the moon, when it is near full, lingers longest in the evening skies of the southern hemisphere.

3.32. Apparent Path in the Sky; Regression of the Nodes. The moon's path among the constellations can be easily observed. It is necessary simply to notice its position each night relative to the stars, and to record the places on a suitable map, or globe. Greater accuracy is obtained by the use of a telescope, from whose circles the right ascension and declination may be read at each pointing; or the moon's coordinates may be taken from the *Nautical Almanac* where they are tabulated for every hour.

The moon's apparent path is nearly a great circle having the average inclination of 5° 9′ to the ecliptic. It therefore intersects the ecliptic at two opposite *nodes*. The *ascending node* is the point where the moon crosses the ecliptic going north; at the *descending node* the moon moves south across the ecliptic.

Regression of the nodes is their westward displacement along the ecliptic, just as the equinoxes slide westward in their precessional motion, but at a much faster rate; for a complete revolution of the nodes is accomplished in 18.6 years. From this and other rapid changes in the moon's orbit, for which the sun's attraction is mostly responsible, the moon's apparent course among the constellations is considerably different from month to month.

3.33. The Moon's Changing Declination. Since the moon's path on the celestial sphere departs only a little from the ecliptic, the moon moves north and south during the month about as much as the sun does in the course of the year. Near the position of the summer solstice it rises in the northeast, sets in the northwest, and is high in the sky (in the northern hemisphere) at meridian transit; near the winter solstice, about two weeks later, the moon rises in the southeast, sets in the southwest, and crosses the meridian at a lower altitude. An interesting example of the many compensations in nature is furnished by the full moon, which, being opposite the sun, rides highest in the long winter evenings and lowest in the summer.

When, however, the inclination of the moon's path to the ecliptic is taken into account, it is seen that the range in declination varies perceptibly as the nodes regress. When the ascending node coincides with the vernal equinox, the moon's path is inclined to the celestial equator 23° 27′ plus 5° 9′, or 28° 36′; this occurred early in 1932. Nine years later, when the ascending node has moved to coincidence with the autumnal equinox, the inclination to the equator is 23° 27′

minus 5° 9′, or 18° 18′. Thus the moon's highest and lowest altitudes at upper meridian transits in latitude 40° average in the first case 78° 36′ and 21° 24′ respectively, and in the second case 68° 18′ and 31° 42′ — a decrease in range of more than 20°.

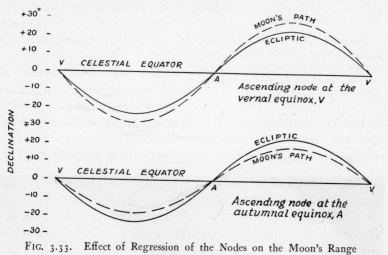

FIG. 3.33. Effect of Regression of the Nodes on the Moon's Range in Declination.

The variation of 10° in the moon's maximum declination in the 18.6-year cycle is chiefly responsible for nutation, the nodding of the earth's axis in this period, which accompanies its precessional motion. Another effect of the regression of the nodes appears in the case of the harvest moon. When the inclination of the moon's path to the celestial equator is the greatest, its inclination to the horizon is least of all at the rising of the ascending node. At such times the retardation in the rising of the harvest moon is unusually small.

3.34. The Moon's Rotation; Librations. *The moon rotates on its axis in the same period in which it revolves around the earth,* namely, the sidereal month of 27⅓ days. In consequence of the equality of the two periods the moon presents nearly the same hemisphere toward the earth at all times. It is always the face of the " man in the moon " that we see at the full phase and never the back of his head. But an examination of the moon's surface throughout the month shows that features near the edge of the disk are turned sometimes into view and at other times out of sight. The moon seems to rock slightly; these apparent oscillations or *librations* arise from three causes.

(1) *The libration in latitude* results from the inclination of about 6½° between the moon's equator and the plane of its orbit. At in-

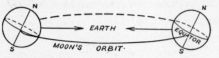

tervals of two weeks the lunar poles are tipped alternately toward and away from us; at times we can see 6½° beyond the north pole, at others the same distance beyond the south pole. The explanation of this libration is similar to that of the seasons.

FIG. 3.34. The Moon's Libration in Latitude. Owing to the inclination of the moon's equator to the plane of its orbit, the poles of the moon are alternately presented to the earth.

(2) *The libration in longitude* is brought about by the failure of the moon's rotation and revolution to keep exactly in step throughout the month, although they come out together at the end. The

FIG. 3.34A. The Moon's Libration in Longitude. The prominent group of seas is nearer the moon's limb in the picture at the right. (From photographs at the Paris Observatory, by courtesy of Carl Zeiss, Inc.)

rotation, like the earth's, proceeds at a very nearly uniform rate; but the revolution is not uniform, because the moon's orbit is an ellipse, and the law of areas holds. Thus the moon seems to rock in an east and west direction, allowing us to see as much as 7¾° farther around in longitude at each edge than we could otherwise.

(3) *The diurnal libration* is produced by the earth's rotation. Even if the other librations were absent, so that the same hemisphere were turned always toward the earth's center, we on the surface view the moon from slightly different directions during the day, and therefore see slightly different hemispheres. From the elevated position nearly 4000 miles above the center of the earth the observer can see, at most, one degree farther over the western edge at moonrise, and the same amount over the eastern edge at moonset.

These are the principal *apparent librations*. There is also a small *physical libration* arising from irregularities in the moon's rotation. When the month is completed, fully 59 per cent of the moon's surface has been visible, while the remaining 41 per cent is never seen. Throughout this region that is hidden from us the earth would be, of course, invisible to lunar observers. As seen from 41 per cent of the moon's surface that always faces us, the earth never sets, but it moves about in the lunar sky in a complicated manner, owing to the librations; from the intervening 18 per cent of the moon the librations cause the earth to rise and set at about the same point of the horizon.

THE MOON'S PHYSICAL FEATURES

3.35. Appearance with the Telescope. Excellent views of the moon's surface are obtained with small telescopes. One of the best of the earlier maps of the moon, by Beer and Mädler in 1837, was made with the aid of a telescope scarcely 4 inches in aperture. Considerably better results may be had with instruments between 6 and 12 inches in diameter. Still larger telescopes are useful under good conditions for examining the finer detail, and for securing photographs.

The most prominent features of the surface are the dark seas, which are also conspicuous to the unaided eye, the mountain ranges, craters, rays, and rills. Mountains, craters, and rills are clearest near the terminator, either the sunrise or sunset line, where shadows are long and the contrast is pronounced. The bright rays and the seas are best at full moon; although at this phase the shadows are too short to afford much contrast between mountain and plain. Altogether, the most pleasing views are offered within about two days of the quarter phases.

Long before the invention of the telescope Plutarch and others appear to have believed that the irregularities of the moon's terminator, which are easily visible to the unaided eye, are caused by mountains and their shadows. Galileo, in 1610, was the first to observe the lunar mountains with the telescope, and to notice that they are, for the most part, nearly circular.

FIG. 3.36. The Moon Shortly After the Full Phase. The sunset line is appearing at the left. The seas and bright rays are conspicuous; the longest ray system radiates from Tycho, near the upper edge. Many short, crooked rays surround the crater Copernicus, to the right of the center and a little below it. The mountains are not prominent near the full phase. (From a photograph at the Hamburg Observatory, Bergedorf, Germany)

3.36. The Lunar Seas. The dark areas which form to the unaided eye the face of the "man in the moon," the profile of the "girl in the moon," the "hare," "frog," and other products of the lively imagination, are the lunar *maria* (*seas*), so-called long ago when they were thought to be bodies of water. Some later writers have preferred the term "plains." There are 14 seas, the largest being distinguished by the rank of ocean (Oceanus Procellarum), and also smaller swamps, lakes, and bays. They have fantastic names, for example, Mare

Serenetatis (Sea of Serenity), and Sinus Iridum (Bay of Rainbows).
All connected, with the exception of two small isolated seas, Mare
Crisium and Mare Humorum, they cover about one half of the
moon's visible surface, and predominate in the northern hemisphere.

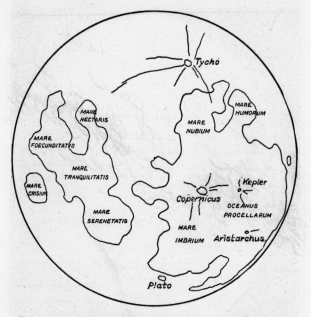

FIG. 3.36A.   Key to Photograph of Nearly Full Moon.

The majority of the seas are roughly circular; of these Mare Imbrium
is the largest with a diameter somewhat more than 700 miles.

Although they lack the extremely rugged scenery of the mountainous country to the south, the seas are far from monotonous as
viewed with the telescope. They are broken by many craterlets and
clefts, and by the summits of partly submerged mountains. Wrinkles,
which resemble flow marks, rise in places to heights of 700 feet; the
great serpentine ridge near the Sea of Serenity is 300 miles long.

3.37. Mountain Ranges.

3.37. Mountain Ranges. Best known of the few lunar mountain
ranges are the three that form the curving western border of the
Mare Imbrium and separate it from the Mare Serenetatis. They are
the Apennines, Caucasus, and Alps — among the few surviving names
from Hevelius' map of the moon (1647), in which the lunar formations have the names of terrestrial ones. These mountains are steep

on one side and slope gradually on the other; and they contain thousands of peaks, the highest one rising nearly 20,000 feet above the plain. In the Leibnitz and Doerfel ranges, near the south pole and

FIG. 3.37. The Moon About Two Days After First Quarter. The moon is inverted and reversed, as it appears ordinarily in the telescope. Near the terminator, which is here the sunrise line, the mountains show to the best advantage. In the upper part (near the south pole) the craters are especially numerous. A little more than halfway down along the terminator is the crater Copernicus, between the Mare Nubium, above, and the Mare Imbrium, below. (From a photograph at the Yerkes Observatory)

almost beyond the moon's limb, there are peaks having elevations of 26,000 feet — comparable with, but not as high as Mount Everest.

While elevations on the earth are given with respect to a single standard, namely, sea level, those on the moon are referred to the surrounding sea, or plain. Since the plains themselves are at different levels, the resulting heights are not so easily compared.

The height of a lunar mountain is determined either by measuring the length of its shadow, and calculating the sun's altitude as seen from that point on the moon, or, as Galileo did, by measuring the distance of its summit from the terminator, as it catches the first rays of the sun in the morning; at this instant, or when the sun is about to set there, the illuminated tip of the peak looks like a little star out in the dark beyond the terminator. A sketch of either situation will show that enough data are then known to make possible the calculation of the height of the mountain by solving a right triangle.

3.38. The Lunar Craters. The most remarkable characteristic of lunar mountains is their preference for nearly circular formations. These are the *craters,* unfortunately named perhaps, as are the seas.

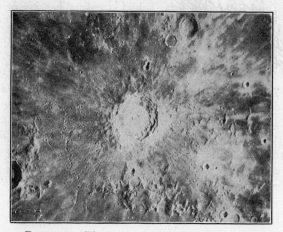

Fig. 3.38. The Crater Copernicus. The nearly circular, terraced wall, about 60 miles in diameter, rises 11,000 feet above the floor. The central mountain has several peaks. (From a photograph by F. G. Pease with the 100-inch reflecting telescope, Mount Wilson Observatory)

Individually, they bear the names of distinguished scientists and philosophers of former times, such as Copernicus and Aristarchus, according to the system of lunar nomenclature introduced by Riccioli in 1651. In number they exceed 30,000, and in size they range from the great walled plains, such as Clavius and Grimaldi, of which the largest measure nearly 150 miles in diameter, to the smallest pits, or craterlets, 1000 feet or less across, that can be seen with large telescopes. They are especially abundant in the regions of the southern hemisphere where the seas do not encroach.

The circumference of a lunar crater is a nearly circular ring of mountains, precipitous and often shelving on the inside, and more gradually sloping without. Lofty peaks surmount the wall, rising abruptly to heights as great as 20,000 feet. Lower peaks appear near the centers of many craters. In some cases the crater floor is depressed several thousand feet below the level of the surrounding plain; in others it is elevated, notably in the crater Wargentin, where the floor is raised nearly to the top of the rampart. Some craters have rough, bright floors; Aristarchus is brightest of all. Others, such as Plato, have floors as smooth and dark as the seas.

3.39. Rays and Rills. *Rays* are bright streaks, often five or ten miles wide, which radiate from points near a few of the craters, and pass over mountain and plain alike without much regard for the topography. Best seen when the sun is high above them, the rays are prominent features of the full moon. The most conspicuous and longest ray system radiates from Tycho near the south pole, giving the full moon in a small telescope an appearance something like that of an orange. A fine system of shorter, more crooked, and somewhat less brilliant rays centers in the crater Copernicus. Pease, observing with the 100-inch reflector, sees the rays " as the illuminated sides of low mounds which always cast their shadows in the same direction that the neighboring craters do."

There are many *rills*, or clefts — cracks of the order of half a mile wide and of unknown depth. Some are very tortuous, while others seem nearly straight for a hundred miles or more and, like the rays, to pay little attention to surface irregularities. Faults are to be seen also.

3.40. History of the Surface Formations. The origin of the moon's surface features is imperfectly understood. At first sight it may seem surprising that an object so open to minute inspection as the moon is should be mysterious in any way, until we reflect that cosmic origins in general are difficult to trace, and that geologists are far from agreement as to the early history of the earth's surface. Two hypotheses concerning the origin of lunar craters have received much attention:

(1) *The craters are the result of volcanic activity on the moon.*
This view, which has been held for more than two centuries, still
finds favor, in some form, among the majority of astronomers. The
chief objection to the hypothesis has been the disparity in size between explosive terrestrial volcanoes, such as Vesuvius, which do not
exceed a few miles in diameter, and the larger lunar craters, particularly the great walled plains. This objection remains after allowance has been made for the smaller surface gravity of the moon.

(2) *The craters were produced by the impacts of large meteors.*
The impact hypothesis appears to have originated with Proctor in
1873. It was revived about twenty years ago and has had a considerable following. Artificial craters formed in the laboratory by
the impacts of projectiles against various materials often resemble
lunar craters, even to the presence of the central peak. These craters
have been studied in this connection, and Meteor Crater (6.34) in
the Arizona desert, four fifths of a mile in diameter, is cited as a
natural example. But the vast size of lunar craters is raised against
this hypothesis also, while the absence of corresponding great scars
on the earth's surface may not be entirely consistent with it.

In the literatures of geology and astronomy there are a great many articles
dealing with the origin of the lunar formations on these and other hypotheses.
Whatever the successful theory may turn out to be, it would seem that it must
explain, among other things, the following:

(1) Formation of great elliptical, or polygonal, areas on the moon's surface, whose remains we see in the curved sweep of the Apennines, Caucasus,
and Alps, in the nearly circular form of the seas generally, and in the great
walled plains.

(2) Diminishing size of the craters. In the cases of overlapping craters,
the smaller one breaks in the wall of the larger. Conditions around the cir-
cumferences, and sometimes in the centers of the elliptical formations were
appropriate for mountain building, and perhaps also for volcanic activity of
the explosive type.

(3) Formation of the seas by material which spread over half the surface,
dissolving and submerging the original features.

(4) Appearance of craterlets. These could be of either igneous or
meteoric origin, or both.

3.41. Reflection of Sunlight from the Moon.

The *albedo* of a celes-
tial body is its efficiency as a reflector of light; it is the ratio of the
total amount of radiation it reflects to the amount that falls upon it.
The average albedo, or reflecting power, of the moon's surface is
0.073 according to Russell; with allowance for shadows, it is com-

parable with that of rather dark brown rock (brown, as he points out, since the photographic albedo is still less). The remaining 93 per cent of the sunlight that falls on the moon is absorbed, and heats the surface. But there are large variations from the average albedo. Portions of the seas are nearly as black as the shadows, while Aristarchus, the brightest spot on the moon, is as white as snow.

Ultra-Violet   Extreme Red

FIG. 3.41. The Full Moon Photographed in Different Colors. Differences in the relative intensities of the details are shown, especially in the seas. A dark spot to the right of Aristarchus, near the right edge of the moon, is prominent in the ultra-violet photograph, and almost absent as photographed with red light. (From photographs by W. H. Wright, Lick Observatory)

Low albedo may be taken to mean the absence of appreciable atmosphere; for air, especially when clouds are suspended in it, has a higher reflecting power. According to Abbot, the earth's atmosphere and its clouds reflect 37 per cent of the incident sunlight.

Something like 465,000 full moons at average distance would be needed to produce an illumination equal to sunlight; there is room in the visible half of the sky for only one fifth of this number. At any other phase the moon's light is reduced far more than the fraction of the disk which belongs to the hemisphere that is then turned away from the sun, because of the shadows along the terminator, and the very slanting and therefore weakened sunlight in these regions. Although half of the visible hemisphere is turned toward the sun at the quarter phases, Stebbins' measurements with the selenium photometer show that the brightness at first quarter is only 12 per cent of that of the full moon; at last quarter it is reduced to 10 per cent, because the dark seas then cover a larger part of the visible sunlit area.

3.42. Temperatures at the Moon's Surface.

According to Pettit and Nicholson the temperature of the moon's surface varies from 400° K (261° Fahrenheit), when the sun is overhead, to 120° K (−243° F.) on the dark side — extreme conditions from day to night that no one would care to experience. These are the temperatures of the rocks; at noon they have been exposed to the sun's rays continuously for a week with no protecting atmosphere interposed. The rapid cooling of the rocks when sunlight is withdrawn is made evident by measurements of these observers during the total lunar eclipse of June 14–15, 1927. During the eclipse the temperature dropped nearly 200° C. (360° F.).

The relations between the temperature of a body and the intensity and character of its radiation are formulated in the radiation laws (7.38). By use of the appropriate law the temperature can be calculated when the radiation has been measured. The radiation received from the moon can be measured by means of a thermocouple placed at the focus of the telescope. Allowance must be made for the fact that some of the radiation is simply sunlight reflected at the moon's surface; what fraction this is of the whole can be learned by interposing in the path of the rays a vessel of water, which transmits the sunlight, but is opaque to the low temperature radiation of the moon itself. In this way the temperatures of the moon and planets have been determined, although the matter is less simple for a planet having an atmosphere.

3.43. Conditions at the Moon's Surface.

From its small velocity of escape we have already concluded (3.14) that the moon can have no appreciable atmosphere. The low albedo points to the same conclusion which is further supported by many other easily observed characteristics of the surface. There is no evidence of twilight, and no haze dims the moon's limb. No clouds obscure the view, and no erosion by weathering can be noticed.

Whenever the moon occults a star, the disappearance is sudden, without preliminary fading and reddening of the starlight; and the interval until the star reappears is precisely the interval calculated geometrically, undiminished by refraction which in our atmosphere delays the sunset and hastens the time of sunrise (3.17). Nor is there any effect at the time of solar eclipse that may be ascribed to a lunar atmosphere.

There are no large bodies of water on the moon. Small amounts

would speedily evaporate in the daytime, or else might persist as ice
in cracks where sunlight does not enter. It is quite possible that
water is present in the composition of the rocks.

FIG. 3.43. Southern Portion of the Moon at Last Quarter. Above the
center of the picture is the crater Tycho from which bright rays radiate. Above
this crater, about halfway to the upper edge, is the walled plain Clavius,
nearly 150 miles in diameter. The shadows lengthen as the terminator (sunset line) is approached. Part of the Mare Nubium is at the lower right.
(From a photograph by F. G. Pease with the 100-inch reflector, Mount
Wilson Observatory)

The totally dissimilar landscape on the moon would impress the visitor from the earth. Absence of air, and the smaller value of gravity would produce many unfamiliar effects. A black sky instead

Fig. 3.43A. Northern Portion of the Moon at Last Quarter. A large part of the picture is occupied by the Mare Imbrium. This sea is bordered above by the Apennines, and at the left by the Caucasus and Alps. To the right of the Alps is the crater Plato whose floor is especially dark, and farther to the right is the Bay of Rainbows. (From a photograph at the Mount Wilson Observatory)

of a blue one would be filled with stars day and night alike. The absence of any sound would be noted, except sound transmitted by the rocks, the sudden transition from the long day to the long night, the sharp contrast between light and shade over the landscape, and the entire absence of life or activity of any kind. The moon is the perfect desert; for steadiness, clearness, and continuity of the view of the celestial bodies it is the perfect site for an observatory.

Eclipses of the Moon and Sun

Eclipses of the moon occur when the moon, at the *full* phase, passes through the earth's shadow, and is therefore darkened. Solar eclipses occur when the moon, then at the *new* phase, passes between the earth and the sun, so that its shadow falls on the earth; the observer within the shadow sees the sun wholly or partially hidden by the moon.

3.44. Shadows of the Earth and Moon. Since the earth and moon are globes smaller than the sun, the shadow of each one is a cone having its apex directed away from the sun. This region, from which

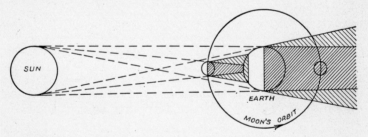

FIG. 3.44. The Cause of Solar and Lunar Eclipses. When the moon is between the earth and the sun, its shadow falls on a portion of the earth; within this region the sun is eclipsed. When the moon is opposite the sun, it is eclipsed by the earth's shadow.

sunlight is geometrically entirely excluded, will be spoken of as the *shadow,* though it is in fact only one part of the shadow, the *umbra;* surrounding it is the larger inverted cone of the *penumbra,* from which the light is only partially excluded. There is no way of observing the shadows except as they encounter objects that shine by reflected sunlight. The dark arch of the earth's shadow on the atmosphere can be seen rising in the east at nightfall.

The average length of the earth's shadow is easily calculated from the following proportion between two similar triangles:

$$\frac{\text{length of earth's shadow}}{\text{length of shadow} + \text{sun's distance}} = \frac{\text{earth's diameter}}{\text{sun's diameter}} = \frac{1}{109.1}.$$

Thus the average length of the earth's shadow is the fraction 1/108.1 of the sun's mean distance (92,870,000 miles), or 859,000 miles, varying each way less than two per cent. Since the shadow is more than a hundred times longer than its greatest width, it is inconvenient to represent it in diagrams in its proper proportions.

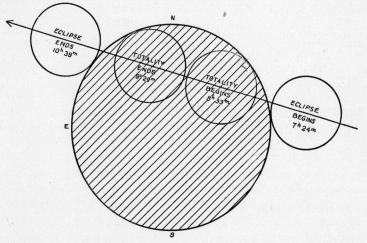

FIG. 3.45.   Path of the Moon Through the Earth's Shadow During the Eclipse of the Moon, November 27, 1928.   The times are Greenwich civil times.

By a similar procedure it is found that the moon's shadow averages 232,000 miles in length when the moon is between the earth and the sun.

3.45. The Moon in the Earth's Shadow.

If a screen could be placed opposite the sun at the moon's mean distance from us, the earth's shadow falling normally upon it would appear as a dark circle whose diameter is found from similar triangles by the relation:

$$\frac{\text{diameter of shadow}}{\text{diameter of earth}} = \frac{\text{length of shadow beyond moon}}{\text{length of shadow}} = \frac{620}{859},$$

since the length of the shadow is 859,000 miles, and the moon's mean distance is about 239,000 miles. The diameter of the shadow, where the moon passes through, is therefore 620/859 of the earth's diameter (about 7920 miles), which is not far from 5700 miles, or 2⅔ times the moon's diameter.

Since the shadow is always opposite the sun, it moves eastward around the ecliptic once a year. At intervals of a synodic month, the faster moving moon overtakes the shadow and, whenever it then encounters the shadow, enters at the *west* side and moves through at the rate which is the difference between the speeds of the moon and shadow; the hourly rate is about 30', or very nearly the moon's diameter.

Eclipses of the moon are total and partial. The longest eclipses occur when the moon passes centrally through the shadow; the duration of the whole eclipse is then about 3ʰ 40ᵐ, and of totality 1ʰ 40ᵐ. Non-central eclipses are shorter, depending on how nearly the moon's path approaches the center of the shadow. When the least distance exceeds the difference between the radii of shadow and moon, there is no total phase.

A lunar eclipse is visible wherever the moon is above the horizon during its occurrence, that is, over more than half of the earth, counting the region that is rotated into view of the moon while the eclipse is going on. The Greenwich civil times when the moon enters and leaves the penumbra and umbra, and of the beginning and end of totality, are published in advance in the various almanacs. To obtain the times at any other place it is necessary simply to add or subtract the difference between Greenwich time and the Standard time of the place.

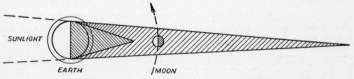

Fɪɢ. 3.46. Visibility of the Moon in Total Eclipse. Sunlight is refracted by the earth's atmosphere into the shadow and upon the eclipsed moon.

3.46. Eclipses of the Moon. In its passage through the penumbra the moon is darkened very gradually; but soon after it enters the umbra, a dark notch appears at the east limb and slowly overspreads the disk. At first, it seems very dark in contrast. As totality comes on, however, the details of the moon's surface often become plainly visible. Even when it is entirely immersed in the shadow, the moon is still illuminated by sunlight. The light has filtered through the earth's atmosphere around the base of the shadow, and has been refracted into the shadow and upon the moon; red predominates in this light, for the same reason that the sunset is red.

The brightness of the totally eclipsed moon varies greatly from one eclipse to another, depending on the state of the weather in the circle of the earth bordering the base of the shadow cone. Obstruction of the light by clouds, and dustiness of the air are both important factors. In Fisher's summary of lunar eclipses over a period of 60 years it appears that the surface features were clearly visible in some instances, while in others they were practically invisible, not only to the unaided eye, but also with small telescopes. Shane's photographs with filters of different colors show a marked increase in the redness of the light toward the axis of the shadow.

Lunar eclipses are interesting spectacles to us, as they have been to people of all times; and they occur often enough to be seen by everyone.

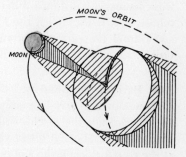

3.47. The Moon's Shadow on the Earth.

On the average, the moon's shadow (umbra) at central eclipse does not touch the earth; for the average length of the shadow at new moon is only 232,000 miles, while the moon's mean distance from the earth's center is 238,900 miles, and not much less than 235,000 miles from the nearest point

Fig. 3.47. Annular Eclipse of the Sun. The umbra of the moon's shadow does not reach the earth's surface. Within this shadow geometrically produced, a thin ring of the sun's disk remains visible around the moon.

on its surface. Owing to the eccentric orbit of the earth-moon system around the sun, the length of the moon's shadow varies from 236,000 miles at aphelion to 228,000 miles at perihelion. The moon's distance from the earth's surface varies from 217,800 miles at perigee to 248,500 miles at apogee. On comparing these values we see that when aphelion and perigee occur together, the moon's shadow falls on the earth's surface 18,200 miles from the apex; but when perihelion and apogee occur together, the shadow is 20,500 miles too short to reach us. These are the extremes.

The first case produces the *total eclipse* of the sun. Within the shadow, which can never exceed 167 miles in diameter, when the sun is overhead, the observer sees the dark circle of the moon completely hiding the sun's disk. The second case gives the *annular eclipse*. In the circle of the geometrical shadow produced beyond its apex, never more than 194 miles across except by distortion around the curving surface, the observer sees the disk of the moon centrally projected upon that of the sun, but slightly smaller, so that a ring, or annulus, of the sun's disk remains uneclipsed. Annular eclipses are 20 per cent more frequent than total eclipses.

Around the small area in which the eclipse is total or annular is the much larger partly shaded region of the penumbra. Measured at right angles to the axis of the shadow, it is a circle some 2000 miles in radius; on the surface it may be increased to 3000 miles. Here the moon hides only a fraction of the sun's disk, the fraction diminishing with increasing distance from the center of the region, and the eclipse is *partial*. When the axis of the shadow is directed slightly away from the earth, as often happens, only the partial eclipse is visible.

3.48. Path of the Shadow. Because of the moon's revolution, the shadow moves generally eastward at the average rate of 2100 miles an hour. Since the earth's rotation at the equator is at the rate of 1040 miles an hour, also eastward, the effective speed of the shadow at the equator, when the sun is overhead, is 1060 miles an hour. In other parts of the earth where the speed of the rotation is less, the effective speed of the shadow is greater; and it is still more when the sun is low, attaining a maximum of 5000 miles an hour. Considering the great speed of the shadow and its small size, it is evident that a total eclipse of the sun can not last long in any one place. The maximum possible duration scarcely exceeds $7^m 30^s$. An annular eclipse may last a little longer, while the partial phase accompanying either type of eclipse may have a duration of more than four hours from beginning to end.

The *path of total eclipse,* or of annular eclipse, is the narrow track of the shadow as it sweeps generally eastward over the earth's surface, from the time when it first touches the earth at sunrise until it departs at sunset. Meanwhile, the penumbra moves over the larger surrounding region in which the eclipse is partial.

Occasionally, the shadow touches the earth at the middle of its path, but at the beginning and end fails to reach the surface. It begins as an annular eclipse, changes to total, and later reverts to the annular type. The eclipse of April 28, 1930 is an example. The eclipse was annular from Polynesia nearly to the British Isles, except from California to Montana where it was total, with a maximum duration of only one and a half seconds.

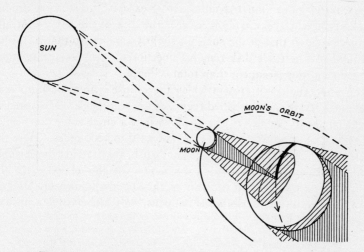

Fig. 3.48. Path of Total Eclipse. Owing to the moon's eastward revolution, the small shadow-dot moves in an easterly direction over the earth's surface. Within the shadow-dot the eclipse is total. Elsewhere, within the larger circle of the penumbra, the eclipse is partial.

The paths of total and annular eclipses, and the regions in which they are partial are calculated in advance and published in the various almanacs for the year in which they occur. The dates, durations at noon, and regions of total solar eclipses, following the eclipse of 1932, are:

Date	Duration (minutes)	Region
1934, Feb. 14	2.7	Borneo, Celebes
1936, June 19	2.5	Greece, Central Asia, Japan
1937, June 8	7.1	Pacific Ocean, Peru
1940, Oct. 1	5.7	Colombia, Brazil, South Africa
1941, Sept. 21	3.3	Central Asia, China
1943, Feb. 4	2.5	China, Alaska
1947, May 20	5.2	Argentina, Central Africa
1948, Nov. 1	1.9	Central Africa, Congo

3.49. Phenomena of the Total Solar Eclipse. As a spectacle the total eclipse of the sun ranks among the most impressive of celestial phenomena. While the details vary considerably from one eclipse to

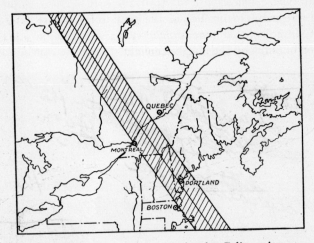

FIG. 3.48A. Path of the Total Solar Eclipse, August 31, 1932. A portion of the path, through Quebec and New England. The shadow traversed this part of its path between 3:10 and 3:35 P.M., Eastern standard time. (From data furnished in advance of its publication by the Director of the *American Ephemeris and Nautical Almanac*)

another, depending on the diameter of the shadow and other factors, the principal phenomena to be noted are much the same on all these occasions.

As the crescent of the sun becomes narrow, an unfamiliar pallor overspreads the sky and landscape, because the quality of the light from the sun's limb differs from that of normal sunlight. Immediately preceding totality the sky darkens rapidly; shadow bands, like ripples, appear on white surfaces; animals grow disturbed and some flowers close; and the shadow rushes in, while the last sliver of the vanishing sun breaks into brilliant " Baily's beads " and quickly disappears.

With the coming of totality the corona appears; it is pearly white, brilliant immediately around the moon and fading out in streamers. Flame-like prominences (7.31) rise from the scarlet chromosphere of the sun. Their bases around the west limb are gradually uncovered, while those at the east limb are covered as the moon moves across. The brighter stars and planets are visible. Totality ends as suddenly as it began, and the phenomena of the partial eclipse recur in reverse order.

The scientific importance of the total solar eclipse arises from the appearance at that time of phenomena which are at other times rendered invisible by the intense sunlight. They are chiefly the sun's

FIG. 3.49. The Total Solar Eclipse of January 24, 1925. From a painting by Howard Russell Butler. (By courtesy of the American Museum of Natural History, New York)

corona, and some aspects of the prominences and the underlying chromosphere. The visibility of stars and planets in the sun's vicinity has permitted special studies, such as the search for the suspected intra-Mercurial planet (5.4), and more recently the observations of the apparent displacement of stars near the sun predicted by the theory of relativity (4.36).

3.50. Eclipse Seasons. Eclipses of the sun and moon take place respectively when the moon is new and full. These phases recur every month, but eclipses are less frequent. The reason is that the moon's apparent path in the sky is inclined 5° 9′ to the ecliptic. Each time, when the moon returns to conjunction with the sun, or with the shadow opposite the sun, both objects have moved eastward from their places at the preceding conjunction. Since they are traveling in different paths, the moon will pass north or south of the sun, or shadow, unless it is near one of the nodes; only then can the moon pass across the sun, or into the shadow.

Eclipses occur, therefore, not every month, but at nearly opposite seasons of the year, when the sun is in the vicinity of one of the nodes of the moon's orbit. These are the *eclipse seasons.* As the nodes regress rapidly westward, the eclipse seasons are more than half a month earlier from year to year. The interval between two successive conjunctions of the sun with the same node of the moon's path is the *eclipse year;* its length is 346.620 days. About the beginning of 1932, the moon's nodes were coincident with the equinoxes (3.33). The middle times of the eclipse seasons then occurred in March and September.

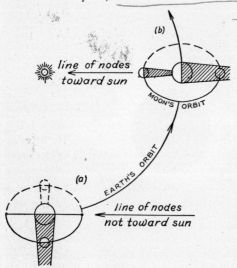

FIG. 3.50. Eclipse Seasons. Since the moon's orbit is inclined about 5° to the plane of the earth's orbit, eclipses can occur only at the two opposite seasons, as at (*b*), when the sun is near the line of nodes of the moon's orbit. At other times in the year, as at (*a*), the moon does not pass between the earth and the sun, nor into the earth's shadow.

3.51. Solar and Lunar Ecliptic Limits. The *solar ecliptic limit* is the distance of the sun from the node, at which it is grazed by the moon, as seen from some station on the earth. Within this distance the sun will be eclipsed; beyond it no eclipse can occur. The value of this limiting distance varies with the changing distances, and therefore apparent sizes, of the sun and moon, and with the fluctuations in the angle between the moon's path and the ecliptic. The extreme values, or *major and minor limits,* are respectively 18° 31′ and 15° 21′. When the sun is beyond the major limit, an eclipse is

impossible; when it is within the minor limit at the time of new moon, an eclipse is inevitable.

The *lunar ecliptic limit* is likewise the greatest distance of the sun from the node at which a lunar eclipse is possible. The major and minor limits are 12° 15′ and 9° 30′. At first sight, it may seem that

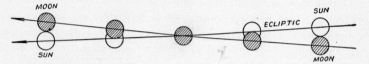

FIG. 3.51. The Solar Ecliptic Limit. In order to be eclipsed, the sun must be near one of the nodes of the moon's path. The maximum distance of the sun from a node, either east or west, at which eclipses are possible, is the solar ecliptic limit.

these limits should be greater, instead of less, than for solar eclipses. But we are concerned with the cone tangent to the sun and earth, which terminates as the umbra of the earth's shadow. In order to eclipse or be eclipsed, the moon must enter this cone. The diameter of the cone, where the full moon passes through, is 5700 miles, as we have seen (3.45); but it is more than 10,000 miles across at the position of the new moon, so that the solar ecliptic limit is the larger.

3.52. Frequency of Eclipses. The number of eclipses during each eclipse season is determined by comparing the double ecliptic limits with the distance the sun moves along the ecliptic in a synodic month with respect to the regressing node; this distance is 29.5/346.6 of 360°, or 30°.6. The question is whether the sun, and the earth's shadow opposite it, can possibly pass through the eclipse region without encountering the moon. They can do so, if the double ecliptic limit is less than 30°.6, although usually they may not escape. If the double limit is greater than 30°.6, one eclipse must take place at each node, and two are possible. Moreover, since the calendar year is over 18 days longer than the eclipse year, the first eclipse season may return at the very end of the year, and in this event *one* additional eclipse may result.

Two solar eclipses of some kind must occur every year; for twice the minor solar ecliptic limit is 30°.7. Five may occur. No lunar eclipse, or total (or annular) solar eclipse need occur during the year, although three of each kind are possible.

The minimum number of eclipses in a year is therefore two, both of the sun. This happens frequently, the next time in 1933. *The maximum number in a year is seven,* five of the sun and two of the moon (in 1935), or four of the sun and three of the moon (1982).

According to Mitchell, the number of solar eclipses in a century averages 237.5, of which 83.8 are partial only, 77.3 are annular, 10.5 are both annular and total, and 65.9 are total. Thus every three years two total solar eclipses take place somewhere in the world. For the earth as a whole, solar eclipses are more frequent than lunar eclipses in the ratio of four to three; but in any one place lunar eclipses are more numerous, owing to the greater area in which they are visible.

3.53. Recurrence of Eclipses. The *saros* is the interval of $18^y\ 11\frac{1}{3}^d$ (10 ⅓ days if five instead of four leap years are included) after which eclipses are repeated. It is equal to 223 synodic months, which contain 6585.32 days, and is nearly the same in length as 19 eclipse years (6585.78 days). Not only have the sun and moon returned to nearly the same positions relative to each other and to the node, but their distances are nearly the same as before, so that the durations of succeeding eclipses in a series differ very little. Knowledge of the saros, as it applies to cycles of lunar eclipses at least, goes back to very early times.

The effect of the one third of a day in the period is to shift the region of the following eclipse 120° west in longitude; after three periods it is nearly the same again. At the end of each period the sun is a half-day's journey, or 28′, west of its former position relative to the node. Thus a gradual change in the character of succeeding eclipses is brought about, together with a shift in latitude of the regions in which they occur.

Eclipses occurring at intervals of the saros fall into series, each series of solar eclipses containing about 70 eclipses and having a duration of 1200 years. A new series is introduced by a small partial eclipse visible near one of the poles. After a dozen partial eclipses of increasing magnitude and decreasing latitude, the series becomes total or annular for 45 eclipses, reverts to about a dozen diminishing partial eclipses, and finally disappears at the opposite pole. At present, twelve notable series of total eclipses are in progress; the one that is represented by the eclipses of 1919, 1937, and 1955 is remarkable because the durations of totality are not far from the greatest possible. A series of lunar eclipses runs through about 50 periods in a total of 870 years.

REFERENCES

Harold Jeffreys, *The Earth* (Cambridge University Press, 1929). " Its origin, history, and physical constitution."

W. J. Humphreys, *Physics of the Air* (McGraw-Hill, 1929).

S. A. Mitchell, *Eclipses of the Sun* (Columbia University Press, 1932).

T. Oppolzer, *Canon der Finsternisse*. This book contains the elements of solar and lunar eclipses between 1207 B.C. and 2163 A.D., and maps showing the approximate tracks of total and annular solar eclipses during this interval.

Total Eclipse of the Sun, August 31, 1932. A series of photographs taken at the Northwestern University observation station, Fryeburg, Maine, showing different stages of the eclipse until totality. (By courtesy of O. J. Lee, and of Wide World Photos, Inc.)

CHAPTER IV

THE SOLAR SYSTEM

MOTIONS OF THE PLANETS — THE LAW OF GRAVITATION — THE SCALE
OF THE SOLAR SYSTEM — MECHANISM OF THE SOLAR SYSTEM — TIDES

The solar system consists of the sun and the many smaller bodies
in its vicinity which, like the earth, revolve around the sun and share
its journey through the stellar system. It includes the planets with
their satellites, comets, and swarms of meteors. Its dimensions are
great as compared with terrestrial standards. The outermost planet,
Pluto, is about forty times farther from the sun than we are, while
the majority of comets have aphelion points even more remote.
But in comparison with the distance of even the nearest star, the
planetary spaces shrink to such insignificance that we look upon the
solar system as our own community, and the other planets as our
neighbors.

It is more than local pride, however, that makes the solar system
an important factor in astronomy; it is the relative ease with which
the motions and other characteristics of the planets may be studied,
owing to their proximity. Before the invention of the telescope,
astronomy was almost entirely confined to the solar system, and even
after its invention, until toward the close of the eighteenth century,
knowledge of the things that lie beyond this system was not far
advanced.

MOTIONS OF THE PLANETS

In its original significance the word *planet* (wanderer) was used
to distinguish from the many "fixed" stars the few celestial bodies
(excepting comets and meteors) that move about among the constellations. Seven were known: the sun, moon, and the five bright
planets, Mercury, Venus, Mars, Jupiter, and Saturn, the last of which
was supposed to be the outermost planet, and not far within the
sphere containing the stars themselves. Thus Omar Khayyam ascended in his meditation "from earth's center through the seventh

gate " to the throne of Saturn — from the center of the universe, as he understood it, almost to its limits.

The current meaning of the word "planet" began with the acceptance of the Copernican theory which added the earth to the list of planets revolving around the sun, and subtracted from the list the sun and the moon. Uranus, which is barely visible to the unaided eye, was discovered in 1781. Neptune, which is always too faint to be seen without the telescope, was found in 1846. The still fainter trans-Neptunian planet discovered in 1930 completes the list of the nine known *principal planets*. In the meantime, in 1801, Ceres, the largest of the asteroids, or *minor planets*, was the first to be discovered.

4.1. The Planets Named and Classified. The names of the planets in order of distance from the sun are:

$$
\begin{array}{l}
\text{Inferior planets} \left\{\begin{array}{l} \text{Mercury} \\ \text{Venus} \\ \text{Earth} \end{array}\right. \\
\text{Superior planets} \left\{\begin{array}{l} \text{Mars} \\ \text{The Asteroids or Minor planets} \\ \text{Jupiter} \\ \text{Saturn} \\ \text{Uranus} \\ \text{Neptune} \\ \text{Pluto} \end{array}\right.
\end{array}
\left.\begin{array}{l} \\ \\ \end{array}\right\} \text{Terrestrial planets}
\quad \left.\begin{array}{l} \\ \\ \\ \\ \end{array}\right\} \text{Outer planets}
$$

They are classified as inferior and superior planets, and also as terrestrial and outer planets. The *inferior planets* are nearer the sun than we are, while *superior planets* have orbits outside the earth's orbit. The *terrestrial planets* are the four inner ones, including the earth; the five *outer planets* are farther from the sun, and, with the exception of Pluto, are larger than the others.

Planets are distinguished from the stars by their motions among them, and in the case of the brighter planets by their steadier light, and by their disks when viewed with the telescope. They are cool, relatively small globes which revolve around the sun, and which shine by reflected sunlight. Venus, Jupiter, and sometimes Mars outshine the brightest stars.

4.2. The Revolutions of the Principal Planets around the sun are characterized by the following regularities:

(1) *Their orbits are nearly circular*. They are in fact ellipses of small eccentricity, but with more marked departure from the circular form in the cases of Pluto, Mercury, and Mars.

(2) *Their orbits are nearly in the same plane*. With the prominent exception of the trans-Neptunian planet, the inclinations of their orbits to the ecliptic plane do not exceed 8°; so that they are located in the sky always near the ecliptic, and mostly within the boundaries of the zodiac. It will be noticed that these characteristics do not apply to the orbits of comets and meteors, and of many asteroids.

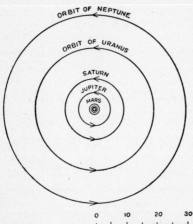

FIG. 4.2. Approximate Orbits of the Principal Planets. They are nearly circles with the sun at the common center, and nearly in the same plane. The orbits of the earth, Venus, and Mercury are too small to show clearly. The orbit of Pluto, averaging 40 units from the sun, is shown in Fig. 5.44.

(3) *The planets revolve from west to east*. This is the favored direction of revolution, and rotation also, for all members of the solar system. Only a few exceptions are known.

(4) Their mean distances from the sun are related approximately by the simple rule with which Bode, in 1772, anticipated the discovery of the asteroids (5.20). *Bode's law* is obtained by writing the numbers 0, 3, 6, 12, 24, . . , doubling the number each time to obtain the next one, and then by adding 4 to each number. When the sums are divided by 10, the resulting series of numbers: 0.4, 0.7, 1.0, 1.6, 2.8, . . , represents the distances of the planets from the sun expressed in astronomical units. The *astronomical unit* is the earth's mean distance from the sun. There was at that time, however, one exception to the rule; the number 2.8 between the numbers for Mars and Jupiter corresponded to no known planet. Bode pointed out that the success of the " law " in other respects justified a search for the missing planet. The discovery of Uranus in 1781, at a distance in satisfactory agreement with the series extended one term further, so strengthened his position that a systematic search was undertaken by a group of European astronomers.

As it turned out, the asteroid Ceres at the expected distance 2.8 was discovered accidentally by Piazzi. The number 2.8 is very nearly the average distance of the many hundreds of asteroids since discovered.

The law is not so successful in representing the distances of Neptune and of the recently discovered planet beyond it, nor would it be in the case of Mercury, if the rule of doubling the number had been adhered to at the beginning of the series. Bode's law has no known physical significance. It is at least an easy way of remembering the distances of the majority of the planets from the sun.

4.3. Sidereal and Synodic Periods. The *sidereal period* of a planet is the true period of its revolution around the sun. The *synodic period* is the interval between successive conjunctions, superior or inferior, or oppositions with the sun; it is the interval in which the faster moving inferior planet gains a lap on the earth, or the earth overtakes the slower going superior planet. The reciprocal of the synodic period, $1/S$, is the difference between the reciprocals of the sidereal period of the planet, $1/P$, and of the earth, $1/E$. Mars and Venus have the longest synodic periods among the principal planets (Table 5.I), because they run the closest race with the earth. The little asteroid Eros has the longest synodic period of all, about $2\frac{1}{3}$ years. It is evident that the synodic periods of the major planets must approach the length of the year as their distances from the sun, and so their sidereal periods, increase.

4.4. Configurations and Phases of the Inferior Planets. Since the inferior planets, Mercury and Venus, complete their revolutions in less time than a year, they gain on the earth, and therefore appear to us to oscillate to the east and west with respect to the sun's position. *Their configurations are unlike those of the moon* (3.26) which has all values of elongation up to 180°. After passing *superior conjunction* beyond the sun, the inferior planet emerges to the east of it as an evening star, and moves out to *greatest eastern elongation*. Here it turns west and, moving now more rapidly, passes between us and the sun at *inferior conjunction* into the morning sky. Turning east again at *greatest western elongation,* it returns to superior conjunction. Greatest elongation does not exceed 48° from the sun for Venus, and 28° for Mercury.

The phases of the inferior planets resemble those of the moon

(3.27); as these planets revolve within the earth's orbit, their sunlit hemispheres are presented to the earth in varying amounts. With the telescope, their disks show the full phase at the time of superior conjunction, quarter phases at the elongations, and new at inferior conjunction. It is worth noticing that these planets would not exhibit the whole cycle of phases, if they revolved around the earth, in accordance with the Ptolemaic system (4.8).

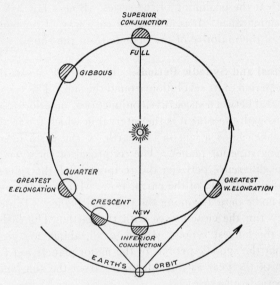

FIG. 4.4. Configurations and Phases of an Inferior Planet. The configurations differ from those of the moon; the phases are the same.

4.5. Configurations and Phases of the Superior Planets.
Since the superior planets have periods longer than a year, they move eastward in the sky more slowly than the sun appears to do, so that they are overtaken and passed by it at intervals. With respect to the sun's position they seem to move westward, and to attain all values of elongation from 0° to 180°. *The configurations of the superior planets are the same as those of the moon.*

Jupiter, as an example, emerges from conjunction to the west of the sun. It is then visible as a morning star, rising at dawn in the east. Moving westward continually with respect to the sun, it comes successively to western quadrature when it rises about midnight, opposition when it rises at sunset, and eastern quadrature when it sets about midnight. Setting earlier from night to night as it approaches the next conjunction with the sun, the planet is finally lost in the twilight in the west.

The superior planets do not exhibit the whole cycle of phases that the moon shows. At conjunctions and oppositions their disks are fully illuminated, and in other positions they do not depart much from the full phase; for the hemisphere turned toward the sun is nearly the same as the one presented to the earth. The *phase angle* is the angle at the planet between the directions of the earth and sun; divided by 180°, it gives the fraction of the hemisphere turned toward the earth that is in darkness. The phase angle is largest when the planet is near quadrature; for the nearest superior planet, Mars, its value may be as much as 47°. The maximum phase angle of Jupiter is 12°, and the values for the more distant planets are smaller. Thus the superior planets show nearly the full phase at all times, with the exception of Mars, which near quadrature resembles the gibbous moon.

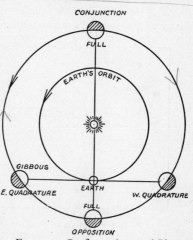

FIG. 4.5. Configurations and Phases of a Superior Planet. The configurations are similar to those of the moon. The only phases are full and gibbous.

4.6. Apparent Motions among the Stars.

It is instructive not merely to notice that the planets change their places among the constellations, but also to observe the paths they follow. Mars serves well as an example. Observe its location in the sky relative to nearby stars, and mark the place and the date on a star map. Repeat the observation about once a week as long as the planet remains in view in the evening sky. A smooth curve through the points, as in Fig. 4.6, represents the apparent path.

Against the background of the stars the planet's motion is for the most part eastward or *direct,* the same as the direction of its course around the sun. Once during each synodic period the planet turns and moves westward, or *retrogrades,* for a time before resuming the eastward motion. On the turns the planet is said to be *stationary*. Thus all the planets appear to move among the stars in a succession of loops, making progress toward the east, and never departing far from the ecliptic.

As long as the earth was believed to be motionless and the center of all planetary movements, these curious looped paths had necessarily to be ascribed entirely to the motions of the planets themselves.

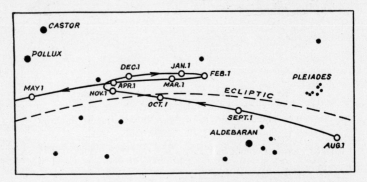

FIG. 4.6. Apparent Path of Mars Between August 1, 1928 and May 1, 1929. From the middle of November to the first of February the motion was retrograde.

Complex motions such as these evidently called for a complicated explanation; and this was forthcoming in the Ptolemaic theory (4.8). The problem was at length simplified by the acceptance of the earth's revolution.

4.7. Retrograde Motions Explained. Owing to the earth's swift movement in its orbit around the sun, the planets are shifted backward, toward the west, against the more distant background of the stars. It is the same effect that one observes as he drives along the highway; objects near the road fly past more rapidly than those in the distance. This effect combines with the planet's real eastward movement to produce the looped path that is observed.

A superior planet, such as Mars, retrogrades near the time of opposition; for the earth then overtakes the planet and leaves it behind. The direct motion becomes most rapid near conjunction, where the planet's orbital motion and its displacement due to the earth's revolution are in the same direction. An inferior planet retrogrades near inferior conjunction. This can be shown by extending the

lines in Fig. 4.7 in the reverse direction, whereupon it is evident that
the earth — an inferior planet relative to Mars, and then near in-

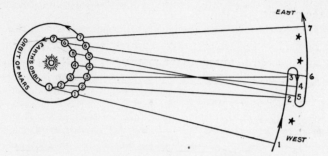

FIG. 4.7. Retrograde Motion of a Superior Planet. Positions of the earth at intervals of a month are numbered on
the inner circle. Positions of Mars in its orbit at the same
times are similarly numbered on the outer circle. As seen
from the faster moving earth, Mars describes a looped path
among the constellations, retrograding, at positions 4 and 5,
around the time of opposition.

ferior conjunction — is retrograding in the Martian sky. Mercury
and Venus exhibit this effect to us. In general, a planet retrogrades
when it is nearest the earth.

4.8. The Ptolemaic System. Ancient watchers of the sky were as
well acquainted as we are with the looped paths of the planets, which
have just been described. It became the major problem of astronomy
to account for these movements so satisfactorily that the places of the
" wandering stars " could be foretold. The problem itself is the same
as the modern one of celestial mechanics. But the whole construction was different from the current interpretation of planetary motions, because the early astronomers accepted as guiding principles
the postulates: (1) The earth is the center of all celestial motions,
and is itself stationary. (2) The celestial bodies move always in
circles with uniform speed. The first statement seemed to be in
agreement with what was observed, while the second one expressed
the prevailing view that uniform circular motion is the only perfect
and dignified motion suitable for the heavenly bodies.

The most notable attempt to reconcile the apparent movements
of the planets with the ancient postulates is ascribed to Hipparchus
(second century B.C.). His theory was elaborated by Ptolemy three

centuries later in his great work, the *Almagest,* and is known therefore as the *Ptolemaic system.* The chief feature of this system is the
resolution of the complicated observed motions into uniform circular
ones.

Each planet is supposed to be moving on the circumference of a small circle,
the *epicycle,* once around in the synodic period. The center of the epicycle
is describing meanwhile a larger circle, the *deferent,* around the earth, completing the circuit in the sidereal period.

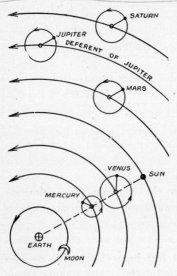

By virtue of the two movements the
planet has a looped path. Not far beyond the deferent of the outermost
planet, Saturn, was the blue sphere of
the fixed stars, the *primum mobile,*
which rotated daily from east to west,
and imparted this additional motion to
the planets, so that they also rose and
set daily.

For many centuries that followed,
this system remained unchallenged, and
its perfection constituted the chief task
of astronomers, namely, to obtain the
specifications for each planet which
would predict correctly its position in
the sky at any future time. As often
as they failed to do so, the specifications
had to be revised. Epicycles were piled
upon epicycles, both centrally and out
of center, until the construction became
very cumbersome, but without satisfactory improvement in its effectiveness.

FIG. 4.8. Ptolemaic Theory of
Planetary Motions. The centers of
the epicycles of Mercury and Venus
remain on the line between the
earth and sun. The line joining a
superior planet and the center of its
epicycle is parallel to the sun's direction from the earth.

4.9. The Copernican System. Copernicus (1473–1543) inaugurated
a new era in astronomy by discard-
ing the postulate of the central,
motionless earth. He showed that
the looped motions of the planets could be interpreted more reasonably and with equal accuracy on the theory of the central sun. The
Copernican system adhered to the postulate of uniform circular motion and, like the older system, employed epicycles to explain the
variable motions of the planets; but the largest of the ancient
epicycles had disappeared with the assumption of the earth's
revolution.

It is not surprising that the heliocentric theory met with disapproval on almost every hand; for it was a radical departure from the common-sense view of the world that had persisted from the very beginning of reflections about it. Moreover, it was supported, at the outset, by no convincing proof; indeed, it seemed to be discredited by the evidence of the celestial bodies themselves.

Tycho Brahe (1546–1601) rejected the Copernican system, because he was unable to observe annual variations in the directions of the stars, which he believed would be noticeable if the earth revolved. As we now know, the stars are so remote that the annual parallax (8.1) of even the nearest star is too minute to be detected with the instruments of that time. Tycho, however, attained a surprising degree of accuracy in his observations. His many careful measurements of the positions of the planets (their right ascensions and declinations) furnished the material for the studies of his assistant, Kepler (1571–1630), which resulted in the three laws of planetary motions.

4.10. Kepler's Laws. Kepler's task was the same as that with which astronomers had been struggling for many centuries, namely, to devise a specific theory on which he could predict correctly the positions of the planets at any time, and in particular those positions which Tycho had faithfully recorded. The successful solution of the problem occupied more than twenty years of study, in the course of which many plans were tried, and then discarded because they did not fit the observed positions. At first, he experimented with combinations of epicycles, until he became convinced that the ancient postulate of uniform circular motion is untenable. Kepler's laws are as follows:

1. *The orbit of every planet is an ellipse with the sun at one of its foci.*

2. *Every planet revolves so that the line joining it to the sun sweeps over equal areas in equal intervals of time.*

3. *The squares of the periods of any two planets are in the same proportion as the cubes of their mean distances from the sun.* $T^2 = k d^2$

Kepler's laws assert that the planets move around the *sun*, having *elliptical* paths, and therefore *non-uniform* motions. Thus they sweep away the Ptolemaic system with its cumbersome epicycles. But in those days new ideas spread slowly. Even now there are some who believe in the stationary, central earth. These laws describe the planetary system as a geometrical construction; they state *how* the planets revolve.

While Kepler was engaged in these studies, his contemporary, Galileo Galilei (1564–1642) was laying the foundations of experimental physics and preparing the way for the question: why do the planets revolve? The interest was beginning to shift from the geometry to the dynamics of the solar system; from the courses of the planets to mighty forces controlling them. ✓

THE LAW OF GRAVITATION

4.11. Force Equals Mass Times Acceleration. The concept of forces acting throughout the universe originates in our own experience with the things around us. If an object at rest, that is free to move, is pulled or pushed, it responds by moving in the direction of the pull or push. We say that force is applied to the object, and, with allowance for disturbing factors such as air resistance and surface friction, we estimate the force by the mass of the object that is moved, and the acceleration, or rate at which it gets up speed. In general, the acceleration of a body anywhere in any direction implies a force acting on it in that direction, and the amount of the force is found by multiplying the mass (3.7) of the body by its acceleration, or $f = ma$.

Acceleration is defined as rate of change of velocity. Since *velocity* is not merely speed, but *directed speed,* acceleration may appear as changing speed or changing direction, or both.

A falling stone illustrates the first case. Its behavior is represented by the relations:

$$v = v_0 + at; \qquad s = v_0 t + \tfrac{1}{2} at^2,$$

where v_0 is the speed when first observed, a is the acceleration toward the earth (about 32.2 feet/sec.^{2}), v and s are its speed and the distance it has fallen after t seconds. If the stone starts at rest ($v_0 = 0$), it will fall 16.1 feet in the first second, 48.3 feet in the next second, and so on, getting up speed at the rate of 32.2 feet/sec.^{2}

A planet moving in a circular orbit illustrates acceleration in direction only; its speed is constant. If the planet describes an elliptic orbit, the speed changes also in accordance with Kepler's second law.

4.12. The Laws of Motion. The conclusions of Galileo and others concerning the relations between bodies and their motions were consolidated by Newton, in the *Principia* (1687), into three statements which form the basis of all mechanics. They are:

1. *Every body persists in its state of rest or of uniform motion in a straight line unless it is compelled to change that state by a force impressed on it.* In this event:

2. *The acceleration is proportional to the force, and inversely to the mass of the body, and it takes place in the direction of the straight line in which the force acts.*

3. *To every action there is always an equal and contrary reaction; or, the mutual actions of any two bodies are equal and oppositely directed.*

The First Law states that a body subject to no external influences moves uniformly in a straight line forever, unless it happens never to have acquired any motion. It contradicts the traditional view that rest is the natural state, and motion the enforced one. Up to the time of Galileo, the continued motion of a planet required explanation; since that time, uniform motion is accepted as no more surprising than the existence of matter. Changing motion demands an accounting.

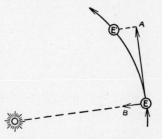

FIG. 4.12. The Earth's Revolution Explained by the Laws of Motion. At the position E the earth, if undisturbed, would continue on to A, by the first law of motion. It arrives at E' instead, having in the meantime fallen toward the sun the distance EB.

The Second Law defines force in the usual way. Since nothing is said to the contrary, it implies that the effect of the force is the same whether the body is originally at rest or in motion, and whether or not it is acted on at the same time by other forces.

The Third Law states that the force between any two bodies is the same in the two directions. The earth attracts the sun just as much as the sun attracts the earth, so that $f_S = f_E$, or $m_S a_S = m_E a_E$. But the effects of the equal forces, that is to say, the accelerations, are not the same, if the masses are unequal; the ratio of the accelerations is the inverse ratio of the masses affected.

4.13. The Law of Gravitation. By means of his laws of motion, and by mathematical reasoning, Newton succeeded in reducing Kepler's geometrical description of the planetary system to a single comprehensive physical law. Since the law of gravitation stands among the most celebrated achievements of science, the sequence and chief results of Newton's investigation will be outlined, although the details may well be reserved for a more advanced study.

According to Kepler's first law, the path of a planet is an ellipse; it is continually curving. Consequently, the planet's motion is continually accelerated and, by the second law of motion, *a force is always acting on the planet.*

Since the planet moves, by Kepler's second law, so that a line joining it to the sun describes equal areas in equal times, it is easily proved that *the force is directed toward the sun.* Kepler had suspected that the sun had something to do with the planet's revolution around it, but he did not understand the connection.

Again from Kepler's first law, since the orbit is an ellipse with the sun at one focus, it can be proved that *the force varies inversely as the square of the planet's distance from the sun.* An elliptic orbit would result also if the force varied directly as the distance, but in this event the sun would be at the center of the ellipse, not at one focus.

From Kepler's third law and the third law of motion it can be shown that *the attractive force between the sun and any planet varies directly as the product of their masses.* In addition, the satellites, such as the moon, are revolving under the attraction of their planets according to the same rules. These were the steps which led Newton to formulate the law of gravitation:

Every particle of matter in the universe attracts every other particle with a force that varies directly as the product of their masses, and inversely as the square of the distance between them.

The statement of the law and its acceptance as a *universal* law, not pertaining merely to the solar system, is a striking example of our faith in the order of nature. Unless this faith is justified, generalizations are impossible, and science becomes a meaningless description of the few fragments of a capricious universe that happen to come under observation. While Newton's experience did not extend beyond the solar system, it is now known that double star systems operate under the same law.

4.14. Examining Newton's Law. The law of gravitation provides the key for the interpretation of the physical universe as an orderly system. Since it constitutes the " rules of the game," the importance of understanding its meaning can not be urged too strongly. The statement is:

$$f = Gm_1m_2/d^2,$$

where f is the force; m_1 and m_2 are the masses of the two particles whose distance apart is d.

(1) *The constant of gravitation*, G, is defined as the force of attraction between two unit masses at unit distance apart. If $m_1 = m_2 = 1$ gram, and d is 1 centimeter, then $G = f$. This constant is believed to be the same wherever in the universe the experiment may be tried, regardless of other physical characteristics of the particles, or of surrounding conditions. It is a universal constant, like the speed of light; but it is even more remarkable as a constant, for the speed of light is reduced by an interposing medium, such as glass, while the force of gravitation is unaffected by anything placed between the attracting bodies. There is no known insulation against gravitation.

The value of G is best determined in the physical laboratory by the method first tried by Cavendish about 1798. It consists in measuring the minute attractions of metallic balls, or cylinders. Heyl's recent determination (1930) at the United States Bureau of Standards is:

$$\text{Constant of gravitation} = 6.670 \times 10^{-8} \text{ dynes.}$$

A *dyne* is that force which, acting on a gram of matter, gives it an acceleration of 1 cm./sec.[2] It is evident that the gravitational forces between ordinary masses are almost negligible, and that they become important for the celestial bodies because of their great masses. The *Gaussian constant of gravitation* is much used in astronomical calculations; it is the acceleration due to the sun's attraction at the earth's mean distance from the sun.

(2) *The attraction of a sphere is toward its center*, as though the whole mass were concentrated there. Owing to their rotations the celestial bodies are not spheres, but the flattening at their poles is usually small, and the intervening spaces are so great, that the distances between their centers may be used ordinarily in calculating their attractions. The attraction of a spheroid in the direction of its equator exceeds that of a sphere of the same mass, and it is smaller in the direction of its poles; but the difference becomes very small with increasing distance.

(3) *The acceleration of the attracted body is independent of its mass.* If the attractive force, f_1, on this body is replaced by the equivalent m_1a_1 in the statement of the law of gravitation, the mass, m_1, cancels out, and the acceleration:

$$a_1 = Gm_2/d^2$$

of the attracted body does not depend on its own mass. Galileo demonstrated this fact to a surprised audience, when he dropped large and small weights from the leaning tower in Pisa. They fell together. Thus he discredited the traditional idea that heavy bodies fall faster than light ones.

The second, or attracting body, as we have chosen to consider it, is itself attracted and has the acceleration $a_2 = Gm_1/d^2$ in the direction of the first. In Galileo's experiment this factor need not be taken into account. It becomes important when the two bodies have comparable masses. The acceleration of one body with respect to the other is the sum:

$$a_1 + a_2 = G\,\frac{(m_1 + m_2)}{d^2}$$

Thus *the relative acceleration of two bodies varies as the sum of their masses.* This relation will be found useful.

omit

4.15. The Moon a Falling Body.

Since the law of gravitation holds everywhere, the moon must be falling toward the earth just as a ball falls to the ground. That the moon fails to arrive is owing to its horizontal motion at such a high speed that the earth's attraction serves only to curve its path around the earth. There are two independent ways of determining the rate at which the moon falls:

(1) *By the observed acceleration of a falling body at the earth's surface, and the law of gravitation.* Using the expression for the relative acceleration of two bodies, in the preceding Section, we have the proportion:

$$\frac{\text{Moon's acceleration}}{\text{Acceleration of the ball}} = \frac{m_E + m_M}{m_E + m_B} \cdot \frac{d^2_B}{d^2_M},$$

where the subscripts refer to the earth, moon, and ball. The acceleration of the ball is about 32.2 feet /sec.^{2}; the moon's distance is not far from 60 times the earth's radius. Neglecting the masses of moon and ball, and the slight effect of the earth's rotation on the descent of the ball, we have for the moon's acceleration about 32.2/3600, or 0.1073 inch/sec.^{2} Thus *the calculated fall of the moon from rest in one second (one half the acceleration) is 0.0536 inch.*

(2) *By the deflection of the moon's orbit from a straight line.* Supposing that the moon's orbit around the earth is a circle, which is not far wrong, it can be shown that the moon's motion is deflected from a straight line by the amount $2\pi^2 d/P^2$ in one second, where d is the moon's distance from the earth, and P is its sidereal period expressed in seconds. The simple calculation shows that the *moon's motion is actually deflected from a straight line 0.0536 inch,* which is in agreement with the value required by the law of gravitation.

Newton was unwilling to publish his law until he became convinced of this agreement. His conclusion, that the moon falls toward the earth under the same rule that a ball falls to the ground, united celestial and terrestrial phenomena decisively for the first time.

omit

4.16. Curvature of the Earth's Orbit; The Sun's Mass.

By the procedure of the preceding Section it is easy to determine the deflection from a straight line of any other body which revolves in a nearly circular orbit, if its period and mean distance from the central body are known. It is left to the reader to calculate in this way that the earth departs from a straight path in one second less than one eighth of an inch, although in that interval it has advanced 18½ miles along its orbit.

Having determined the curvature of the earth's orbit, and so the earth's acceleration toward the sun (twice the deflection, or 0.233 inch/sec.²), we are in a position to evaluate the sun's mass from the statement of the relative acceleration (4.14). The sun's mass is 1.983×10^{33} grams. It is 332,000 times greater than the earth's mass, and 700 times greater than all the rest of the solar system together. Herein lies the explanation of the sun's dominance in this system.

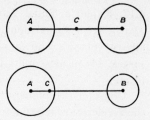

4.17. The Center of Mass. Imagine the earth and sun joined by a stout rod. The point of support for which the two bodies exactly balance is their *center of mass;* it is the point around which they revolve in orbits of the same shape. If the masses were the same, this point would be halfway between their centers. Since the earth and sun have unequal

FIG. 4.17. The Center of Mass. For two equally massive bodies the center of mass, *C*, lies halfway between their centers. For unequal masses it is nearer the center of the heavier body. The ratio of the masses of *A* and *B* is *BC/AC*.

masses, the center of mass is closer to the heavier body, the sun. The proportion is:

$$\frac{\text{Earth's mass}}{\text{Sun's mass}} = \frac{\text{sun's center to center of mass}}{\text{earth's center to center of mass}}.$$

The distance from the sun's center to the center of mass of the earth-sun system is therefore 92,870,000 miles divided by 332,000, which equals 280 miles.

It is to be noticed that the ancient problem of whether the earth or the sun revolves no longer concerns us. Both revolve. The earth, however, does most of the revolving; and the point around which it revolves is within the sun, though not exactly at its center.

Similarly, the centers of mass of the other planets and the sun are readily found, the required data for each planet being taken from Table 5.I. All are within the sun, except the center of mass of the sun-Jupiter system, which lies in the sun's atmosphere, less than 30,000 miles outside the sun's visible surface. It follows that all the planets revolve around the sun, though not around its center, and that the center of the sun has meanwhile a very small motion.

Whenever the center of mass can be found by observations independently, the relative masses of the two bodies become known by the above proportion. Opportunities for determining relative masses in this way occur in the case of the earth-moon system (3.24) and in certain double star systems (8.35).

4.18. Kepler's Third Law Restated. As it was originally stated (4.10), Kepler's harmonic law relates to the periods and distances of any two planets, and says nothing about their masses. The law is so serviceable in astronomy that it must now be put in its more precise form.

Consider two planets, Mars and the earth. For each planet write the acceleration relative to the sun, first, as a consequence of the law of gravitation, second, from the observed curvature of its orbit, which is supposed for convenience to be circular. The relative accelerations are:

$$\text{For Mars,} \qquad G\,\frac{(m_M + m_S)}{d^2_{MS}} = \frac{4\pi^2 d_{MS}}{P^2_{MS}};$$

$$\text{for the earth,} \qquad G\,\frac{(m_E + m_S)}{d^2_{ES}} = \frac{4\pi^2 d_{ES}}{P^2_{ES}}.$$

Now divide the upper expressions by the lower ones, obtaining the proportion:

$$\frac{(m_M + m_S)P^2_{MS}}{(m_E + m_S)P^2_{ES}} = \frac{d^3_{MS}}{d^3_{ES}}.$$

The restatement of Kepler's third law, in accordance with the law of gravitation, is: *The squares of the periods of any two planets, each multiplied by the sum of its mass and the sun's mass, are in the same proportion as the cubes of their mean distances from the sun.*

It is now clear why the law in its original form serves very well for the planetary system. The masses of the planets are so small in comparison with the sun's mass, that $\dfrac{m_M + m_S}{m_E + m_S}$ practically becomes unity.

4.19. Measurement of Mass. The law of gravitation treats the solar system, and the universe generally, as a mechanism to be interpreted in terms of masses and distances. It is important, therefore, to understand the procedure by which these fundamental data are determined.

The mass of a celestial body is always measured by the acceleration it produces on a neighboring body whose distance from it is known. In theory, we might visit each planet in turn, drop a ball, and from its acceleration, assuming the radius known, calculate the planet's mass. As we have seen in the case of the moon (4.15), a satellite serves this purpose as well as a ball. The curvature of its orbit denotes the amount of the acceleration; or, what comes to the same thing, *if the planet has a satellite, the planet's mass plus the mass of the satellite is found by the harmonic law.*

In Kepler's third law, as it is restated in Section 4.18, let the units of time, distance, and mass be respectively the sidereal year, the earth's mean distance from the sun, and the combined mass of the earth and sun. The denominators then disappear because their terms are all unity. Further, in place of Mars and the sun, take any two mutually revolving bodies *anywhere,* denoting them by the subscripts 1 and 2. They may be the sun and a planet, a planet and its satellite, or a double star. Kepler's third law now becomes:

$$(m_1 + m_2) = \frac{d^3{}_{12}}{P^2{}_{12}}.$$

The sum of the masses of two mutually revolving bodies, in terms of the sun's mass, equals the cube of their mean distance apart, expressed in astronomical units, divided by the square of their period in sidereal years.

In this way, and in others, values of the masses are known for the sun, and for planets having one or more satellites. The law does not serve for the solitary planets, such as Mercury and Venus, nor for the asteroids, the satellites themselves, comets, and meteor swarms. Their masses are known only in case they disturb noticeably the orbits of their neighbors.

The Scale of the Solar System

4.20. The Astronomical Unit. The relative distances of the planets from the sun are deduced with considerable accuracy from the original statement of Kepler's third law, in which the planets' masses are neglected. If we take, as before, the earth's mean distance from the sun and the sidereal year as units, the law for any planet is:

(mean distance from sun) ^{3} = (period of revolution) ^{2}.

Suppose that a planet's period is observed to be exactly 8 years. Its mean distance from the sun is therefore the cube root of 64, or 4 astronomical units.

The astronomical unit is the earth's mean distance from the sun; its length is 92,870,000 miles. It is the unit employed for the measurement of distances, not only in the solar system, but in the stellar system as well, so that the greatest importance is attached to the determination of its length as accurately as possible. Before considering the methods that are used to measure the length of the astronomical unit (4.25), let us understand the principle underlying the measurements of celestial distances in general.

4.21. Parallax; Relation to Distance. *Parallax* is the difference between the directions of an object as seen from two places, or from the two ends of a *base line*. As an example of the parallax effect, one has only to notice the shifting of a nearby object against a more distant background, when the eyes are covered alternately. Evi-

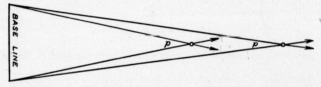

FIG. 4.21. Relation of Parallax to Distance. For the same base line the parallax, *p*, of an object diminishes as its distance increases.

dently, for the same base line the parallax becomes smaller as the distance of the object is increased, and for the same distance the angle becomes greater as the base line is lengthened. If this line is so short that no change in the direction of the object can be detected, the rule is to lengthen it. The parallax and distance of an object are connected by the relation:

$$\text{Distance} = \frac{206,265''}{\text{parallax}''} \times \text{length of base line,}$$

supposing that the parallax is small, and that the direction of the object is perpendicular to the base line at its center. This is the fundamental rule by which astronomical distances are measured; whenever the parallax of a celestial body has been observed from two points of known separation, the distance can be calculated.

The earth's motions cause periodic parallax displacements of the nearer celestial bodies with respect to the more distant ones. The rotation of the earth produces *geocentric* or *diurnal* parallax, while its revolution is accountable for the observed *heliocentric* or *annual* parallaxes of the nearest stars (8.1).

With the latter effect we are not concerned for the present, except to recall that Tycho Brahe rejected the Copernican theory of the earth's revolution partly because he was unable to observe this effect (4.9). The annual parallaxes of the stars, whose evaluation is now an important part of the programs of a number of observatories, constitutes a convincing proof of the earth's revolution.

4.22. Geocentric Parallax. The parallax of a nearby object, such as the moon or a planet, is usually determined by simultaneous obser-

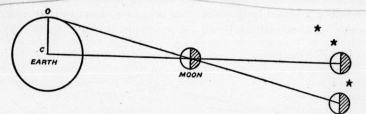

Fig. 4.22. The Moon's Geocentric Parallax. The difference in direction of the moon from the center of the earth and from the surface, when the moon is at the horizon, is nearly one degree, or about twice the moon's apparent diameter.

vations of its positions relative to the stars as seen from two places, although it may be obtained at a single station from observations made after sunset and before sunrise; meanwhile, the earth's rotation has transported the station a distance equal to something like the diameter of the earth. Whatever stations are used, the parallax is standardized by calculating from it the angle that would have resulted, if the base line had been the earth's equatorial radius, the object being on the horizon. This *equatorial horizontal parallax* is the geocentric parallax of the object.

Two examples will illustrate the relation between geocentric parallax and distance.

(1) The least possible distance of the asteroid Eros is 13,840,000 miles. What is its parallax at that time?

Using the rule of the preceding Section, and substituting the value of the equatorial radius, 3963.34 miles, we have:

$$\text{Parallax of Eros} = 206{,}265'' \times \frac{\text{earth's equatorial radius}}{\text{distance of Eros}} = 59''.1.$$

(2) The moon's parallax at its mean distance from the earth is $57' \, 2''.7$. Required its mean distance.

This is by far the largest geocentric parallax of any celestial body (meteors excepted); in this case it is a good plan to use the exact relation:

$$\text{Moon's distance} = \frac{\text{earth's equatorial radius}}{\text{sine of moon's parallax}}.$$

The moon's mean distance is therefore about 238,860 miles.

Geocentric parallax may also be defined as the apparent radius of the earth viewed from the object. Thus the moon's parallax of about one degree informs us that the earth's diameter fills an angle of 2° as seen from the moon, or about four times the moon's apparent diameter, as we see it.

From a place not on the equator the horizontal parallax is slightly less than the standard value (it is less by 1/300 at the poles). The difference in direction of a celestial body as seen from any station and from the center of the earth decreases with increasing altitude of the object, to nothing at all when it is in the geocentric zenith. The *American Ephemeris* and similar almanacs give the positions of the sun, moon, and planets as seen from the center of the earth. Viewed from a place on the earth's surface, the celestial body is a little lower than its predicted geocentric position. The difference is not enough to be detected with the unaided eye, except for the moon.

The geocentric parallax of the nearest bright star, α Centauri is $0''.000032$, an angle about as large as the apparent diameter of one of the periods on this page viewed from a distance of a thousand miles. No telescope is powerful enough to detect so small an angle. Evidently geocentric parallax is of no avail for determining the distances of the stars. This is fortunate, however, because the unvarying stars may then be safely employed as reference points for observing the parallaxes of the nearer bodies.

4.23. Apparent and Linear Dimensions. When the distance of a celestial body from the earth becomes known, from its parallax or otherwise, then if its apparent diameter has been measured, it is easy to calculate the linear diameter in miles or similar units, that is to say, the actual size that it must have in order to fill the observed angle at that distance. In this way also the size of a lunar crater can be found from its apparent size, or the distance of a satellite of Jupiter from that planet, when the greatest apparent separation of the two has been observed. If the apparent diameter does not exceed a degree and is expressed in seconds of arc, the relations are very nearly (Fig. 4.23):

$$\text{Linear diameter} = \text{distance} \times \frac{\text{apparent diameter}}{206,265''};$$

$$\text{apparent diameter} = \frac{\text{linear diameter}}{\text{distance}} \times 206,265''.$$

Some applications are given in the following examples:

(1) The moon's apparent diameter is $31'5''$ at its mean distance, 238,857 miles. Calculate its diameter in miles and in kilometers.

$$\text{Moon's diameter} = 238,857 \text{ miles} \times \frac{1865''}{206,265''} = 2160 \text{ miles.}$$

Since 1 mile equals 1.6093 kilometers, the moon's diameter in kilometers is 3476 km.

(2) At what distance must a penny be held away from the eye to make it appear as large as the full moon?

Supposing that the diameter of the penny is three quarters of an inch, we find:

$$\text{Distance} = 0.75 \times \frac{206,265''}{1865''} = 6 \text{ feet } 11 \text{ inches.}$$

Another aspect of the relations is brought out in this example; if the apparent diameter of an object is measured, and the linear diameter is known independently, then the distance of the object may be calculated.

Unless the distance of a celestial body is known, its linear dimensions are generally unknown, and such dimensions can not properly be used in its description. Nothing useful is conveyed by the statement that the full moon appears to be a foot in diameter, unless the distance of the foot rule is specified. The moon may appear no larger than a penny, as we have just now seen; it may appear as large as a distant house, and it does seem to be as large as the sun, all depending on the distances of these objects.

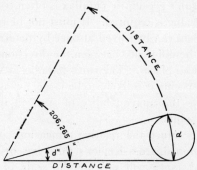

Fig. 4.23. Relation Between Linear Diameter, d, Apparent Diameter, d'', and Distance. When the radius of a circle is bent around the circumference, it subtends an angle of 206,265''. Therefore,

$$d/\text{distance} = d''/206,265''.$$

4.24. Expression of Angular and Linear Dimensions. *Apparent, or angular dimensions* relate to differences in direction from the point of observation. They are expressed in angular units: (1) *in degrees, minutes, and seconds of arc,* either in terms of the angle at the observer's eye between the directions, or of the arc of the great circle in the sky which includes them; it makes no difference, for angle and arc have the same value; (2) *in radians.* The radian is the angle subtended by the radius of a circle, when it is bent around the circumference; it is therefore $360°/2\pi$, which equals $57°.30$, $3437'.7$, or $206,264''.8$.

Linear dimensions are expressed in a greater variety of units, depending on the order of the dimensions and the traditions of those who are describing them. In physical science, the use of the metric system has become almost universal. For many purposes the centimeter-gram-second system of units is the most convenient; but for expressing the great distances and high speeds of the celestial bodies, astronomers have employed the kilometer more often than the centimeter as the unit of length. Either one often necessitates appalling rows of ciphers. The remedy is the adoption of larger units, such as the astronomical unit or the light-year, or of the very convenient device in which the number appears as a power of 10; thus the moon's mean distance is 38,440,000,000 centimeters, or 3.844×10^{10} cm.

Dimensions are given in this book not so much as a basis for calculations as to show the relations of things. This seems to justify the frequent use of the more familiar units, such as inches and miles, wherever the descriptive purpose is better served by so doing, and the use of metric units in other places.

4.25. The Sun's Parallax. The important problem of finding the sun's distance may be called the solar parallax problem, because the sun's geocentric parallax is often considered to be the constant whose value is required. It must not be imagined, however, that the problem can be solved at once by determining this parallax directly from the difference between the directions of the sun's center as seen from two places. The sun's parallax is very small, while the error in observing it is likely to be large, owing to the large disk of the sun, and to the unavailability of stars in the daytime to serve as reference points.

Since the relative dimensions in the solar system can be determined, from Kepler's third law or by more rigorous procedure, one distance will provide the scale of miles as well as another. The smallest possible *percentage* of error is the goal to be attained. Suitable objects for this purpose are those whose positions can be accurately measured, and whose parallaxes are large, namely, the nearer planets, and in particular Mars and some of the asteroids. The asteroid Eros (5.23) received much attention on this account at its exceptionally close approach to the earth in 1931. When the parallax of a suitable object has been measured, the solar parallax is readily calculated from it.

All the recent reliable determinations of the solar parallax have given values not far from 8".80. The sun's distance is accordingly (4.21) 206,265"/8".80 × 3963.34 miles, or about 92,900,000 miles. By international agreement the *American Ephemeris* and the nautical almanacs of other nations, beginning with 1900, have adopted 8".80 as the value of the solar parallax. There is considerable evidence that the correct figure in the third decimal place is greater than zero.

But with each new determination the mean of all is likely to change slightly.

The general mean of the most dependable determinations, according to Russell, is the following:

Solar parallax = 8″.803 ± 0″.001.

Sun's mean distance = $\begin{cases} 92,870,000 \text{ miles} \pm 11,000 \text{ miles,} \\ \text{or } 149,450,000 \text{ kilometers.} \end{cases}$

The separate results that enter into the mean are derived only partly from measurements of parallax. Methods which involve the perturbations of the moon and nearer planets, and others which depend on the velocity of light have made valuable contributions.

MECHANISM OF THE SOLAR SYSTEM

4.26. The Relative Orbit of Two Bodies. We have seen (4.17) that two bodies, such as the earth and sun, mutually revolve around their common center of mass, which is nearer the more massive body, so that the less massive component has the larger orbit. It can be shown (1) that the orbits are independent of any motions of the center of mass, that is to say, of the system as a

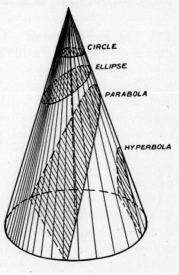

CIRCLE

ELLIPSE

PARABOLA

HYPERBOLA

FIG. 4.26. The Conics.

whole; (2) that they are the same in form, and that this is also the form of the *relative orbit,* of one body with respect to the other. The relative orbit is often the only one that can be calculated; it is the one understood when a body is said to revolve around another.

Kepler's first law states that the orbits of the planets are ellipses. Newton proved that the orbit of a body revolving in accordance with the law of gravitation must be a conic, of which the ellipse is an example.

The *conics,* or conic sections, are the ellipse, parabola, and hyperbola. They are sections cut from a circular cone, which for this purpose is the surface generated by one of two intersecting lines when it is revolved around the other as an axis, the angle between them remaining the same.

The ellipse (eccentricities 0 to 1) is obtained when the cutting plane passes entirely through the cone, so that the section is closed; when it passes at right angles to the axis the eccentricity is zero, and the section is a *circle*.

The parabola (eccentricity = 1) results when the cutting plane is parallel to one side of the cone. This curve extends an indefinite distance, its directions at the two ends approaching parallelism. The orbits of many comets are nearly parabolas. All parabolas, like all circles, have the same form, but not the same size.

The hyperbola (eccentricity greater than 1) is obtained when the cone is cut at a still smaller angle with the axis. It is an open curve like the parabola, but the directions of the two ends approach diverging lines. When a star passes another and is deflected by attraction from its original course, the orbit is hyperbolic; if it were repelled instead, its path would be the other branch of the hyperbola.

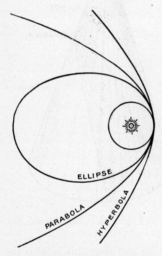

FIG. 4.27. Orbits Having Same Perihelion Distance. The size and eccentricity of the orbit increase with the speed of the revolving body at perihelion.

4.27. Form of the Relative Orbit.

The particular conic in which a celestial body revolves is determined by the central force and the velocity with which the body is started; for it is evident that the curvature of the orbit depends on the distance the body has fallen toward its companion, and the distance it has moved forward meanwhile in the orbit. This conclusion, among others, is derived formally from the *equation of energy:*

$$V^2 = G(m_1 + m_2)\left(\frac{2}{r} - \frac{1}{a}\right),$$

where V is the velocity of revolution when the two bodies are the distance r apart, and a is the semi-major axis of the resulting relative orbit.

It can be seen from this equation that the semi-major axis lengthens as the velocity is increased. For a moderate speed the orbit is an ellipse; for increasing speeds the length and eccentricity of the orbit grow greater, until a critical speed is reached at which the orbit becomes parabolic.

If the orbit is a circle, then $a = r$ in the above formula, so that V^2 is proportional to $1/r$. If it is a parabola, a is infinite and V^2 is proportional to

$2/r$. Therefore, if the speed of a body revolving in a circular orbit is multiplied by the square root of 2, or about 1.41, its orbit becomes a parabola. Since the earth's orbit is nearly circular, the *parabolic velocity* at our distance from the sun is the earth's velocity, $18\frac{1}{2}$ miles a second, multiplied by 1.41, or 26 miles a second. If its velocity should ever become as great as this value, the earth would depart from the sun's vicinity. Many comets and meteor swarms, whose aphelion points are far beyond the orbit of Neptune, cross the earth's orbit with speeds of this order.

4.28. The Elements of the Orbit are the specifications necessary to define it uniquely, and to fix the place of the revolving body in the orbit at any time. The elements of the elliptical orbit of a planet, with their symbols, are the following:

(1) *Inclination to ecliptic, i.* If the plane of the orbit is inclined to the ecliptic plane (i denotes the numerical value of the inclination), the line of

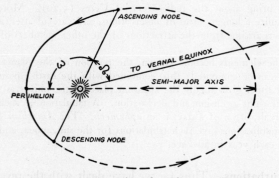

FIG. 4.28. The Orbit of a Planet. The plane of the planet's orbit is inclined to the plane of the earth's orbit, represented by the plane of the paper.

their intersection is the *line of nodes*, which passes through the sun's position. The *ascending node* is the point at which the planet crosses the ecliptic plane going from south to north.

(2) *Longitude of the ascending node, Ω.* It is the celestial longitude of this node as seen from the sun, that is, the angle between the line of nodes and the direction of the vernal equinox. It fixes the orientation of the orbit plane, and, together with the inclination, defines this plane precisely.

(3) *Angle from the ascending node to the perihelion point, ω.* It is measured from the ascending node along the orbit in the direction of the planet's motion, which must be specified; it gives the direction of the major axis of the orbit with respect to the line of nodes, and thus describes the orientation of the orbit in its plane.

(4) *Semi-major axis, a.* This element, which is known also as the planet's *mean distance* from the sun, defines the size of the orbit and, very nearly, the period of revolution; for by Kepler's third law, P^2 is proportional to a^3 regardless of the shape of the ellipse.

(5) *Eccentricity*, *e*. The eccentricity of the ellipse is the ratio c/a, where c is the sun's distance from the center of the ellipse (one half the distance between the foci). These five elements define the relative orbit uniquely.

(6) *Time of passing perihelion*, *T*. (7) *Period of revolution*, *P*. These elements permit the determination of the planet's position in the orbit at any time.

If the orbit is circular, the longitude of perihelion drops out; if it is a parabola, the semi-major axis, which is then infinite, is replaced as an element by the *perihelion distance*, *q*, which defines the size of the parabola.

The approximate elements of the orbit of a newly discovered planet or comet can be derived usually as soon as its positions relative to the stars (right ascensions and declinations) have been measured on three different occasions. The methods employed for elliptical orbits are generally adaptations of the method which Laplace developed in 1780, or of that which Gauss invented in 1801 to bring about the rediscovery of Ceres (5.20). More accurate elements require a longer series of observations, and careful attention to disturbing effects arising from the attractions of the other members of the solar system.

When the elements become known, the position of the planet or comet at any time can be computed; this, combined with the earth's position in its orbit at that time, gives finally the apparent place of the object as seen from the earth, its right ascension and declination. A tabulation of such places at regular intervals, often of a day, is an *ephemeris*. The *American Ephemeris* and similar publications give such tabulations for the sun, moon, and principal planets, for each year in advance.

4.29. Perturbations.

Thus far we have dealt with the revolution of a planet around the sun as though the planet were acted on only by the sun's attraction. This is the *problem of two bodies*, which is solved directly and completely in terms of the law of gravitation. But the planet is subject to the attractions of all the other members of the solar system as well, so that it departs in a complicated manner from simple elliptic motion. Thus we have in practice the *problem of three or more bodies*, whose solution is much more troublesome. It is fortunate for the orderly description of planetary movements that the masses of the planets are very small in comparison with the sun's mass, and that their distances apart are very great. If it were not so, the mutual disturbances of the revolving bodies would introduce so much confusion that simple approximations, such as Kepler's laws, would have been impossible.

Since the sun's mass is dominant, it is possible at first to derive the planet's orbit with reference to the sun alone, and then to consider the departures from this simple elliptic motion, that are imposed by the attractions of other members of the system. *Perturbations* are the small alterations so produced in the planet's position and orbit; they are classified as periodic and secular.

Periodic perturbations are small departures from simple elliptic motion, which run through cycles generally not exceeding a few hundred years. *Secular perturbations* are changes in the elements of the orbit, which go on fairly steadily in the same direction from century to century, but are themselves periodic in cycles of tens and hundreds of thousands of years. In general, the eccentricities and inclinations of the orbits fluctuate, perihelia advance, and nodes regress, while the lengths of major axes and the periods of revolution are not much affected.

Laplace and Lagrange both concluded that all perturbations in the solar system are oscillatory in the long run, and that they can not permanently alter the arrangement of the system. Poincaré's more rigorous discussion shows, however, that stability is not perfectly assured when a very long period of time is considered.

4.30. Energy, a Fundamental Concept.

The concept of forces operating throughout the solar system is intermediate between considerations of what the forces can accomplish, and the capability of the system to produce the forces. *Work is the product of the force by the distance* the body is moved in the direction of the force. When a stone is lifted from the ground, work is performed against the force of gravity; the higher it is lifted, the greater the amount of work done. On the other hand, *energy is the capacity of a body, or system of bodies, for doing work.*

Kinetic energy is the energy a body possesses by virtue of its motion; it is equal to the amount of work it can do before it is brought to rest. Numerically, it is equal to one half the product of the mass of the body and the square of its velocity, or $\frac{1}{2}mv^2$. Since the energy increases as the square of the velocity, a small body can do as much damage as a large one, if it moves fast enough. A tiny meteor weighing only a gram, entering the atmosphere with the speed of 26 miles a second, has as much kinetic energy as a 1-ton truck that is traveling at the rate of 100 miles an hour.

Potential energy is the energy a system possesses owing to the relative positions of its parts. A stone on the ground is not in the position to do work; but if it is raised above the ground, it acquires potential energy equal to the product of its mass, the force of gravity, and the distance it is raised, or *mgh*.

Energy has various forms which are convertible one to another.

The heat a body possesses is ascribed to the kinetic energy of the molecules of the body. Radiant energy is emitted from heated bodies, such as the sun and stars. Electrical and magnetic energy are also familiar forms.

The importance of the energy concept is its great generality; it is the chief basis for the interpretation of all physical phenomena. *Astronomy has been defined as the study of the distribution and redistribution of energy (and matter) in the universe.*

4.31. Conservation of Energy. The energy that is required to raise a stone above the ground is taken from the muscles of the arm, from steam, electricity, or whatever means is employed. This energy is transferred to the stone, which is then enabled to do work because of its elevated position. When the stone is released, the potential energy it has acquired is changed to kinetic energy; and when it strikes the ground this energy of motion is transformed into heat. Helmholtz, in 1847, reached the conclusion that energy is indestructible; the disappearance of any amount of energy in one form is always accompanied by the appearance of the same amount in another form. This principle of the *conservation of energy* asserts that *the total amount of energy in an isolated system is always the same.*

No system is in fact perfectly isolated; it must continually be losing energy and gaining some from outside. Moreover, the transformations of the energy within the system are not likely to proceed with perfect efficiency; some of the energy is dissipated, as the result of friction, into unavailable heat. It is true that friction does not play a leading part in the movements of the solar system, although the tides produce considerable dissipation of energy on the earth, and perhaps elsewhere.

Thermodynamics is the study of the conversion of heat into other forms of energy, and of these again into heat. It has many important applications in astronomy. This study is based on two principles known as the first and second laws of thermodynamics. The *first law* is the statement of the conservation of energy. The *second law,* formulated by Clausius in 1850, is concerned with the *degradation of energy;* it asserts that *the amount of unavailable energy is increasing always.* This has been taken to mean that the machinery of the whole universe will eventually run down, unless it is wound up again by some agency not specified.

4.32. Moment of Momentum. The *momentum* of a body is the product of its mass and velocity, or *mv*. The *moment of momentum* of a revolving body, such as a planet revolving around the sun, or a particle of the rotating earth, is the product of the momentum and the distance from the center of motion, or *mvr,* the velocity being measured at right angles to the direction of that center. The total moment of momentum of a system is obtained by adding together the values for all the separate parts. The *angular momentum,* which many prefer to use, has the same value as the moment of momentum; it is equal to the product of the mass and the area swept over by the radius in unit time.

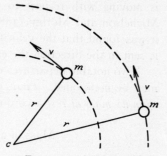

FIG. 4.32. Conservation of Moment of Momentum. In an isolated system of revolving bodies the sum of all the products *mvr* remains the same. The total moment is increased by the rotation of the bodies.

The total moment of momentum (or angular momentum) of a system is always the same, if no external force acts on the system. This conservation law is of great value in studies of the solar system, and of revolving systems in general, particularly in the attempt to trace their development.

As a consequence of this law, the contraction of a rotating body causes it to rotate faster; for as the distances of its parts from the axis become smaller (the total mass remaining the same) the velocities must increase. A shrinking of the earth would diminish the length of the day, while expansion would increase it. Slight variations in the size of earth would account for the observed variations in the rate of the earth's rotation (2.7).

Similarly, the shrinking of the solar system would increase the speeds of the planets, and shorten their periods of revolution. It will be understood that the conservation of moment of momentum does not hold, if the system gains or loses mass.

4.33. The Special Theory of Relativity. It has been known since Newton's time that the relative motions of bodies within any system, such as the solar system, are the same whether the system as a whole is at rest or in uniform motion. Einstein, in 1905, based his theory of relativity on the principle that *all* physical phenomena (including optical and electrical) are likewise relative and unaffected by any *uniform* motion of the whole system.

Thus the velocity of light in a vacuum, as measured by any observer, is invariable, regardless of the direction in which the observer is moving with respect to the light. The classical experiment of Michelson and Morley (1887) established the theory at this point; it was found that the velocity of light is the same, whether the light is sent in the direction the earth is revolving, or at right angles to it.

Two notable departures of the theory from Newtonian mechanics may be mentioned. *First, the mass of a body in motion is greater than its mass at rest* according to the relation:

$$\text{Mass of a body} = \frac{\text{mass at rest}}{\left(1 - \frac{v^2}{c^2}\right)^{\frac{1}{2}}},$$

where v is the velocity of the body, and c is the constant velocity of light. Mass, like velocity, is therefore a relative quantity. In acquiring additional kinetic energy the body gains mass, which has been taken to mean that energy possesses the mass E/c^2. This relation has assumed great prominence in current theories of the history of the stars (10.33).

The second remarkable characteristic of the Einstein theory is the relativity of time. As Newton understood it, time flows on, absolute and independent of whatever occurs in the universe. Minkowski's world (1908) is a geometrical representation of the special theory; it is the world of *events,* having four dimensions in which the time is included.

4.34. General Theory of Relativity.

The special theory considers only uniform motion. In 1915, Einstein extended the basic principle to include accelerated motion as well, and therefore motion in the presence of matter. Here he encounters the law of gravitation.

In the Newtonian scheme the emphasis is on the *force* that makes a planet revolve. The relativity theory directs the attention to the *course* the planet pursues. If we hold to the simple geometry of Euclid or Minkowski, the region near a material body now appears to be warped; in the curved region around the sun the natural path of a planet is a conic, just as its natural path in otherwise empty space is a straight line. No force is acting in either case.

The mathematical development of the theory is so highly generalized that we shall leave it to the specialist in this field, and simply notice the results. It is found that under ordinary conditions in the laboratory and in the sky the calculations of phenomena are practically the same, whether the formulae of Einstein or Newton are employed. A few exceptional cases are known in which predictions

FIG. 4.34. The Einstein Tower of the Astrophysical Observatory, Potsdam, Germany. A fixed vertical telescope (7.13) employed in the study of the sun.

of phenomena on the two theories differ widely enough to be subject to the test of observation. These cases involve the presence of large masses, or velocities large enough to have some significance in comparison with the velocity of light; they relate mostly to celestial phenomena.

4.35. Physical Tests of the Theory of Relativity. Three astronomical test cases have received considerable attention, and in each case the observational evidence appears to support the theory of relativity. They are:

(1) *The advance of Mercury's perihelion* (5.4). For a long time it has been known that the major axis of Mercury's orbit is rotating faster than can be predicted by the law of gravitation. The faster rate is required by the new theory.

(2) *The " Einstein shift "* of the lines in the spectra of the sun (7.9) and of the companion of Sirius (10.12).

(3) *The apparent outward displacements of stars near the sun.* This effect, which the general theory predicts, was first observed by English astronomers at the total solar eclipse of 1919 in the southern hemisphere. The favorable outcome of the test aroused wide-spread interest in the theory of relativity.

4.36. Apparent Displacements of Stars Away from the Sun.

The curvature of space and time in the vicinity of a massive body affects the course of a ray of light as well as that of a material body. A ray of starlight which passes near the sun describes a hyperbolic orbit;

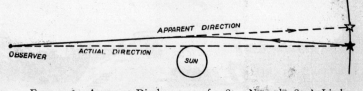

Fig. 4.36. Apparent Displacement of a Star Near the Sun's Limb. By the theory of relativity, starlight passing near the sun is deflected in such a way that the star is apparently displaced outward from the sun's position.

its direction changes by an amount which varies inversely as its least distance from the center of the sun. Thus stars that appear close to the sun in the sky must be apparently displaced away from the sun. The maximum displacement is 1″.75 for a star at the sun's limb, according to the theory of relativity.

But the stars can be observed near the sun only during a total solar eclipse. The " Einstein effect " was therefore a special problem for eclipse observers. The procedure has been to compare photographs of the field of stars immediately surrounding the totally eclipsed sun with other photographs of the same region of the sky taken at night a few months earlier, or later, when the sun is out of the way.

Photographs of the 1919 eclipse showed that the amount of the deflection of starlight at the sun's limb is not far from that required by the theory of relativity. This conclusion was confirmed at the eclipse of 1922, in Australia, by expeditions from the Greenwich, Toronto, and Lick observatories. Trumpler's analysis (1932) of the results from three eclipses gives 1".79 ± 0".06 for the outward displacement of a star at the limb, in satisfactory agreement with the predicted value.

TIDES

˅ The regular rise and fall of the ocean *twice* in a little more than a day, or more exactly 24ʰ 50ᵐ on the average, which is also the interval between upper transits of the moon, was connected definitely with the moon by a number of early writers; but the association of the moon with the tides was not generally recognized until after Galileo's time. Newton correctly ascribed the tides to the attractions of the sun and moon, and accounted for their general behavior by means of the law of gravitation. Laplace's treatment of the subject goes more thoroughly into its many complexities.

We are not specially concerned here with the ocean tides themselves, but rather with some possible contributions of the tides on the earth and elsewhere in the development of the solar system, and the stellar system also. Since the studies of G. H. Darwin, son of the naturalist, on the action of the tides in shaping the earth-moon system, tidal theories have assumed commanding positions in cosmogony.

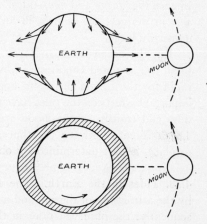

FIG. 4.37. Tides in a Very Deep Ocean. If the whole earth were covered by very deep water, and if the earth's rotation were slower, high tides would occur under and opposite the moon. The upper figure, after Darwin, shows the tide-raising force of the moon at different places.

4.37. Lunar and Solar Tides in the Ocean.
To simplify the explanation of the tides, let us suppose, as Newton did, that the whole earth is covered by very deep water. Since the moon's attraction varies inversely as the square of the distance, it is greater than the average for that part of the ocean nearest the moon, and less than the average for the most distant part, so that the water rises in the regions under and opposite the moon. The ocean therefore assumes

the figure of an ellipsoid of revolution having its longest axis directed toward the moon, and slowly rotating as the moon revolves around the earth. The earth's daily rotation under the tide figure carries the place of observation from one crest to the other in $12^h 25^m$.

The sun also raises appreciable tides in the ocean, although they are not so high as the lunar tides. It can be shown that the tide-producing force of a body varies inversely as the cube of its distance, and accordingly that the sun, despite its overwhelmingly greater mass, is less than half as effective as the moon in raising tides on the earth. The two sets of tides may be supposed to operate independently, their relative positions varying with the moon's phases. Solar tides reinforce lunar tides, on Newton's assumption, when the moon is new or full, and partly neutralize them at the quarter phases; whence the *spring* and *neap* tides. When the moon is new or full and also in perigee, the change in level between low and high tides is unusually large.

But the ocean is not uniform in depth, nor is it deep enough to fulfill the assumed condition. Moreover, the earth's rotation is too rapid for the simple theory to apply; and other factors which have important effects on the tides have not been taken into account. High tides and transits of the moon are generally far from simultaneous. The difference between the times, which varies greatly from place to place, is best determined by observations.

4.38. Tides in the Earth. The earth, like the ocean, is deformed by the attractions of the sun and moon, but to a smaller extent. Consequently, the observed tides in the ocean represent the differences between ocean and earth tides, their heights depending on the extent to which the earth yields to the tide-raising forces. If the earth yielded as much as the water, no appreciable ocean tides could be observed. On the other hand, if the earth were perfectly rigid, tides in the ocean would have greater heights. Thus if the heights of the tides can be observed, a comparison with the theoretical values gives a measure of the earth's rigidity. As early as 1863, Kelvin reached the conclusion that the earth is a very rigid body, which has been confirmed by many others.

Michelson and Gale conducted (1913, 1919) a remarkable study of the tides exhibited in horizontal iron pipes half filled with water. The pipes were 500 feet long with glass ends, so that the variations in the water level could be observed. Evidently the amount of the tidal deformation must be very small in such limited space; the highest tide was, in fact, less than a thousandth of an inch, but they could measure it within one per cent.

In the course of these experiments, the principal phenomena of the tides in the ocean, such as spring and neap tides, were plainly observed. The results agree perfectly with the theory, except that the height of the tide is 0.69 of the calculated value for a perfectly rigid earth. In other words, the height of the tide in the earth itself is 31 per cent of what it would be if the earth were fluid. Two conclusions of great interest follow from these results: first, the rigidity of the earth is about the same as that of good steel, that is to say, the earth yields to the tide-raising forces no more than a similar great ball of steel would yield. The second conclusion is that the earth has high elasticity; it so quickly resumes its original shape, when the deforming force is withdrawn, that the earth tides keep in step with the fluid tides.

4.39. Tidal Friction. The tides act as a friction brake on the earth's rotation; for they are held in position by the sun and moon, while the earth rotates under them. The incessant movement of the water over the uneven floor of the ocean, especially in the shallow places, must gradually lengthen the day. According to MacMillan's calculations the day can not increase in length on this account more than one second in 500,000 years; this appears to be of the right order, but other more recent considerations suggest a somewhat more rapid increase.

From a thorough examination of the records of ancient solar and lunar eclipses Fotheringham finds (1920) that the moon in its motion relative to the stars has moved forward 4".3 at the end of a century with respect to the position calculated from the theory. In the course of 2000 years, this small gain accumulates to nearly the moon's apparent diameter, causing eclipses to come an hour too soon. Likewise, the sun's motion outstrips the theory to the extent of 1".5 in a century. Both discrepancies are satisfactorily explained, *if we suppose that the day is increasing in length 1/1000 of a second a century.*

Jeffreys has shown that an increase of this order in the length of the day requires continuous dissipation of energy by the friction of the tides at the rate of two billion horsepower. The question arises as to whether the tides are capable of promoting this gigantic enterprise. According to the same authority, friction in the open ocean and in the earth's interior is relatively negligible; but in the shallow seas and straits, for which data are available, the average dissipation of energy by tidal friction is altogether 60 per cent of that required to lengthen the day 0^s.001 a century, and two thirds of it takes place in Behring Sea. Assuming the correctness of these results, it is not improbable that the full quota of friction might be found, if complete data were available.

4.40. Tidal Theory of the Earth-Moon System. The slow retardation of the earth's rotation by tidal friction is accompanied by a transfer of moment of momentum (4.32) from the earth to the moon. The moon's gain in this respect appears as increasing speed of its revolution around the earth. The increase of speed causes the moon to spiral outward from the earth; and as the size of its orbit increases, the length of the month increases also. These very gradual variations in the day and month, when they are extended over long periods of time, may greatly alter the configuration of the earth-moon system.

Darwin has traced the possible past and future history of the system. Beginning at the time when the moon was about 10,000 miles from the earth, the length of the month was then something less than a quarter of the present month, and the day was still shorter. Under the action of the tides, both month and day have slowly increased in length, the month faster than the day. After a time, however, the day will lengthen faster than the month, and will finally overtake it, when the day and month have become equal to 55 of our present days (Jeffreys prefers 47). At this remote period in the future, when the moon is much farther away than it is now, the earth-moon system will be internally stable, the earth turning the same hemisphere always toward the moon, just as the moon now presents one hemisphere to the earth. If it happens not to be our hemisphere that is turned moonward, the moon may become one of the sights to see on a trip abroad. At this stage lunar tides can not alter the system; but solar tides still operate on it, and they will force the earth and moon out of step. The history of the system will then be repeated in reverse order, until the moon is brought close to the earth again.

As in the case of any theory that contemplates vast periods of time, the tidal theory of the earth-moon system may properly be regarded with considerable caution; for other factors, which may now seem inconsiderable, or for which experience has not yet prepared us, may eventually dominate the situation. The fact that the moon now turns one hemisphere toward us always is favorable to the theory. Owing to its smaller mass and to the larger tide-raising force of the earth, it is perhaps not surprising that equality of rotation and revolution has already come about on the moon, even though the more effective friction of ocean tides is absent there. Moulton states that, if the earth and moon were physically alike, tidal friction would change the period of the moon's rotation about half a million times as fast as it changes the earth's rotation. The planet Mercury, and Jupiter's bright satellites appear to provide other instances of equality of rotation and revolution resulting from tidal friction.

REFERENCES

J. L. E. Dreyer, *History of the Planetary Systems* (Cambridge University Press).

Robert Grant, *History of Physical Astronomy* (1852), " from the earliest ages to the middle of the nineteenth century."

. F. R. Moulton, *An Introduction to Celestial Mechanics* (Macmillan).

A. S. Eddington, *Space, Time, and Gravitation* (Cambridge University Press, 1921). "An outline of the general relativity theory."

R. T. Crawford, *Determination of Orbits of Comets and Asteroids* (McGraw-Hill, 1930).

Dome of the 60-inch Reflector, Mount Wilson Observatory.

CHAPTER V

THE OTHER PLANETS

MERCURY — VENUS — MARS AND ITS SATELLITES — THE ASTEROIDS — JUPITER AND ITS SATELLITES — SATURN, ITS RINGS AND SATELLITES —URANUS AND NEPTUNE, THEIR SATELLITES — PLUTO — TABLES OF THE PLANETS AND SATELLITES

MERCURY

This planet is nearest of all to the sun, at the mean distance of 36 million miles. It therefore revolves more rapidly than any other planet; at perihelion, where its distance from the sun is reduced to 28½ million miles, the speed is 36 miles a second — twice the swiftness of the earth's movement. Its orbit is more eccentric (0.206) and more highly inclined to the ecliptic (7°) than that of any other principal planet, except Pluto. Mercury is the smallest of the principal planets; the diameter (3100 miles) is only 50 per cent greater than that of the moon, and is slightly exceeded by two of Jupiter's satellites. Like Venus it has no known satellite. The sidereal period of revolution is 88 days. The least distance from the earth at inferior conjunction is 50 million miles.

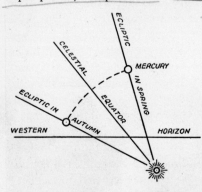

FIG. 5.1. Mercury as Evening Star. It is most conspicuous as evening star at greatest eastern elongations in the spring.

5.1. As Morning and Evening Star. Mercury is occasionally visible to the naked eye for a few days near the times of its greatest elongations, which take place, on the average, 22 days before and after inferior conjunctions. Since the synodic period is only 116 days, three western and as many eastern elongations may occur in the course of a year. They are by no means equally favorable. The apparent distance from the sun at greatest elongations varies from 28°, when the planet is at aphelion, to as little as 18° at perihelion. Moreover, since the planet is never far from the ecliptic, it is highest in the sky at sunrise and sunset when the ecliptic is most inclined to the horizon. This condition is fulfilled (1.20) when the autumnal equinox is rising and the vernal equinox is setting.

As a morning star, therefore, Mercury is most conspicuous at greatest western elongations in September and October, and as evening star at greatest eastern elongations which occur in March and April. It then appears in the twilight near the horizon as a star of the first magnitude — at times nearly as bright as Sirius, twinkling like a star because of its small size and low altitude. Although most people have never seen it, this planet was known to astronomers of very early times.

The terms "morning star" and "evening star" are applied generally to appearances of the inferior planets, especially Venus because it is the more noticeable of the two. But they are employed for the superior planets as well, to designate that they rise after or set before midnight.

5.2. Telescopic Appearance and Rotation. Through the telescope Mercury shows phases, as an inferior planet should (4.4). The phase is full at superior conjunction, quarter at greatest elongation, and new at inferior conjunction. The best views are likely to be obtained in the daytime, when the planet is far above the unsettled atmospheric conditions near the horizon. But even under the best conditions, the markings on its disk are difficult to see. Daylight photographs of Mercury at the Lowell Observatory show unmistakable markings.

The rotation period is somewhat uncertain. As the result of repeated observations of the hazy markings Schiaparelli, in 1889, announced that the period is 88 days. Mercury is so small and so near the sun that it may well be constrained by powerful solar tides to rotate and revolve in the same period, just as the moon does in relation to the earth. If this is so, then aside from librations the planet turns the same hemisphere always toward the sun; one side is continually baked, the other is forever frozen. Owing to the considerable eccentricity of the orbit, the libration in longitude may bring one fourth of the other hemisphere into the sunlight for a part of the time.

5.3. Resemblance to the Moon. Physically, this planet *Mercury* resembles the moon rather than the earth. It does not greatly exceed the moon in diameter and mass, and consequently in surface gravity. The low velocity of escape (2.2 miles a second as compared with 1.5 miles a second at the moon's surface) suggests scarcely better success in retaining an atmosphere. The low albedo (0.07) is about the same as the moon's, this small efficiency as a mirror probably arising from the same cause, namely, the reflection of sunlight from a dark, broken, airless surface. That this surface is at least as mountainous as the moon's surface is inferred from the similar, or even greater increase in the brightness of the planet between the quarter and full phases.

The surface of Mercury must be as barren as the moon's surface, and is subjected to even greater extremes of temperature. Pettit and Nicholson's radiometric measurements indicate a temperature of 340° C. (about 650° Fahrenheit) on the sunward side of the planet — hotter than the melting points of tin and lead. They were unable to detect any radiation from the dark side; it must be intensely cold there.

5.4. Advance of the Perihelion. The major axis of Mercury's orbit is slowly rotating at the rate of 574″ a century, owing to disturbing effects of Venus and other planets, which are subject to calculation. Leverrier, in 1845, found that the observed advance of the perihelion point exceeds the calculated advance by 38″ a century. A slightly greater value, 40″, is now preferred. This planet, which " seems to exist for no other reason than to throw discredit on astronomers," had to be reckoned with. Either the observations were at fault, or it was further disturbed by a body or bodies unknown, or else the law of gravitation, the basis of all the calculations, had finally failed.

After completing the investigations of the equally strange behavior of Uranus, which resulted in the discovery of Neptune (5.40), Leverrier returned to the problem of Mercury, and came to the conclusion that the excessive motion of its perihelion is caused by an undiscovered planet within the orbit of Mercury. This planet he named " Vulcan." But in spite of careful searching for its transits of the sun, and for its appearance near the sun at times of total eclipse, this intra-Mercurial planet has never been seen. In all probability it does not exist. An alternate theory was advanced by Seeliger, namely, that the effect on Mercury is produced by the inner portions of the material that causes the zodiacal light (6.26). This theory is disputed on the ground that enough material to give this effect would cause an illumination far brighter than the observed one.

Scientific and popular interest in the perihelion advance was re-awakened, in 1915, when Einstein's general theory of relativity (4.34) was successful in predicting an advance of 43″ a century above that calculated by Newton's theory of gravitation, in practical agreement with the observed excess. This was the first physical test of the relativity theory. It is one of the very few known differences be-tween predictions of the same effect by the two theories, which are great enough to be observed.

5.5. Transits of Mercury and Venus. The inferior planets usually pass north or south of the sun at inferior conjunction, because their orbits are slightly inclined to the ecliptic. Occasionally they *transit,*

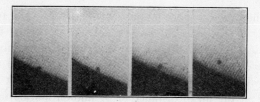

Fig. 5.5. Transit of Mercury, November 7, 1914. The planet appears as a small dark dot against the sun's disk. The interval of time between the first and fourth exposures was less than five minutes. (From photographs at the Royal Observatory, Greenwich)

or cross the sun's disk. The additional condition necessary for a transit is similar to the requirement for solar and lunar eclipses, namely, that the sun must be near one of the nodes of the planet's apparent path.

The sun, in its annual circuit, passes Mercury's nodes on May 8 and November 10. Transits are possible only within 3 days of the former date, and within 5 days of the latter; this difference, owing to the eccentricity of the planet's orbit, makes the November transits twice as numerous as those in May. Altogether, there are about 13 transits of Mercury in a century. The last one occurred on November 10, 1927. The next transit, on November 11, 1940, will be partly visible in the United States; and the following one, on November 14, 1953, will be wholly visible here. With the telescope at these times

Mercury appears as a small black dot moving slowly over the sun's disk.

Transits of Venus are possible only within about two days before or after June 7 and December 9, the dates when the sun passes the nodes of this planet's path. They are much less frequent because the limits are narrower, and also because conjunctions come less often. At present, the transits of Venus occur in pairs having a separation of eight years. A pair of transits took place in 1874 and 1882. The next ones are due June 8, 2004 and June 6, 2012. Formerly they were carefully observed for the purpose of improving the value of the sun's distance; but more available methods have proved better for this purpose. Transits of Venus are visible without the telescope.

VENUS

Venus, the familiar morning and evening star, is the brightest of the planets. It outshines all the celestial bodies except the sun and moon, and near the times of greatest brilliancy it is plainly visible to the naked eye at midday, when the attention is directed to it. The second in order from the sun, this planet revolves next within the earth's orbit at the mean distance of 67 million miles from the sun, completing the circuit of the sun in 225 days. Its orbit is the most nearly circular in the planetary system. Like Mercury it has no known satellite. In some of its characteristics Venus resembles the earth so closely that it has been called the earth's "twin sister."

5.6. As the Morning and Evening Star. Since the orbit of Venus is within the earth's orbit and nearly in the same plane with it, this planet, like Mercury, appears to swing back and forth with respect to the sun's position. At superior conjunction its distance from the earth is 160 million miles, or the *sum* of the earth's and its own distance from the sun. From this position Venus emerges slowly to the east of the sun as the evening star; it appears a little higher from night to night, and sets a little later after sunset, until it reaches greatest eastern elongation, 220 days after the time of superior conjunction.

The entire westward swing to greatest western elongation is accomplished in 144 days. Midway, the planet passes nearly between the sun and the earth into the morning sky. At inferior conjunction it is only 26 million miles from the earth, or the *difference* between the earth's and its own distance from the sun. This is the closest approach to us of any of the principal planets, although some of the asteroids come at times still closer to the earth. Turning eastward again after greatest western elongation, Venus moves slowly back to superior conjunction, again requiring 220 days for this part of the

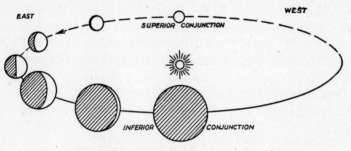

FIG. 5.7.   Changing Phase and Apparent Size of Venus.

journey. The synodic period, between similar conjunctions or elongations, is accordingly 584 days.

Greatest brilliancy as the evening or the morning star occurs about 36 days preceding or following the times of inferior conjunction. On these occasions Venus is six times brighter than the planet Jupiter, and 15 times brighter than Sirius, the brightest star.

5.7. Through the Telescope; the Phases. As a visual object with the telescope the most interesting feature of Venus is its phases, which Galileo, in 1610, was the first to observe. As an inferior planet, Venus exhibits the complete cycle of phases; it is full at superior conjunction, quarter at elongation,

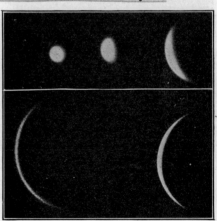

FIG. 5.7A.   Venus at Different Phases. (From photographs by E. C. Slipher, Lowell Observatory)

and new at inferior conjunction, although a thin illuminated crescent usually remains at the last named configuration, because as a rule the planet crosses a little above or below the sun.

Unlike the moon which is brightest at the full phase, Venus attains greatest brilliancy when its phase resembles that of the moon two days before the first quarter. At the full phase the planet's apparent diameter is 10″; at the new phase it has increased over six times, because the distance from the earth is then reduced to less than one sixth of the former value. Diminishing phase is more than offset by increasing apparent size, until the crescent phase is reached. At greatest brilliancy, the sunlit crescent sends us two and a half times more light than the smaller, fully illuminated disk at superior conjunction.

A small telescope gives a satisfactory view of the phases of Venus; but even the largest telescopes fail to reveal visually any conspicuous markings on the planet's surface. Indeed, to many observers the silvery disk has seemed always perfectly blank.

5.8. The Planet Photographed with Filters; Markings. At the favorable eastern elongation in 1927, Ross secured a remarkable series

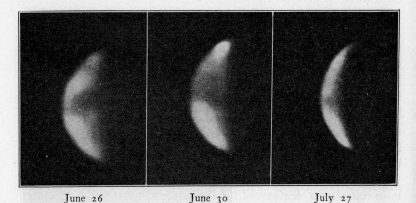

June 26   June 30   July 27

FIG. 5.8. Venus Photographed in Ultra-Violet Light. The belts and bright spots are clearly shown. (From photographs, in 1927, by F. E. Ross at the Mount Wilson Observatory)

of photographs of Venus with the telescopes at Mount Wilson, using filters of different colors before the plates. It might be supposed that any markings on the planet would be most likely to appear on plates exposed behind red and infra-red filters. This procedure gives the clearest views of the earth's surface from airplanes at high elevations. But the red and infra-red photographs of Venus reveal no markings at all. Some of the plates taken with blue light show very weak markings, while all the photographs with ultra-violet light show considerable detail on the planet's disk.

The elusive character of the markings with the eye at the telescope is now accounted for, because the eye is most sensitive to colors between the blue, in which the markings are very weak, and the red which shows them not at all. The complete failure of the infra-red photographs to exhibit details informs us of the great difficulty of dealing by present methods with the surface of the planet. The markings on the ultra-violet photographs are located in the planet's atmosphere, probably at high levels.

These markings (Fig. 5.8) are in the form of parallel dark bands presumably parallel to the equator, and bright " clouds " which appear at the north and south points of the disk, and which might be supposed to overlie the poles of Venus, like the polar caps of Mars; but they lack the greater permanence of the Martian caps, appearing and disappearing in a way not yet understood.

5.9. Rotation of Venus. The failure to observe well-defined markings on the planet's disk, up to the time of recent photographs, is responsible for the conflicting views concerning the rotation period. Until 1890, a period of about 23½ hours was generally agreed upon. In this year, Schiaparelli's observations led him to the conclusion that the period is 225 *days*, equal to the revolution period, so that Venus, like Mercury, turns the same hemisphere always toward the sun. More recent observers were divided between the long and the short period. At present, the evidence seems to require the rejection of both.

Spectroscopic observations of Venus at the Lowell and Mount Wilson observatories leave little doubt that the rotation is considerably slower than that of the earth. Further evidence against rapid rotation is found in the lack of appreciable flattening at the poles of the planet.

A period of rotation as long as 225 days seems equally improbable. The belted aspect of the disk, and the rapid changes in all the markings on the recent photographs suggest a shorter period. Ross points out that a stable condition would exist in the atmosphere of Venus, if the same hemisphere always faced the sun, and that gradations would be symmetrical, not with the equator, but with that point on the planet having the sun in its zenith. He suggests the provisional period of thirty days as the best compromise possible at the present time.

5.10. Venus Compared with the Earth.

The diameter of Venus is about 7700 miles. Its mass is 80 per cent of the earth's mass. In these two respects it is more nearly like the earth than any other planet. The high density, about 90 per cent of the earth's, indicates the existence of a solid surface beneath the obscuring atmosphere. Gravity is 85 per cent of its value here. Since surface gravity is an important factor in determining the extent and behavior of the atmosphere, meteorological conditions, so far as this goes, may bear some resemblance to those of the earth.

Air is certainly present; for twilight effects have been observed. Near the times of inferior conjunction the horns of the illuminated crescent are extended more than halfway around the circumference of the disk. The planet's albedo is 0.59. Such high efficiency of the reflecting surface indicates usually, though not always, the presence of a cloudy atmosphere.

The dark bands which appear on the disk of Venus in the ultra-violet photographs bear some resemblance to what Clayden believes would be the earth's appearance to outsiders. "There is no question," he wrote in 1909, "that the earth is a belted planet." A bright cloud belt, marking our equatorial region of uprushing, moisture-laden currents of air, is bordered north and south by two dark bands where the currents are downward and clouds are rare. Cyclonic and anticyclonic areas, forming, migrating, and disappearing, may well contribute changing bright and dark spots, as viewed from outside.

Radiometric observations contribute another similarity. They indicate for both the day and night sides of Venus a uniform temperature of $-23°$ C. at the level, or levels under observation. Above the highest clouds of the earth's atmosphere there is a corresponding isothermal region whose temperature is $-55°$ C.

Dissimilarities are to be noted also. Since the distance of Venus from the sun is seven tenths of the earth's distance, the sun's radiation has twice the intensity there. If water is abundant, the amount of evaporation, the percentage of cloudiness, and the heights of the clouds may be greater than they are on the earth. The longer period of rotation, if it is really several weeks in length, constitutes another notable difference.

No evidence of water vapor or of oxygen is revealed by the spectrum of the planet, as it was studied at Flagstaff and Mount Wilson. The absence of water is not surprising, because all observations of Venus would seem to be restricted to its upper atmosphere, above the cloud levels, where water vapor ought to be scarce. But the statement that the amount of oxygen above the visible surface is less than one thousandth of the supply in our atmosphere is not so easily dismissed.

Surface conditions on the planet are entirely unknown, because the surface has never been seen. Whether life in any form has gained a foothold there is so far purely a matter of speculation.

Mars and its Satellites

The red planet Mars is next in order beyond the earth. It revolves in its rather eccentric orbit at the mean distance of 142 million miles from the sun, completing the sidereal revolution in 687 days. The synodic period is 780 days. Inconspicuous at times, it becomes occasionally a very brilliant object, and sometimes outshines Jupiter, its lurid light contrasting in a startling way with the pale yellow hue of that planet. Its diameter (about 4200 miles) exceeds only that of Mercury; its mass is one tenth of the earth's mass. The surface may be observed with the telescope far better than that of any other planet. Among the larger planets it is the only one, except Mercury, whose surface is not hidden beneath its atmosphere. Considerations of the possibility of life on its surface have been stimulating to the imagination, and have been the cause of much popular interest in the planet.

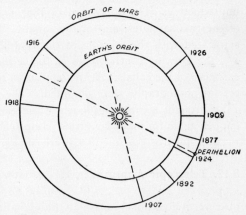

5.11. Favorable Oppositions. When it is in conjunction with the sun, the distance of Mars from the earth averages 234 million miles, and its stellar magnitude is

FIG. 5.11. Varying Distances of Mars at Opposition. At the favorable opposition of 1924, Mars was very near perihelion.

+1.6, so that it is hardly more noticeable than the brightest star in the Great Dipper. At the average opposition the distance is reduced to 49 million miles, while the brightness has increased nearly 25 times. A superior planet is best observed at opposition, because it is then nearest us.

Another consideration is introduced in the case of Mars by the eccentricity of the orbit (0.093), and the resulting range in distance at the different oppositions. *Favorable oppositions* are those that occur when the planet is near perihelion. On these occasions the distance from the earth approaches the minimum of 34,600,000 miles; the stellar magnitude is then −2.8, and the brightness exceeds that of any other planet except Venus. At the most remote opposition, when the planet is at aphelion, its distance is 63 million miles, and it is not so bright as Sirius.

Oppositions recur, on the average, at intervals of the synodic period, 780 days, or nearly two years and two months. Favorable oppositions occur in August and September. On August 28 the earth has the same heliocentric longitude (334°.8) as the perihelion of Mars. The least favorable oppositions come in February and March.

Favorable oppositions recur at intervals of 15 or 17 years. The disk of the planet may then attain the apparent diameter of 25″, so that a telescope magnifying only 75 times shows it as large as the moon appears to the naked eye. These opportunities have not been unproductive. The opposition of 1877 is notable for the discovery of the two satellites, and of the canals. The opposition of 1892 is associated with the erection of the Lowell Observatory in Arizona, and the growing controversies as to the interpretation and even the existence of the canals. At the opposition of 1909 the first really successful photographs were obtained. The opposition of August 22, 1924, brought a closer approach of the planet to the earth than will happen again for many centuries. Improved photographic, radiometric, and spectroscopic methods were employed at that time.

5.12. Telescopic Appearance. The first view of Mars with the telescope, even a large one, is likely to be disappointing. To the casual observer it does not compare favorably with Jupiter or Saturn. What is glimpsed seems meager in contrast with the varied detail that astronomers describe and exhibit in their drawings. It is important to remember that these descriptions are given by trained observers who have made good use of moments of exceptionally fine definition. In some parts of the country such moments rarely come.

From the full phase, at conjunction and opposition, the illuminated part of the disk decreases to the gibbous phase at quadrature, when it resembles the moon about three days before full. At favorable oppositions the planet's southern hemisphere is always easier to observe, because the south pole is then tipped partly toward the earth.

The *orange background,* which imparts to Mars its ruddy color, occupies three fifths of the planet's surface. Upon this background dark *blue-green markings* appear; some are large, fairly conspicuous blotches, while others are evanescent streaks — the *canals.* Great *white spots* mark the poles during the winter seasons. Other white spots appear at times along the sunrise line, and elsewhere.

The dark markings are permanent features of the surface, although they are not at all times of equal conspicuousness. They were formerly supposed to be bodies of water, while the orange part was interpreted as land. Accordingly, they were named seas, bays, lakes, and so on; and these designations on the earlier maps have survived, like the lunar " seas," although these markings are no longer regarded as water areas. Prominent among them are the *Solis Lacus* (*Lake of the Sun*), and the *Syrtis Major* which Huyghens observed and sketched as early as 1659.

The white polar caps are products of the cold seasons, forming rapidly as winter comes on in each hemisphere. The southern cap has attained a maximum radius of 50° from the pole. Since a degree of latitude on the surface of Mars averages 37 miles, the diameter of the cap was then 3700 miles. The northern one is somewhat smaller. The caps shrink with the approach of the summer season. Their visual behavior is about what might be expected if they are snow caps. But the recent photographs (5.14) indicate that they are, at least partly, atmospheric and not surface phenomena.

5.13. The Canals of Mars were discovered, in 1877, by Schiaparelli at the Milan Observatory. He saw relatively narrow streaks connecting the large dark markings, and named then *canali* (*channels*) to match the rest of the watery nomenclature. Unfortunately, the word was translated into English as " *canals,*" thus conveying the idea of artificiality which the discoverer did not propose. This novel point of view was later advanced by Lowell and others, namely, that the canals are evidence of a vast irrigation project on the planet — not the narrow waterways themselves, but the strips of vegetation that they water. This construction requires the presence of intelligent life on Mars, a conclusion of permanent public and scientific interest, if it is correct.

The existence of the canals is established by the many observers who have seen and sketched them in the same places. Photographs

give confirmatory testimony, so far as it goes; for they are not usually as effective as the eye at the telescope in detecting delicate planetary detail. But the sharply defined, uniform, and geometrical char-

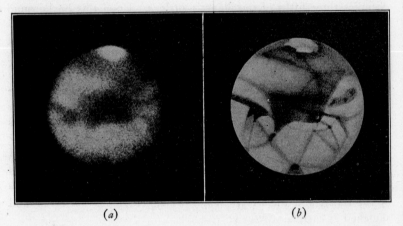

(a)   (b)

FIG. 5.13. Photograph and Drawing of Mars, September 2, 1924. The
south polar cap is at the top. The large "sea" in the center is Mare Eryth-
raeum. Several canals are clearly shown. (From a photograph, with red
filter, and a drawing by R. J. Trumpler with the 36-inch refractor, Lick
Observatory)

acter of the canals, as they appeared to Lowell, is in question — the
characteristics on which his position as to their artificiality funda-
mentally rests.

5.14. Photographs of Mars with Color Filters. At the favorable
oppositions of 1924 and 1926, instructive photographs of Mars were
made through light-filters of different colors. The principle involved
is easily understood. The reddening of the sun as it sinks toward the
horizon demonstrates the ability of red light to penetrate farther
through an atmosphere than blue or violet light; the latter colors are
more readily scattered by the air, as shown by the blue of the sky.
The clearest views of a planet's surface ought, therefore, to be obtained by exposing plates behind red filters. On the other hand, the
planet's atmospheric features ought to be emphasized when violet
filters are used. For still greater contrast infra-red and ultra-violet
filters were employed.

The dark markings are delineated most clearly on the infra-red
photographs. This is accordant with expectation. But the polar

" snow caps " and other more transitory white spots appear faint, or not at all in red light; they are prominent features of the ultra-violet photographs instead. From this surprising result Wright infers that

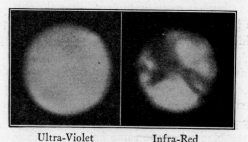

Ultra-Violet   Infra-Red

FIG. 5.14. Photographs of Mars in Ultra-Violet and Infra-Red Light, November 2, 1926. The polar caps are shown in ultra-violet light, while the dark markings are brought out clearly in infra-red light. (From photographs by W. H. Wright with the Crossley reflector, Lick Observatory)

the polar cap is an atmospheric phenomenon, but that there is some evidence of a smaller surface cap below it.

5.15. Rotation of Mars.

The period of rotation is 24^h 37^m $22^s.58$. The rotation of Mars has the same direction as the earth's rotation, and its period so nearly equals the earth's period that at the same hour from day to day almost the same face of the planet is presented to us, except that everything has stepped backward ten degrees. Thus the various markings pass slowly in review, completing their apparent backward revolutions in about 38 days. The permanence and definiteness of the dark markings, and the fact that they have been observed and mapped for 275 years, allows the rotation period to be determined with a high degree of accuracy.

The planet's equator is inclined $23°.5$ to the plane of its orbit, according to Lowell. Other authorities give slightly different values, but all agree that it is nearly the same as the angle between the earth's equator and ecliptic. The orientation of the Martian axis differs about 90° from that of the earth's, the northern end, instead of pointing toward Polaris, is directed to the point of the celestial sphere in right ascension 22^h 11^m, declination $+55°$. This point is 8° south of the star α Cephei and not far from the location of our own north celestial pole 6000 years hence.

Notwithstanding the slightly longer rotation period, the oblateness of Mars (1/192) is more pronounced than the earth's polar flattening. This is a consequence of smaller density, and perhaps also of less rapid increase in density toward the center of the planet.

5.16. The Seasons of Mars. Mars presents its poles alternately to the sun in much the same way that the earth does, owing to the similarity of its axial tilt. The seasons resemble ours geometrically, except that they are nearly twice as long. The winter solstice of Mars occurs when the planet has the same heliocentric longitude that the earth has about September 10, and not long after the time of perihelion, when it has the same direction from the sun as the earth on August 28. Summer in the southern hemisphere is therefore warmer than the northern summer which comes when the planet is near the aphelion point; while the southern winters are colder than the northern ones. For the same reason, the earth's southern hemisphere would have the greater seasonal range in temperature, if there were no compensating factor (2.37).

While the whole variation in our distance from the sun is only 3 per cent, Mars in its more eccentric orbit is fully 20 per cent (more than 26 million miles) farther from the sun at aphelion than at perihelion. The effect in the two hemispheres is more marked. The southern polar cap becomes larger than the northern cap in the winter season, and it disappears completely in summer, which the other has not been observed to do.

5.17. Seasonal Changes. Not only the polar caps, but also the dark surface markings, including the canals, exhibit conspicuous seasonal changes, which have been carefully studied for many years at the Lowell Observatory, and elsewhere. The darkening, or the appearance, of the dark markings, occurs in both hemispheres during the Martian seasons corresponding to our late spring. They become more intense in early summer, remain near maximum intensity for 50 days or more, and begin to fade as the fall season approaches. The fading, which extends into the winter, is in color as well as intensity; the blue-green of the spring and summer turns to chocolate brown. *The dates of the changes in the intensity and color of the dark markings are such as would be expected, if these changes are produced by the* *growth and decline of vegetation.* This view is expressed by Lowell and by E. C. Slipher, and many astronomers concur in it.

But the actual existence of vegetation on the surface of Mars remains an open question in the minds of many. Evidence from other

Martian Date		Martian Date
May 11		June 23
May 29		July 31

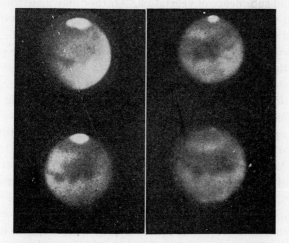

FIG. 5.17. Seasonal Changes on Mars. The series of photographs shows the shrinking of the south polar cap, and the gradual darkening of the dark markings with the advance of the summer season in the southern Martian hemisphere. (From photographs by E. C. Slipher, Lowell Observatory)

directions is to be desired, and in this connection V. M. Slipher's comparison of the spectrum of the planet with that of light reflected from vegetation is interesting. That he did not detect the reflection spectrum of chlorophyl in the planet's light may indicate merely the difficulty of this test.

5.18. Life on Mars Considered. The question as to the presence of life in other worlds is a fascinating one, but in general it is difficult to approach except by way of pure speculation. There is no known means of observing life beyond the solar system, or even the presence of possible planets attending the stars, on which life might flourish. Within the solar system the majority of the members are at once withdrawn from consideration, either because they are too small to retain atmospheres, or because they seem to be too far removed from the sun to have a suitable temperature, or for other reasons. Venus and Mars survive the first sweeping elimination; but the surface of the former is wrapped in cloud and mystery. Mars then remains as the most promising subject for discussion.

The seasonal changes in the dark markings may result from the growth and subsidence of vegetation. Or they may arise from a cause unrelated to life. As an example of an alternate interpretation, it is suggested that seasonal variations in the transparency of the Martian atmosphere might produce the observed cycle in the intensity and color of these areas. *The artificial aspect of the canals,* as they appear to some observers, requires, in their opinions, the presence of human life on the planet. But other observers are unable to see in the canals this appearance of artificiality.

Life, as we know it, requires air, water, and a temperature within rather narrow limits. It is important to inquire whether the conditions on Mars meet these demands. *Air is certainly present.* A twilight band extends 8° onto the hemisphere that is turned away from the sun. The surface markings fade toward the edge of the disk, where they are viewed obliquely through a greater thickness of the air. The ultra-violet photographs (5.14) give equally conclusive evidence. Wright's estimate of the height of the atmosphere that can be photographed is 60 miles.

The atmosphere of Mars is considerably rarer than ours. The low albedo (0.15), and the distinctness of the surface markings lead to this conclusion, while the smaller surface gravity, 0.38 that of the earth, and the consequently reduced velocity of escape (3 miles a second), give a reason for it. The oxygen content of the planet's atmosphere is less than that above the level of Mount Everest, according to Adams and St. John's spectroscopic analysis; and for equal areas the amount of water vapor above its surface is as low as five per cent of that in the earth's atmosphere. *Water is probably scarce on the surface as well as in the atmosphere.* Lowell and Douglass pointed out long ago that the "seas" are not oceans, because the canals traverse them, as they do the orange areas.

Theoretical considerations based on the greater distance of Mars from the sun assign to it a mean surface temperature far below the freezing point of water. Radiometric measurements at the Lowell and Mount Wilson observatories indicate, however, that *the surface is above freezing at noon in the tropics.* This value must not be compared directly with terrestrial temperatures which have to do with the air immediately above the surface. The air may be much colder than the surface. As the abode of life Mars seems unattractive. On the other hand, no one can say conclusively that life does not exist there.

5.19. The Two Satellites of Mars were discovered, in 1877, by Asaph Hall at the Naval Observatory in Washington. He named them *Phobos* and *Deimos* — Fear and Panic, the companions of Mars.

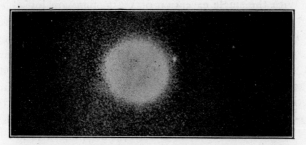

FIG. 5.19. The Satellites of Mars. Photographed August 21, 1924. Phobos is close to the planet. Deimos is considerably fainter, and about ⅔ inch farther to the right. (From a photograph by E. C. Slipher, Lowell Observatory)

They are very small (perhaps not exceeding 10 miles in diameter), and so near the planet as to be invisible except with large telescopes at favorable times.

Phobos, the inner satellite, revolves at the distance of 5800 miles from the center of Mars, and 3700 miles from the surface; it completes a sidereal revolution in only $7^h 39^m$, a period less than one third that of the planet's rotation. As viewed from the planet, therefore, it rises in the west and sets in the east. *No other known satellite in the solar system revolves in a shorter interval than the rotation period of its primary.*

The distance of Deimos from the center of Mars is 14,600 miles, and its period of revolution is $30^h 18^m$. It is smaller than the inner satellite, and only one third as bright.

More than a hundred years before the discovery of these satellites, Voltaire mentions them in the story of Micromegas; and Swift's Gulliver, in reporting the scientific achievements of the Laputans, refers to their observation of two satellites of Mars, " whereof the innermost is distant from the center of the planet exactly three of his diameters, and the outermost five; the former revolves in the space of ten hours, and the latter in twenty-one and a half."

THE ASTEROIDS

The *asteroids,* or *minor planets* (or *planetoids*) are the many small bodies which revolve around the sun, mostly between the orbits of Mars and Jupiter, the majority having periods between 3½ and 6 years. With the single exception of Vesta, they are invisible to the naked eye. The name "asteroid" (star-like) describes very well their appearance with the telescope, except that a few of the larger ones show tiny disks. Although lacking in telescopic interest, the asteroids present problems of considerable theoretical importance in their grouping and in the variety of their movements. From the standpoint of celestial mechanics they form a perfect connecting link between the planets on the one hand, and comets and meteor swarms on the other. Four, at least, of the asteroids approach the earth much closer than any of the large planets.

5.20. Discovery of the Asteroids. Ceres, the largest of the asteroids, and the first to become known, was discovered accidentally by Piazzi in Sicily, on the first evening of the nineteenth century, January 1, 1801. Its motion from night to night relative to the stars attracted his attention. At first, there was danger of losing this strange object while it was passing the sun into the morning sky. Piazzi's observations did not determine its path among the stars well enough to make certain its recovery. To meet this emergency the mathematician Gauss invented his method for calculating the orbit of a celestial body from three observations of its position. He then computed the orbit of this body and its apparent path, along which it was later found again. The orbit was that of a planet revolving between Mars and Jupiter at the mean distance from the sun 2.8 times the earth's distance, in close agreement with Bode's law (4.2).

In the following year another asteroid, Pallas, was discovered by Olbers in the region of the sky where he had been searching for Ceres. The fact that the orbits of the two bodies nearly intersect, and their small size in comparison with the older planets, led Olbers to the theory that they are fragments of a disrupted planet. Others were looked for, and two more were soon found, Juno in 1804, and Vesta in 1807. The four first discovered are relatively bright.

Vesta, the brightest of all, becomes visible at times to the naked eye.

Nearly forty years elapsed before the fifth asteroid, Astraea, was discovered, in 1845, by the amateur Hencke, who had been searching for fifteen years in the belief that other, fainter asteroids were to be found. His success encouraged others. Since 1847, every year has added at least one new little planet to the list.

5.21. Photographic Search for Asteroids.

For many years, the search for asteroids was entirely visual. The observer at the telescope compared a region of the sky with a star chart of that region.

FIG. 5.21. Trails of Three Asteroids. (From a photograph by M. Wolf, Königstuhl-Heidelberg)

If an uncharted star was seen, it was watched hopefully for movement among the stars, which would reveal its planetary character. It was slow procedure.

Photography was substituted in 1891 by Wolf at Heidelberg, who now heads the list of successful asteroid hunters with more than 500 discoveries. Plates are exposed to the sky for two or three hours in large cameras which are mounted equatorially and driven by clockwork. On the developed plates the stars appear as dots, while an asteroid in that region is shown as a short streak, because of its motion among the stars while the exposure is going on (Fig. 5.21).

In Metcalf's photographic searches the camera was given a slow motion in addition to that supplied by the clockwork, so as to follow the movement of the average asteroid. The stars then trailed slightly on the plate, while the asteroid, if it was present, appeared as a dot, an arrangement which was more likely to show faint ones. For very slow moving asteroids two plates of the same region are taken at different times and compared with a blink microscope (8.9).

As soon as the discovery of a new member is announced, the Recheninstitut in Berlin assigns it a probationary designation, the year of discovery followed by two letters, of which the first (the letters I and Z are omitted) indicates the half-month, and the second the order in which the announcement was received (I is omitted). Thus the asteroid 1932 ED was the fourth to be announced in the first half of March, 1932. If more than 25 are discovered in a half-month, the order is repeated, with the suffix $_1$.

When the orbit is determined, and the asteroid proven to be a new one, a permanent number is given to it, and the discoverer may name it whatever he wishes. It is customary to employ the feminine form in the naming, except for a few in the extreme edges of the group, such as Eros and Achilles. At the end of the year 1930, number 1152 had been reached.

5.22. Compared with the Principal Planets. The orbits of the asteroids exhibit more variety than those of the large planets. While some are nearly circular and only slightly inclined to the ecliptic, others depart considerably from the circular form and are not confined within the bounds of the zodiac. The orbit of Hidalgo has an eccentricity of 0.65, and is inclined 43° to the ecliptic; the aphelion point is as far away as Saturn. The direction of revolution is invariably from west to east.

The largest asteroid, Ceres, is 480 miles in diameter, according to Barnard's measurements. Pallas is second with a diameter of 300 miles. Vesta is half the size of Ceres, but outshines it under the same conditions; evidently its surface is a better reflector of sunlight. Since only a few show disks even with large telescopes, the sizes of most of them can only be estimated from the brightness. About a dozen exceed one hundred miles in diameter; the majority are less than fifty miles. All are too small to have atmospheres. Stroobant estimates at 100,000 the number of asteroids brighter than magnitude 20, and their combined mass as 1/2000 of the earth's mass, or four per cent of the moon's mass.

5.23. Eros. Since its discovery, in 1898, this asteroid has been of special interest owing to its occasional close approaches to the earth. At perihelion its distance from the sun is 105 million miles, and its least distance from the earth's orbit, near its perihelion also, is therefore only 14 million miles.

Eros comes to opposition at intervals of 845 days, but only rarely is it near perihelion at the same time. At the close approach of January 30, 1931, preceding the opposition of February 17, its distance from the earth was 16 million miles. The next favorable opposition will occur in 1975. On these occasions, only a small telescope is required to show this 20-mile asteroid as a star of the seventh magnitude. The astronomical importance of the near approach is that it provides data for more accurate determinations of the sun's distance (4.25) and of the moon's mass (3.24). Periodic fluctuations in the brightness of Eros, which other asteroids exhibit also, can be observed advantageously at such times.

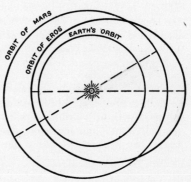

FIG. 5.23. Orbit of Eros.

Campbell's studies, at Harvard, of the light variations of Eros show that the period, slightly more than five hours and a quarter, has not changed a measurable part of a second during the past 30 years. But the extent of the fluctuation varies greatly; at times it exceeds a full magnitude, while at other times it is barely perceptible.

The view that the light variation is produced in some way by the rotation of Eros was clarified at the close approach of 1931. Van den Bos and Finsen, with the 26-inch refractor of the Union Observatory, saw the asteroid in the form of the figure eight, or of a notched double star, rotating in the period of the light variation. The irregularity in the extent of the variation is not yet completely accounted for.

5.24. Close Approaches of Asteroids. Two asteroids are known which come nearer the earth than Eros does. The first was discovered by Delporte, at Uccle, Belgium, in March, 1932. It bears the provisional designation 1932 EA_1, showing that it was the twenty-sixth asteroid discovered in the second half of that month. Although its mean distance from the sun is twice the earth's distance, the eccentricity of the orbit is so high, around 0.44, that the perihelion is only 10 million miles outside the earth's orbit. This was the distance of the asteroid from the earth on March 22, 1932. Another close approach will occur in 1943. The faintness of this object will make it difficult to observe except near perihelion.

An even more striking case is presented by asteroid 1932 HA, discovered by Reinmuth, at Heidelberg. A preliminary orbit by Whipple and Cunningham has the eccentricity 0.6, and the mean distance from the sun 1.6 times the earth's distance. At perihelion, therefore, the asteroid is nearer the sun than the orbit of Venus. It is the only asteroid known to come within the earth's orbit, and it can pass within two million miles of the earth — the closest approach of any known planet. It can transit the sun, but there is no certainty of observing it in transit; for this little object is estimated to be only a mile in diameter. At closest approach it is no brighter than a star of the tenth magnitude.

5.25. Grouping of Asteroids. The orbits of the asteroids are not distributed at random through the region which the majority frequent. As early as 1866, Kirkwood called attention to wide gaps in the neighborhoods of mean distances from the sun where the periods of revolution would be ⅓ and ½ of Jupiter's period; narrower but well-defined gaps correspond to other simple fractions. It is natural to suppose that a period commensurate with that of the chief disturbing planet would be unstable, because the same types of disturbances would recur frequently. The divisions in Saturn's rings (5.35) suggest a similar explanation. For asteroids having periods equal to that of Jupiter, however, there are two regions where stability is assured.

Long ago, the mathematician Lagrange explained a particular solution of the problem of three bodies, when the three bodies occupy the vertices of an equilateral triangle. Since no celestial example was then known, he took as a hypothetical case an asteroid moving in such a way that its distances from Jupiter and the sun remained the same, and equal to the distance separating those two bodies. If the asteroid is disturbed, it will oscillate around its vertex of the triangle; but the system will not be broken up, at least, not for a long time.

Ten asteroids are now (1932) known which are not far from examples of this interesting case. Achilles was the first of these to be discovered, in 1906. Named after the Homeric heroes, they are known, therefore, as *the Trojan group.* In their revolutions around the sun they oscillate about points which are equally distant from Jupiter and the sun. Five are east and five are west of Jupiter. Owing to their greater distances from the earth, these asteroids are visible only with large telescopes.

It may appear strange that this group should have a mean period the same as Jupiter's, when the others, in general, avoid periods which are simply related to that of the planet. But in this special case the asteroids are always far away from Jupiter.

Hirayama, at Tokyo, has drawn attention to remarkable groupings of many asteroids into " families." The members of each family have nearly the same mean distance from the sun; their orbits differ little in eccentricity and in inclination to the plane of Jupiter's orbit. At least five families are recognized.

JUPITER AND ITS SATELLITES

This great planet is one of the brightest objects in the sky; it is usually more brilliant than any of the stars or other planets, except Venus and occasionally Mars. In even a small telescope it is a fine object, owing to its large banded disk and its four bright satellites. Jupiter has nine satellites in all, five of which are very faint. Its mean distance from the sun is 483 million miles, and its distance from the earth at the closest approach is 367 million miles. The sidereal period of revolution is 11.86 years; the synodic period is 399 days, so that from year to year the planet advances among the stars about one constellation of the zodiac.

Jupiter is the *largest planet.* Its equatorial diameter (88,600 miles) is eleven times the earth's diameter and one tenth that of the sun. Its mass, which is 1/1047 of the sun's mass, is much greater than the combined masses of the other planets.

5.26. The Belts and Other Markings. A small telescope shows a few dark streaks across the disk of Jupiter, parallel to its equator. These are the *belts,* first noticed in 1630. In the larger telescopes they exhibit a great variety of detail and color, and often rapid changes in form, which reveal their fluid nature; for we are observing the upper levels of the clouds in the planet's atmosphere. The attention may well be transferred to the bright *zones* or *currents* between the belts, which are presumably the regions of maximum cloudiness at these levels.

The bright *equatorial zone* extends some 10° on each side of the equator, having a maximum width of 15,000 miles. It is bordered by the dark *north and south equatorial belts,* the most conspicuous of the belts. Beyond them are the bright *north and south tropical*

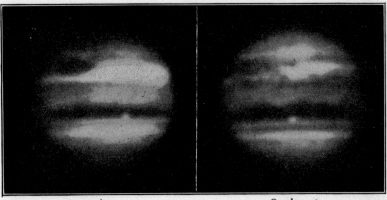

September 14   October 6

FIG. 5.26. Jupiter in 1928. Two photographs of the same face of Jupiter showing rapid changes in its southern (upper) hemisphere. The great red spot is seen at the left side of the disk. The small white spot in the north tropical belt is overtaking the red spot. (From photographs by E. C. Slipher, Lowell Observatory)

zones; then come the less conspicuous temperate belts and zones, and finally the polar regions. Bright patches and streaks appear in the belts, and dark ones in the zones.

In contrast with the short-lived markings which persist usually only a few weeks, the *great red spot* has had a remarkably long career. First noticed in 1878, this elliptical, brick-red spot was 30,000 miles long, and was set in a larger bright spot of the same shape, an enlargement of the south tropical zone. Eventually the red nucleus faded, but the bright spot is still to be seen; and the records show that it was present as early as 1831.

5.27. Rotation of Jupiter; Interior Conditions. The rotations of the outer planets are more rapid than those of the terrestrial planets, and the *rotation period of Jupiter is the shortest of them all — about* $9^h 55^m$. The speed of the rotation at Jupiter's equator is more than

27 times greater than at the earth's equator, which results in the marked degree of flattening at the poles. The oblateness is 1/15.4, according to H. Struve. The planet's equator is inclined $3°\ 7'$ to the plane of its orbit.

The period of the rotation is determined by timing the well-defined cloud markings; but these are drifting meanwhile in the various currents. Thus the period varies from one zone to another, and even in the same zone. According to Phillips, the mean period of the equatorial zone is $9^h\ 50^m\ 26^s$, while in other parts of the disk it varies from $9^h\ 55^m\ 5^s$ to $9^h\ 55^m\ 42^s$, with little regard for latitude. The "south tropical disturbance," which is a little south of the great red spot, has a period of rotation twenty seconds shorter than that of the spot; it drifts by the spot and gains a lap on it every two years.

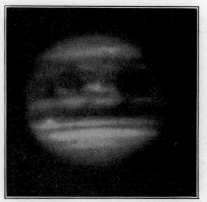

November 30

FIG. 5.26A. Jupiter in 1928. A later photograph by E. C. Slipher, showing the same face as in Fig. 5.26.

Wright has photographed Jupiter at short intervals through a complete rotation. The films were assembled by Mees into an instructive moving picture.

An important clue to the interior condition of a planet is derived from the ratio ϵ/m (3.4), which for the earth we have found equal to 0.97. The value for any other planet is proportional to its mean density and oblateness, and the square of its period of rotation. By a simple calculation the following information is derived concerning the distribution of material within some of the planets:

For uniform distribution	$\epsilon/m =$	1.25
For the planets:	Mars	1.14
	Earth	0.97
	Jupiter	0.76
	Saturn	0.72
For very high central condensation		0.50

It is evident that the masses of Jupiter and Saturn are highly concentrated toward their centers.

5.28. Physical Constitution of Jupiter. The planet's mean density is 1.34 times that of water, and therefore slightly less than the sun's density. On this account, and owing to its great mass, Jupiter was formerly supposed to be gaseous throughout — still too hot to solidify, though not appreciably luminous. But radiometric measurements give *no evidence of internal heat*. Coblentz and Lampland's

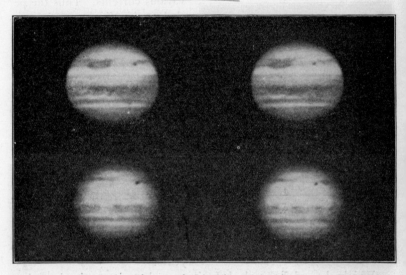

FIG. 5.28. Jupiter Photographed in Ultra-Violet and Extreme Red Light, October 2, 1927. In ultra-violet light (upper pair) the planet shows a sharper edge, larger disk, and different surface details than in red light (lower pair). The great red spot is prominent in the upper photographs, and scarcely visible in the lower ones. The exposures at the right were made eleven minutes later; in the meantime, the planet had rotated 6¾° toward the left, and the shadow of satellite II, which was in transit, had moved noticeably toward the left. (From photographs by W. H. Wright, Lick Observatory)

measures, in 1924, indicate that the temperature of the effective radiating layer in the planet's atmosphere is −130° C., which is entirely ascribable to sunshine. Since the mass of Jupiter is highly concentrated toward its center, it is quite possible that the planet has a solid surface underneath its extensive cloudy atmosphere of undetermined depth.

The atmospheric phenomena are in many respects mysterious. Rapid changes in the clouds suggest vigorous vertical convection, and strong horizontal currents, which run ahead of the rotation, sometimes at rates of the order of 200 miles an hour, comparable with the high winds in the earth's upper atmosphere.

It is certainly not water that enters into the Jovian weather, but some ingredient that evaporates at a temperature far below 0° C.; carbon dioxide has been suggested. V. M. Slipher's spectrograms of the outer planets show the presence of some unidentified constituent in their atmospheres, which strongly absorbs sunlight, particularly in the orange and red. This absorption is greater for the more distant planets, Uranus and Neptune, and may well account for the blue-green color of their disks. Dunham finds (1933) a striking similarity between absorption bands in the spectra of the outer planets and of ammonia.

5.29. The Four Bright Satellites. Four of Jupiter's nine known satellites are bright enough to be visible to the naked eye as faint stars, if they were farther removed from the brilliant planet. The

FIG. 5.29. Jupiter's Four Bright Satellites. Photographed February 16, 1921, and May 25, 1923. The four satellites are visible with a small telescope. (From photographs by E. C. Slipher, Lowell Observatory)

smallest telescope shows them plainly. These four bright satellites were discovered by Galileo early in 1610. They have received names, but are oftener designated by number, in order of their distance from the planet. The first and second satellites are about the moon's size. The third and fourth are 50 per cent greater in diameter; they are the *largest of all satellites,* surpassing even the planet Mercury. The orbits of these satellites are nearly circular, and nearly in the planes of the planet's equator and of its orbit.

Their periods of rotation and revolution are the same. Stebbins' measurements (1926) with the photo-electric cell have shown that the brightness of each of these satellites varies slightly in the period of its revolution. The slight periodic variations in the light are almost certainly caused by the rotations of the satellites; they indicate that the surfaces are unevenly marked, so that the hemispheres facing the earth vary in reflecting power as the satellites rotate. This interesting result was anticipated for the third satellite, and perhaps also for the fourth, by Douglass and others from observations of the markings.

The velocities of escape at the surfaces of the four bright satellites are comparable with that of the moon; it seems doubtful, therefore, that they have atmospheres. Their densities are somewhat less than the moon's, with the exception of the fourth satellite, which has the remarkably small density 0.6 times that of water. The combined light of these satellites upon Jupiter is not more than thirty per cent of the light of the full moon on the earth.

5.30. Eclipses and Transits of the Satellites. Since the orbits of the bright satellites are nearly in the plane of the planet's orbit, they are always nearly edgewise to the earth. As the satellites revolve around Jupiter, they appear to us to move back and forth almost on the same straight line; the forward swing takes them behind the planet and

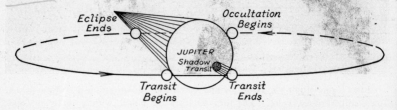

FIG. 5.30. Phenomena of a Satellite of Jupiter.

through its shadow (the fourth satellite often clears it), the backward swing in front of the planet, when their own shadows are cast upon it. These phenomena: occultations, eclipses, transits, and shadow-transits add considerable interest to observations of Jupiter with the telescope. The times of their frequent occurrences are predicted in the *Nautical Almanac*.

It was by observations of the eclipses of Jupiter's satellites that Roemer first demonstrated the finite speed of light (2.11). Inasmuch as the times of the disappearances and reappearances can not be observed with any great accuracy, Pickering at Harvard adopted the better plan of determining by means of photometers the instants at which the light of the satellite is reduced one half. These numerous observations were employed by Sampson in constructing new tables from which the phenomena are now predicted. But the observed times of the eclipses are not always in agreement with the predicted ones, perhaps, as Sampson suggests, owing to variations of as much as 200 miles in the height of Jupiter's cloud level, and so in the diameter of its shadow.

5.31. The Faint Satellites.

The other five satellites are difficult objects to see even with large telescopes; probably no one of them is much greater than 100 miles in diameter. They have never received names, being designated simply by numbers, following those of the Galilean satellites, in the order of their discovery. Four were discovered at the Lick Observatory, namely, the fifth satellite by Barnard in 1892, the sixth and seventh by Perrine in 1904 and 1905, and the ninth by Nicholson in 1914. Melotte at Greenwich found the eighth satellite in 1908.

The fifth satellite, like the four bright ones, has a nearly circular and only slightly inclined orbit. It is remarkable for its nearness to the planet, which adds much to the difficulty of observing it, and for its short period of revolution, which is slightly less than 12 hours. It is the *swiftest of all the satellites,* revolving at the rate of a thousand miles a minute. The line of apsides advances and the nodes regress at the very rapid rate of 2°.5 a day, owing to the satellite's small distance from the oblate planet.

The four outer satellites have little in common with the inner ones; their orbits have greater eccentricity, and are not in the same plane with the others. They are paired in an interesting way. The mean distances of the sixth and seventh satellites from the planet are a little more than 7 million miles; those of the eighth and ninth are about 15 million miles, and their greatest distances may be as much as 20 million miles. The eighth and ninth satellites are the *most distant of all satellites from the primary;* and *they are further remarkable because they revolve from east to west.*

Jupiter's control over its remote satellites is disputed by the sun, whose attraction greatly disturbs their orbits. The question has arisen as to whether these satellites are asteroids captured by Jupiter under favorable circumstances, and whether their allegiance to the planet is only temporary. Moulton has shown that the stability of the eighth and ninth satellites is rendered more probable because of their retrograde revolutions.

As seen from Jupiter, the outer satellites would be invisible to the unaided eye, except the sixth satellite, which would appear as a rather faint star.

SATURN; ITS RINGS AND SATELLITES

Saturn is the most distant of the bright planets from the sun, and the most remote planet known to early astronomers. It completes a revolution once in 29½ years, at the mean distance of 886 million miles from the sun. Its least distance from the earth is 745 million miles — nearly twice that of Jupiter. It shines with a steady yellowish light, often brighter than a star of the first magnitude, and sometimes brighter than Capella.

The planet ranks second to Jupiter in size and mass; its equatorial diameter is 74,100 miles. It ranks first, with Jupiter, in number of satellites. Of all the planets Saturn has the *least density* (*0.7 times that of water*), *and the greatest oblateness*. It is unique in the possession of a *system of rings*, which surround the planet and make it one of the most impressive of the celestial objects.

5.32. Physical Constitution of Saturn. In many respects this cloud-enveloped planet resembles Jupiter. The clouds here are likewise arranged in bands, although they are more regular, less distinct, and apparently less rapid in their variations. A broad yellow zone overlies the planet's equator, and large bluish caps mark its poles, with bright and dark bands intervening. Again, the period of rotation is not the same for all the markings. But distinct spots suitable for determining the rotation are not so often found on Saturn. Hall, in 1876, observed a bright spot near the equator, which went around in a period of $10^h 14^m$. Barnard's observations, in 1903, of spots farther north gave the longer period of $10^h 38^m$.

It is generally agreed that the observed surface of Saturn is gaseous; but there remains considerable difference of opinion concerning the interior. According to Coblentz's measurements, the temperature at the visible levels is $-150°$ C.; this may be entirely the effect of sunshine, and not at all of internal heat of the planet. As we have seen (5.27), the material of Saturn is highly concentrated toward its center. Jeffreys points out that, if the solid part of Saturn has a density equal to about the moon's density, half of its volume is gaseous, so that the solid surface would be one fifth of the radius, or 3700 miles, below the visible surface.

5.33. Satellites of Saturn. Saturn has nine satellites. The largest, Titan, discovered by Huyghens in 1655, is visible in small telescopes as a star of the eighth magnitude; it is somewhat larger than the moon. Five or six other satellites can be seen with telescopes of moderate aperture; they appear as faint stars in the vicinity of Saturn, and are easily identified by means of convenient tables in the *Nautical Almanac*. With the single exception of Titan, the satellites are too small to show disks in the telescope at the great distance of Saturn. Their diameters are uncertain on this account, but on the basis of brightness they appear to range from 1100 miles in the case of Rhea to about 200 miles for Phoebe. This smallest satellite, discovered by W. H. Pickering, in 1898, is the most distant from Saturn. *It revolves from east to west,* like the two outer satellites of Jupiter. Possibly other tiny distant satellites await discovery.

Some, at least, of Saturn's satellites rotate and revolve in the same period, and so turn one hemisphere always toward the planet. This is made evident by their variations in brightness in the same periods as their revolutions, which shows also that their surfaces are unevenly spotted. Iapetus is most remarkable in this respect; it is five times brighter at western elongation than at eastern elongation.

5.34. Discovery of Saturn's Rings. Saturn is encircled by three concentric rings in the plane of its equator, which are designated by name and letter as follows: the outer ring (A), the bright ring (B), and the " crape " ring (C).

The rings are invisible to the unaided eye, and were therefore unknown until after the invention of the telescope. Galileo began to observe Saturn in 1610, and saw what seemed to be two smaller planets touching the large one on each side; they disappeared two years later, and afterwards reappeared. Subsequent observers for nearly half a century were equally mystified by the strange phenomenon. It remained for Huyghens, in 1655, to recognize that the planet is surrounded by a broad, flat ring.

In 1675, D. Cassini, at the Paris Observatory, was the first to notice the fine dark circle which separates the ring into two, although it was not until a century later that " Cassini's division " was found

to be an actual division in the ring. The discovery of the crape ring
is usually credited to Bond, of Harvard, who observed it in 1850.

5.35. Description of the Rings. A very small telescope is sufficient
to show the rings; a large one is needed to study them in detail.
They are very nearly circular, although they appear always elliptical,
because we view them obliquely. The diameter of the entire ring
system is 171,000 miles, according to Lowell's measurements, or 2.3
times the equatorial diameter of the planet (74,100 miles). Since
they have nearly twice the diameter of Jupiter and are about twice
as far away from us, the rings have nearly the same apparent diameter
in the telescope as that of Jupiter.

FIG. 5.35. Saturn, January 7, 1888. Drawing by J. E. Keeler, with the
36-inch refractor of the Lick Observatory, on the first night on which this telescope was used.

The width of the outer ring is 10,000 miles; that of the dark Cassini division is 3000 miles or less. The bright ring is 16,000 miles
wide; it is brighter than the outer ring, and at its outer edge is as
luminous as the brightest parts of the planet itself. The crape ring
(or dusky ring) is about 11,500 miles in width; it is separated from
the bright ring by a division 1000 miles across, and from the planet's
equator by a space of 7000 miles. The appreciable thickness of the
rings can scarcely exceed 10 miles. It is not surprising that they
become invisible when they are presented to us edgewise.

In addition to the prominent Cassini division and the far less
obvious one between the bright and the crape rings, other narrow
dark lines have been seen occasionally, notably the " Encke division "

February 11, 1916

May 24, 1922

FIG. 5.36. Saturn's Rings at Different Angles. The southern side of the rings was presented in 1916, the northern side in 1929. Cassini's division is clearly shown, between the two bright rings. In the first and third photographs the crape ring can be seen against the ball of the planet. The large oblateness of the planet, the parallel bands across its disk, and the shadows are to be noted. (From photographs by E. C. Slipher, Lowell Observatory)

September 10, 1929

in the outer ring. Lowell measured several others in the bright ring. Kirkwood called attention to the fact that the divisions in the rings are at the distances from the planet at which the periods of revolution would be simple fractions of those of the nearer satellites. Thus a small satellite revolving in the Cassini division would have a period one half that of Mimas. The divisions are probably regions in which material can not remain very long, because of perturbations produced by the satellites. There are corresponding gaps in the asteroid region, in which the periods of revolution around the sun would be simple fractions of Jupiter's period (5.24).

5.36. The Rings at Different Angles. The rings are inclined 27° to the plane of Saturn's orbit, and keep the same direction, as the planet revolves around the sun. Thus their northern and southern sides are presented alternately to the sun, and to the earth also; for these two bodies, as viewed from Saturn, are never more than 6°

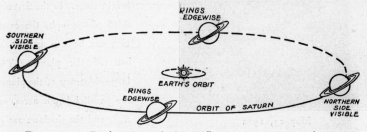

FIG. 5.36A. Explanation of the Different Appearances of Saturn's Rings. The plane of the rings is inclined about 27° to the plane of Saturn's orbit.

apart. Twice during the sidereal period of 29½ years the plane of the rings passes through the sun's position. It occupies, however, nearly a year in sweeping across the earth's orbit; and in this interval the rings become edgewise to us from one to three times, when they can not be seen for a few days even with the best telescopes.

In 1921, the rings were edgewise to the earth. Thereafter, they opened gradually, until at the beginning of 1929 the northern side attained its maximum apparent width; but the planet was then far south in the constellation Sagittarius. The next disappearance will take place in 1936, after which the southern side will come into view. At the next maximum opening of the rings, in 1943, the planet will be in Gemini, in excellent position for observation in the northern hemisphere, and in addition not far from its perihelion.

When the rings are widest open, their apparent width is 45 per cent of their length, and one sixth greater than the planet's polar diameter. Then Saturn is perhaps the finest visual object that the telescope shows. On these occasions it is much brighter, for the rings at this angle can reflect 1.7 times as much light as the planet alone. When it is also near perihelion and in opposition, Saturn appears nearly twice as bright as the brilliant star Capella; but at opposition, when the rings are closed, its brightness is that of a standard first magnitude star, such as Altair.

5.37. Stability of the Rings; Roche's Limit. Saturn's rings are composed of many separate pieces, each one reflecting a little sunlight and revolving independently, like a tiny satellite, in the plane of the planet's equator. They may be said to resemble a compact

Ultra-Violet   Violet

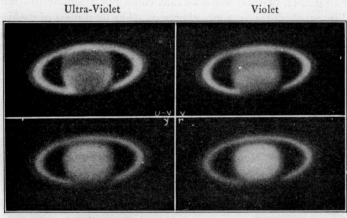

Yellow   Red

FIG. 5.37. Saturn Photographed with Filters. The equatorial band on the planet was bright in red light and dark in violet light. This change was not noticeable in 1930–31. (From photographs, July 13, 1927, by W. H. Wright, Lick Observatory)

swarm of meteors, revolving in a nearly circular orbit, and presenting the appearance of a continuous surface, aside from the divisions, because of their great distance from us. In fact, until nearly a century ago the rings were supposed to be either solid or liquid surfaces. Maxwell, in 1857, showed theoretically that a solid ring around a planet would be shattered by the strains to which it would be subjected; he further proved that a ring of many small satellites would ordinarily be stable. Roche, in 1848, had already disposed of the liquid ring.

Roche's limit is the distance from the center of a planet, 2.44 times its radius, within which a liquid satellite of the same density would be torn into small pieces by the tide-raising forces of the planet. Just as the ocean is raised at opposite points by the moon's attraction (4.37), so the satellite is deformed; the tides increase rapidly in height with approach to the planet, and when Roche's limit is reached, the disruptive force of the tides exceeds the cohesive force of gravity.

All parts of Saturn's rings lie within Roche's limit. The greatest radius is less that 2.4 times the planet's mean radius. The nearest satellite, Mimas, is safely outside the limit. It is a matter for speculation whether the rings were formed from the material of a disrupted satellite, or from material that could not assemble to form a satellite, or, of course, in some other way. The total mass of the rings can not exceed 1/27,000 of Saturn's mass, according to H. Struve, and is probably much less; this upper limit is 600 times greater than the mass of Mimas.

5.38. Meteoric Structure of the Rings.

The theoretical evidence that Saturn's rings are discontinuous is well supported by the observa-

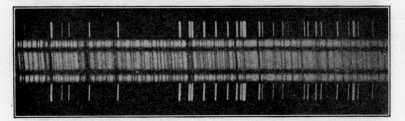

FIG. 5.38. Spectrum of Ball and Rings of Saturn. The direction of the red end of the spectrum is toward the right. In the spectrum of the ball of the planet, in the middle, the lines slant because of the planet's rotation (7.7). In the spectrum of the rings (above and below) the lines have the opposite slant. This shows that the rings are revolving more rapidly at their inner edges, proving their meteoric nature. The bright " pickets " are comparison spectra. (From a photograph by V. M. Slipher, Lowell Observatory)

tions. *The rings A and C are transparent.* Barnard saw one of the satellites, still shining, though somewhat dimmed, within the shadow of the crape ring. More recently, two observers watched the outer ring pass over a star without entirely hiding it.

The inner parts of the rings revolve faster than the outer parts.
The reverse would be the case, if the rings were continuous surfaces;
for all parts would then rotate in the same period, and the outside,
having farther to go, would move faster. Keeler, in 1895, observed
with the spectroscope (Fig. 5.38) that the inner edge of the bright
ring is revolving 2½ miles a second faster than the outside of the
outer ring, quite in accordance with Kepler's third law for separate
bodies in revolution.

The distances of Mimas, the outer edge of ring A, and the inner
edge of B from the center of Saturn are respectively 3.11, 2.31, and
1.52 times the planet's equatorial radius; and the revolution period
of Mimas is 22^h 37^m. By Kepler's third law (4.10) the periods of
the outer edge of A and the inner edge of B are respectively 14^h 27^m
and 7^h 46^m, while the material in the crape ring revolves in still
shorter periods. Since Saturn's equator rotates in 10^h 14^m, it appears
that the outer parts of the ring system move westward across the
Saturnian sky; but a considerable part of the bright ring, and all of
the crape ring rise in the west and set in the east as seen from the
surface of Saturn, duplicating the behavior of Phobos (5.19) in the
Martian sky.

Uranus and Neptune; Their Satellites

At distances nineteen and thirty times the earth's distance from
the sun, these two planets complete their revolutions in periods of 84
and 165 years respectively. Uranus is barely visible to the unaided
eye, while Neptune is never a naked eye object, appearing as a star of
the eighth magnitude. In the telescope they show small blue-green
disks, on which no markings can be clearly seen. They are nearly
alike in size, having diameters somewhat greater than 30,000 miles,
and probably in other respects. Physically they appear to resemble
the nearer outer planets, Jupiter and Saturn.

5.39. Discovery of Uranus. This planet was discovered accidentally,
in 1781, by William Herschel who was observing in the region of
Gemini with a 7-inch reflecting telescope of his own making, and
came upon an object which appeared larger than a star. Herschel,
at first, believed that he had found a comet. An examination of the
records revealed the interesting fact that Uranus had been observed
fully twenty times in the hundred years preceding its discovery;
each time the position had been measured and set down as that of a
star.

Since the old observations extended over a complete revolution of the planet, they were at once employed in the calculation of the orbit. But no orbit could be found to fit them perfectly. At length, the old positions were discarded, and an orbit was derived, in 1821, from the new observations alone, with proper allowance for the disturbing effects of known planets. It was not long, however, before Uranus began to depart appreciably from the assigned course, until in 1844 the difference between the observed and calculated positions amounted to something over 2′, an angle scarcely perceptible to the unaided eye, but regarded as an " intolerable " discrepancy by astronomers. There seemed no longer any room for doubt that the motion of Uranus was being disturbed by a planet as yet unseen.

5.40. Discovery of Neptune. Leverrier, in France, discovered Neptune in 1846. As the result of a thorough investigation of the discrepancies in the motion of Uranus, he was able to calculate the location of the disturbing body, and its direction from the earth. All that remained was to observe it. Leverrier wrote to Galle at the Berlin Observatory, telling him where in the constellation Aquarius to direct his telescope in order to see the new planet; and Neptune was found within a degree of the specified place. It was a great triumph for the law of gravitation, on which the calculations were based, and a notable example of the so-called " astronomy of the invisible " — the detection of celestial bodies before they are seen, by their gravitational effect on known bodies.

The account of Neptune's discovery is not complete without mention of the English astronomer, J. C. Adams, who also successfully solved the problem, and was indeed the first to determine the planet's location. But those to whom he applied for telescopic aid did not have a suitable chart of this region of the sky, and perhaps also did not fully recognize the knock of opportunity.

5.41. Satellites of Uranus and Neptune. The four satellites of Uranus are named Ariel, Umbriel, Titania, and Oberon, in order of distance from the planet. The outer two were discovered by Herschel in 1787; they are perhaps a thousand miles in diameter, and are fainter than most satellites. The inner two were discovered in 1851 by Lassell. They are smaller and even fainter than the others. The orbits of all four satellites are practically circular, and they must lie in the plane of the planet's equator.

The orbits of the satellites are inclined 97°.8 to the plane of the ecliptic, if we regard the revolutions as direct; or what amounts to

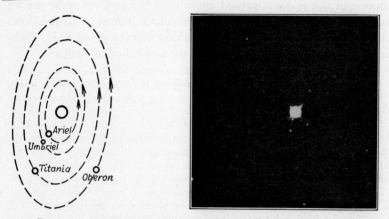

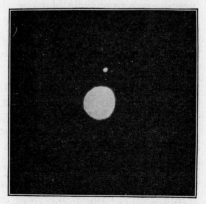

Fig. 5.41.   Uranus and Its Four Satellites.   The planet is enlarged by the exposure required to show the extremely faint satellites.   The diagram represents the apparent orbits of the satellites in 1915, and the positions of the satellites on September 6, when the exposure was made.   (From a photograph by C. O. Lampland with the 42-inch reflector, Lowell Observatory)

the same thing, they are inclined 82°.2 and *the revolutions are retrograde.*   At any rate, the orbits are nearly perpendicular to the ecliptic. As the planet revolves, the orbits are presented to the earth at various angles; they were edgewise to us in 1924, and in 1945 they will appear nearly circular.

Neptune has one satellite, discovered by Lassell in 1846. The diameter is about 3000 miles, and the distance from the planet is 220,000 miles.   In these two respects the satellite is not much different from the moon; but its period of revolution is 5^d 21^h instead of a month, owing to the greater mass of its primary.   *It revolves from east to west* in a nearly circular orbit which is inclined 20° to the planet's equa-

Fig. 5.41A.   Neptune and Its Satellite.   (From a photograph by E. E. Barnard with the 40-inch refractor, Yerkes Observatory)

tor, and which regresses, eastward, upon this plane, once around in 585 years, according to Eichelberger and Newton (1926). If this motion of the nodes is caused entirely by the bulging of Neptune's equator, and if the interior condition of the planet is between the states of Jupiter and Saturn, its oblateness must be about 1/40, which is too small to be surely observed in the small disk of Neptune.

The regression of the nodes of a satellite's orbit, always contrary to the direction of its revolution, has been mentioned several times. This perturbation, and the advance of the line of apsides in the same period are, in general, produced partly by the planet's oblateness, and partly by the sun's attraction. In the first case the nodes regress on the plane of the planet's equator, and in the second on the plane of its orbit. Neptune's satellite and the fifth satellite of Jupiter (5.31) are instances in which the sun's effect is relatively small; on the other hand the regression of the moon's nodes (3.32) is almost entirely caused by the sun. Often both factors conspire, and then the nodes regress on a *proper plane*, a compromise between the planet's equator and orbit, with which the satellite's orbit maintains a constant inclination.

5.42. Rotations of Uranus and Neptune.

The most direct method of determining the rotation of a planet is by timing its markings as they turn around. But only a few members of the planetary system exhibit markings distinct enough for this purpose. Mars and the moon are favorable cases. Jupiter shows well-defined *cloud* formations, while similar markings on Saturn and Venus are more difficult to distinguish, one from another. The tiny disks of Uranus and Neptune are practically blank in the best telescopes; their rotations have been studied by means of the spectroscope (7.7).

Uranus rotates once in 10.8 hours, according to V. M. Slipher's spectroscopic observations, in the same direction as that in which the satellites revolve.

The period of Neptune's rotation is 15.8 hours, according to the spectroscopic results of Moore and Menzel. The rotation is direct, although the revolution of the satellite is retrograde.

PLUTO

5.43. Discovery of Pluto.

On March 13, 1930, the Lowell Observatory announced the discovery of a faint star-like object in the constellation Gemini, whose slow motion relative to neighboring stars distinguished it as a planet beyond the orbit of Neptune. This date, the anniversary both of Lowell's birth and of Herschel's discovery of

Uranus (5.39), also in Gemini, seemed a doubly suitable one for making the announcement.

The search for the planet at this observatory, which had extended over a quarter of a century, was brought to a successful conclusion through the use of a 13-inch camera designed specially for the purpose. The planet was first seen, by Tombaugh, on photographs taken with this camera in the latter part of January. Further observations were required, however, before the discovery could be announced

FIG. 5.43. Pluto, Near the Time of its Discovery. The arrows point to the planet which appeared as a star of the fifteenth magnitude. The bright star below the planet is δ Geminorum. (From a photograph at the Lowell Observatory)

with complete confidence. A faint slow-moving object might be, after all, only a nearby asteroid in the neighborhood of a stationary point. If so, its speed would soon increase. But as weeks went by, the object gave no indication of speeding up. Moreover, its position and motion in the heavens were in reasonable agreement with those predicted from Lowell's theoretical investigations.

After the discovery of Neptune, small departures of the outer planets from the calculated paths remained to suggest the presence of a planet more remote than Neptune. Lowell's determination of the orbit of the trans-Neptunian planet, in 1915, was based on discordances between observed and predicted positions of Uranus. W. H. Pickering's determinations were derived chiefly from discrepancies in the motion of Neptune which is more strongly perturbed by the planet beyond it, although the interval since the discovery of Neptune has been scarcely long enough to permit the most satisfactory computation of its own orbit.

Widely different opinions are held as to the bearing of these predictions on the discovery of the new planet. Many astronomers believe that the agreement between the predicted and actual orbit is too close to be ascribed to accident. Yet Brown and others maintain that the outstanding discordances on which the predictions of its existence were based can not be attributed to perturbations by that planet.

The recently discovered planet is named Pluto. The first two letters of the name, which have been adopted as the symbol for the planet, are appropriately the initials of Percival Lowell, whose calculations led to the search, and who founded the observatory at which the discovery was made. Pluto appears as a star of the fifteenth visual magnitude, having a yellowish hue rather than the blue-green color of its near neighbors. In size and mass it bears a closer resemblance to the terrestrial planets than to the other outer planets.

5.44. The Orbit of Pluto. Since its discovery, Pluto has been found on earlier photographs at a number of observatories; and these fortunate records have greatly enhanced the accuracy in the computations of its orbit. The mean distance from the sun is 39.5 astronomical units, or 3670 million miles, which exceeds by nearly 900 million miles the distance of Neptune. The most remote planet known, Pluto is accordingly the most leisurely in its revolution around the sun; its sidereal period is 248 years, almost exactly one and a half times Neptune's period. The eccentricity of the orbit is 0.25, and its inclination to the ecliptic is 17° 9′, both larger values than for any other principal planet. These elements of the orbit were computed by Nicholson and Mayall.

The high eccentricity of the orbit introduces still another unusual feature. At aphelion Pluto is nearly fifty astronomical units from the sun; at perihelion it is only 29.7 units distant, and therefore some 35 million miles *within the orbit of Neptune*. Owing to the great inclination of Pluto's orbit there is no danger of collision. The nearest possible approach of the two planets is around 240 million miles.

In the diagram (Fig. 5.44), the plane of the page represents the ecliptic plane, and very nearly the plane of the orbit of Neptune. The portion of Pluto's orbit which lies south of the ecliptic plane is shown by the broken line. At the time of its discovery Pluto was near the ascending node of its orbit, and therefore near the ecliptic. Now at about its average distance from the sun, it will gradually draw nearer, passing its perihelion toward the end of the year 1989.

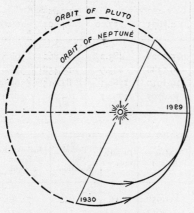

FIG. 5.44.   Orbit of Pluto

TABLES OF THE PLANETS AND SATELLITES

In the Tables at the end of this Chapter the elements of the planetary orbits are taken from *The American Ephemeris and Nautical Almanac,* to which the reader is referred for a more complete tabulation. The adopted length of the astronomical unit is 92,870,000 miles. To express any distance in kilometers, multiply the value in miles by 1.6093. The other data are taken from what seem to be the most reliable sources.

The diameters of the majority of the satellites are subject to large uncertainty. With the exceptions of the moon, Jupiter's four bright satellites, and Titan, they do not show appreciable disks in the telescope; the diameter has been calculated from the observed brightness and assumed reflecting power of the satellite.

THE OTHER PLANETS

TABLE 5.I. THE PLANETS

	Name	Symbol	Mean Distance from Sun		Period of Revolution		Eccentricity of Orbit	Inclination to Ecliptic
			Astron. Units	Millions of Miles	Sidereal	Synodic		
Terrestrial	Mercury	☿	0.3871	35.95	days 87.969	days 115.88	0.206	7° 0′
	Venus	♀	0.7233	67.18	224.701	583.92	0.007	3 24
	Earth	⊕	1.0000	92.87	365.256	——	0.017	0 0
	Mars	♂	1.5237	141.50	686.980	779.94	0.093	1 51
	Ceres	①	2.7673	257.00	years 4.604	466.60	0.077	10 37
Major	Jupiter	♃	5.2028	483.2	11.862	398.88	0.048	1 18
	Saturn	♄	9.5388	885.9	29.458	378.09	0.056	2 29
	Uranus	♅	19.1910	1782.3	84.015	369.66	0.047	0 46
	Neptune	♆	30.0707	2792.7	164.788	367.49	0.009	1 47
	Pluto		*39.5*	*3670*	*248*		*0.25*	*17° 9′*

Name	Equatorial Diameter in Miles	Mass ⊕ = 1	Density Water = 1	Period of Rotation	Inclination of Equator to Orbit	Oblateness	Stellar Magnitude
Sun ☉	864,100	331,950	1.41	24ᵈ.65	7° 10′	0	− 26.7
Moon ☾	2,160	0.012	3.33	27 .32	6 41	0	− 12.6
Mercury	3,100	0.04	3.8	88		0	− 1.2
Venus	7,700	0.81	4.86	30 ?		0	− 4.3
Earth	7,927	1.00	5.52	23ʰ 56ᵐ	23 27	1/296	——
Mars	4,215	0.11	3.96	24 37	23 30	1/192	− 2.8
Jupiter	88,640	316.94	1.34	9 50	3 7	1/15	− 2.5
Saturn	74,100	94.9	0.71	10 14	26 45	1/9.5	− 0.4
Uranus	32,000	14.7	1.27	10 45	98	1/14	+ 5.7
Neptune	31,000	17.2	1.58	15 48	151	1/40	+ 7.6

Elements of the orbit of Pluto are given in Section 5.44.

TABLE 5.II. THE SATELLITES

Name	Discovery	Mean Distance in Miles	Period of Revolution	Diameter in Miles	Stellar Magnitude at Opposition
Moon		238,857	27^d 7^h 43^m	2160	−12

SATELLITES OF MARS

Name	Discovery		Mean Distance in Miles	Period of Revolution			Diameter in Miles	Stellar Magnitude at Opposition
Phobos	Hall,	1877	5,800	0	7	39	10 ?	+12
Deimos	Hall,	1877	14,600	1	6	18	5 ?	13

SATELLITES OF JUPITER

	Name	Discovery		Mean Distance in Miles	Period of Revolution			Diameter in Miles	Stellar Magnitude at Opposition
	Fifth	Barnard,	1892	112,600	0	11	57	100 ?	13
1.	Io	Galileo,	1610	261,800	1	18	28	2300	5
2.	Europa	Galileo,	1610	416,600	3	13	14	2000	6
3.	Ganymede	Galileo,	1610	664,200	7	3	43	3200	5
4.	Callisto	Galileo,	1610	1,169,000	16	16	32	3200	6
	Sixth	Perrine,	1904	7,114,000	250	16		100 ?	14
	Seventh	Perrine,	1905	7,292,000	260	1		40 ?	16
	Eighth	Melotte,	1908	14,600,000	739			40 ?	16
	Ninth	Nicholson,	1914	14,900,000	758			20 ?	17

SATELLITES OF SATURN

Name	Discovery		Mean Distance in Miles	Period of Revolution			Diameter in Miles	Stellar Magnitude at Opposition
Mimas	Herschel,	1789	115,000	0	22	37	400 ?	12
Enceladus	Herschel,	1789	148,000	1	8	53	500 ?	12
Tethys	Cassini,	1684	183,000	1	21	18	800 ?	— 11
Dione	Cassini,	1684	234,000	2	17	41	700 ?	11
Rhea	Cassini,	1672	327,000	4	12	25	1100 ?	10
Titan	Huyghens,	1655	759,000	15	22	41	2600	8
Hyperion	Bond,	1848	920,000	21	6	38	300 ?	13
Iapetus	Cassini,	1671	2,210,000	79	7	56	1000 ?	11
Phoebe	Pickering,	1898	8,034,000	550			200 ?	14

SATELLITES OF URANUS

Name	Discovery		Mean Distance in Miles	Period of Revolution			Diameter in Miles	Stellar Magnitude at Opposition
Ariel	Lassell,	1851	119,100	2	12	29	600 ?	16
Umbriel	Lassell,	1851	165,900	4	3	28	400 ?	16
Titania	Herschel,	1787	272,000	8	16	56	1000 ?	14
Oberon	Herschel,	1787	364,000	13	11	7	900 ?	14

SATELLITE OF NEPTUNE

Name	Discovery		Mean Distance in Miles	Period of Revolution			Diameter in Miles	Stellar Magnitude at Opposition
Nameless	Lassell,	1846	220,000	5	21	3	3000 ?	13

CHAPTER VI

THE SOLAR SYSTEM, Continued

COMETS: THEIR MOTIONS AND PHYSICAL CHARACTERISTICS — METEORS
AND METEOR STREAMS — METEORITES — ORIGIN OF THE SOLAR SYSTEM

The description of the solar system has thus far dealt chiefly with
the planets and their satellites — single bodies of considerable size
and approximately spherical form, although this may not apply to the
smaller asteroids and satellites. The rings of Saturn, as aggregations of small bodies, have introduced to us a different type of organization within the solar system. We have now to consider other
aggregations of this type, namely, comets and meteor swarms.

COMETS

6.1. In ancient times, the appearance of a great comet was an
omen of impending disaster, and was likely to be recorded. The
records of comets go back at least 25 centuries, as many as four
hundred being definitely reported before the invention of the telescope. The superstitious fear of comets, and the more recent appre-
hension of the damage that might result from collision with one are
now largely replaced by the admiration and wonder that are aroused
whenever one of these strange spectacles is displayed in the sky.
Donati's comet of 1858, the great comet of 1882, and Halley's comet
in 1910 were of great interest to everyone.

A large comet consists of a hazy, globular *coma,* with a star-like
nucleus near its center, sometimes as bright as the brightest stars,
and a filmy *tail,* perhaps as much as 50° in length. Such comets
are rare and, with the single exception of Halley's comet, have arrived unheralded.

Comets were formerly regarded as atmospheric rather than celestial phenomena by almost everyone, until Tycho showed that the
comet of 1577 was more remote than the moon, because it had a
smaller parallax. Doerfel proved that the comet of 1681 was moving

in a parabola, and soon afterward Newton enrolled comets as law-
abiding members of the universe, moving in accordance with the law
of gravitation.

6.2. Discovery of Comets. Comets are sometimes discovered by
accident, but more often by those who are searching for them. Pons,
at Marseilles, was the most successful comet hunter, having 37 discoveries to his credit between 1803 and 1827. Amateurs have found

FIG. 6.1. Donati's Comet, October 5, 1858. As it appeared to the naked eye.
Not long before this drawing was made, the comet passed over Arcturus (to the
right of the comet's head) without obscuring it. (From a drawing by Bond
at Harvard College Observatory)

many comets. The chief requirements are a small telescope with a
large field, perseverance, and a catalogue of the nebulae and star
clusters which may easily be mistaken for comets, although the motion of the comet will soon identify it. The western sky after nightfall, or the east before dawn are the most promising regions.

The announcement of the discovery of a comet, giving the comet's
position and the direction of its motion, is telegraphed at once from
the Harvard Observatory to other observatories in this country, so
that the comet may be under observation the following night. As
soon as three positions have been measured at intervals of a few days,
the preliminary orbit is calculated; then it is often possible to de-

cide whether the comet is a new one, or the return of a comet that has appeared before, and what may be expected of it. Many of the preliminary orbits are computed under Leuschner's direction at Berkeley.

Provisionally, a comet is designated by the year of its discovery followed by a letter in the *order of discovery* in that year, for example, comet 1929b. The permanent designation is the year (not always the year of discovery) followed by a Roman numeral in the *order of perihelion passage;* an example is comet 1929 I. Many comets, especially the remarkable ones, are known also by the name of the discoverer, or discoverers, or of the astronomer whose investigations of the comet entitle him by common consent to the ownership. Halley's comet and the Pons-Winnecke comet are examples.

In recent years, five comets have passed perihelion, on the average, each year; of these about 35 per cent are returns of previously observed comets, while 65 per cent are new ones. But the yearly number varies greatly. In 1925, the banner year thus far, eleven comets were discovered, and ten were found in 1927. The majority are visible only with the telescope. Comets that are bright enough to be seen with the naked eye average less than one a year; perhaps one in ten of these is spectacular enough to attract the attention of those who are not astronomers.

6.3. Orbits of Comets. A comet has no permanent individuality by which it may be distinguished from other comets. The only identification mark is the path it pursues. If a newly discovered comet is traveling in an orbit similar to that of a comet previously seen, it is fairly safe to say that it is the return of that comet; and it is certain, if the comet returns again after an equal interval of time.

The orbits of more than four hundred comets are known with varying degrees of precision. One fourth of them are certainly ellipses, the periods of revolution varying from 3 to 10,000 years. The remaining 75 per cent are so nearly parabolas that it is very difficult to tell the difference, in the small portions of the orbits near the sun where the comets become visible. It is the custom to calculate these orbits as though they were parabolas, thereby shortening the computations, although there is good reason for believing that they are really ellipses. Probably the majority of comets recede to distances from the sun as much as thirty times the distance of Neptune. But this great distance is only 1/300 of the way to the nearest star. The sun is still in control there.

In contrast with the regularities which have been noticed (4.2) in the motions of the principal planets, the characteristics of the motions of comets, especially those of long period, are as follows: (1) Their orbits are nearly parabolas. (2) They have no special relation to the plane of the ecliptic. (3) Some comets revolve from west to east, and others in the opposite direction. The orbital motions of comets of short period more nearly resemble those of the asteroids.

6.4. Jupiter's Family of Comets. Of more than a hundred known comets having well-established elliptical orbits, with periods of revolution up to 10,000 years, *40 per cent have periods between five and*

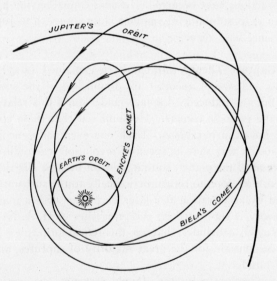

Fig. 6.4. Orbits of a Few Comets of Jupiter's Family. Encke's comet has the smallest orbit of all.

nine years, averaging a little more than one half the period of Jupiter. These are the members of Jupiter's family of comets. Without exception the aphelion points, and the ascending or descending nodes of their orbits are near the orbit of this planet; and more than half of these comets may approach within 15 million miles of the planet. The orbits are generally not much inclined to the ecliptic, and the revolutions are all from west to east around the sun.

The comets of Jupiter's family are never conspicuous objects. A few become visible without the telescope, when they pass near the earth. The Pons-Winnecke comet was dimly visible to the naked eye for several nights in the summer of 1927, as a foggy spot in the sky twice the size of the full moon. On June 27 of that year its distance from the earth was 3½ million miles — the second closest approach of a comet's *head* to the earth on record. Lexell's comet, in 1770, passed us within 1½ million miles.

The membership of Jupiter's family is subject to change. Brooks' comet, first seen in 1889, was recruited in 1886, according to Chandler's calculations, when it passed closer to Jupiter than the nearest satellite; the comet's period was diminished from 29 to 7 years. A new member was added to the list as recently as 1922. On the other hand, subtractions have occurred. Lexell's comet, having a period of 5.5 years in 1770, subsequently made a close approach to Jupiter, and has never since been seen. .

6.5. The Capture Theory. It has been explained (4.27) that the eccentricity and size of an orbit are diminished, if the speed of the revolving body is reduced. Laplace made use of this relation to account for the periodic comets. He supposed that these comets had originally moved in parabolas. Each one eventually encountered a planet in such a way that its speed of revolution was reduced by the backward pull of the planet, so that its orbit became elliptical; it was constrained, therefore, to return periodically to the sun, until it might be released by acceleration at a later encounter with a planet. The capture theory is supported by the researches of H. A. Newton and others. Russell concludes that on theoretical principles Jupiter is probably responsible for the great majority of captures, and Saturn for the remainder.

In its application to Jupiter's family of comets the capture theory is the most convincing. The direct motions of these comets, their close approaches to Jupiter's orbit, and the rather small inclinations of their own orbits are favorable to the theory. But the degree of precision that Jupiter has attained in placing the aphelia of its captives in proximity to its orbit is surprising.

In order to have its orbit converted by a single encounter, from a parabola to one of the small ellipses of this family, a comet must pass nearer Jupiter than its first satellite. The supporters of the theory recognize the probable infrequency of such close approaches, and suppose that the orbits are reduced gradually as the result of several encounters. Crommelin, however, recalls the fact that accelerations as well as retardations may take place, and considers the capture process inadequate to recruit Jupiter's family to its present size in the face of the inevitable losses. Callandreau and Fayet lighten the burden on the theory at this point by supposing that tidal disruptions at the close approaches have multiplied the comets of this family.

6.6. Comets of Longer Period.

Comets whose periods are between ten and a hundred years are grouped into three families, for each of which the aphelion points average about the same distance from the sun as Saturn, Uranus, or Neptune. It is convenient to identify each family with the corresponding planet, *without implying that any one of these comets was captured by the planet to whose family it is said to belong.* H. C. Wilson, Russell, and others have called attention to the fact that in most cases the high inclination of the comet's orbit places the aphelion far above or below the planet's orbit. Indeed, all the members of Neptune's family pass much closer to Jupiter than they do to Neptune.

Saturn's family contains three comets, including Tuttle's comet which returns faithfully and is associated with the August meteors (6.24). The family of Uranus has at least two comets; one of them, Tempel's comet of 1866, has the same orbit as the Leonid swarm of meteors. Neptune's family has eight members, of which five have been seen more than once; its most distinguished member is Halley's comet. Among the comets which recede far out beyond Neptune's orbit there is some indication of groupings of aphelia around two or three distances from the sun.

The Schwassmann-Wachmann comet, discovered late in 1927, appears to be one of the most remarkable of known comets. According to the preliminary orbit computed at Berkeley, this comet revolves entirely between the orbits of Jupiter and Saturn. The eccentricity of the orbit is 0.14 — less than that of Mercury. At perihelion the comet is 30 million miles farther from the sun than Jupiter's mean distance.

6.7. Halley's Comet.

This famous comet, *the first known periodic comet,* made one of its many appearances in 1682. Halley determined its orbit from the observed positions, by the geometrical method which Newton had explained, and found it identical with the orbits he had also calculated for the comets of 1531 and 1607. Concluding that these were appearances of the same comet, which must therefore be moving in an ellipse, Halley predicted that it would reappear in 1759. The comet returned in that year according to prediction, and again in 1835 and 1910. Halley's comet is a member of Neptune's family; it is the only conspicuous comet having a period less than a hundred years. The revolution is retrograde.

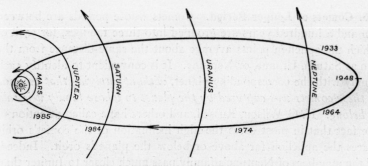

Fig. 6.7. Orbit of Halley's Comet. The comet remains for nearly half the time in the small portion of its orbit beyond Neptune's orbit. It passes aphelion in 1948, and will return to the sun in 1985.

Previous to its 1910 appearance, Cowell and Crommelin at Greenwich made a thorough study of the orbit. They were able to identify from the records 28 observed returns, as far back as 240 B.C. It was Halley's comet that appeared in 1066, at the time of the Norman conquest of England. In the meantime, the period has varied nearly five years, owing to disturbing effects of the planets. The average interval between perihelion passages is 77 years; but the period at present is considerably less.

6.8. Halley's Comet in 1910. At its recent return, Halley's comet was first sighted photographically by Wolf in September, 1909, as a minute star-like object; it was then more than 300 million miles away. Astronomers knew in advance precisely where to search for it. In May, 1910, the comet had become a spectacular object in the eastern sky before dawn. The head was as bright as the brightest stars, and the tail was more than 50° long. On May 19, the comet's head passed directly between the earth and the sun at the distance of 14 million miles, and two days later, the tail may have encountered the earth, although there was no observational evidence of either event. Afterwards, the comet appeared in the evening sky, for a time plainly visible to the unaided eye, although it was no longer a striking object. It was followed with the telescope until July, 1911,

when it had passed beyond the orbit of Jupiter. Bobrovnikoff lists
709 photographs of the comet in the years 1909–11.

Halley's comet has now receded beyond Neptune's orbit, where
it will remain for more than 30 years, passing the aphelion point in

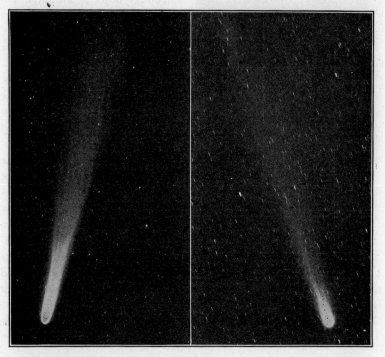

Fig. 6.8. Halley's Comet. On May 6, 1910, the comet was visible in
the east before dawn. On May 31, it had passed between the earth and the
sun into the evening sky and was rapidly diminishing in brightness. (From
photographs by H. E. Wood, Union Observatory, South Africa)

1948. Since the motion of a comet is in accordance with the law
of equal areas, it is evident that its progress at the present great
distance from the sun can not be very rapid. It will return in
1985.

6.9. Diminishing Period of Encke's Comet. The *second periodic
comet* to be recognized is remarkable in several respects. Encke
calculated the orbit at its appearance in 1819, and identified it with
the orbits of comets which had appeared in 1786, 1795, and 1805.

The period, 3.3 years, is the shortest of any known comet. Since 1819, it has not been missed at a single return; the return in 1928

was the 37th to be recorded. Encke's comet is never a conspicuous object, although at times, as in 1924, it becomes faintly visible to the unaided eye.

In the past hundred years the period of this comet has diminished two and a half days, and the mean distance from the sun has been reduced 275,000 miles, for a reason not connected with the attractions of the planets. A resisting medium of some sort in the comet's path would account for the effect. Any reduction of the comet's speed by such a medium would result in a shrinking of the orbit, and consequently in a shorter period of revolution. Backlund concluded

FIG. 6.9. Encke's Comet. During the exposure, the telescope was made to follow the comet's rapid motion with respect to the stars. Thus the stars appear as trails. (From a photograph, in October, 1914, by E. E. Barnard, Yerkes Observatory)

that the retardation takes place near perihelion, and that its amount is not the same at all returns.

At aphelion, the comet is nearly a whole astronomical unit inside Jupiter's orbit. On this account, some writers have excluded it from Jupiter's family. In view of the shrinkage of the orbit, however, the aphelion may have been near Jupiter's orbit only a few thousand years ago, according to Backlund.

6.10. Comet Groups; the Great Comet of 1882. It is not always safe to suppose that a newly discovered comet is the return of a former one, simply because it is moving in the same orbit. Comet 1880 I is an example. When its orbit was calculated and found to resemble that of the great comet of 1843, it was at first supposed to be the return of that comet, although periods of several hundred years had been deduced for both. The appearance of the great comet of 1882, having practically the same orbit as the other two, settled the matter. These comets are different ones.

A *comet group* is composed of a number of comets which follow nearly the same path *in the vicinity of the sun.* The most remarkable group is the one that has been mentioned; it includes the great comets of 1668, 1843, 1880, 1882, and 1887, all of which passed unusually close to the sun. It seems probable that they are parts of a single comet which divided at a previous close approach to the sun, the separate parts having widely different periods thereafter. It is to be noticed that a comet group is not the same as a comet family (6.4).

The great September comet of 1882, the most notable of the group, was one of the finest comets of modern times, plainly visible in full daylight. It passed through the sun's corona, within 300,000 miles of the sun's surface, with a speed exceeding a million miles an hour. *278 mi/sec* Effects of the close approach were evident soon after perihelion passage. The nucleus divided into four parts, which spread out in the direction of the comet's motion, and which will return as four comets about a century apart, according to Kreutz's calculations, their periods varying from 660 to 960 years. In addition, Barnard and others observed several small companion comets traveling parallel to the principal one.

6.11. Comets as Members of the Solar System. Conforming with the earlier view that comets move in parabolas, it was natural to suppose that they come to us from interstellar space, swing once around the sun, and depart forever. Periodic comets, such as Halley's comet, were accounted for by the capture theory. It was interesting to imagine them visiting about from star to star, with journeys of millions of years between visits. At the same time, the chance is very small that a comet, having left a neighboring star, would approach the sun near enough to be observed.

It is now generally believed that the comets we see are, at present, members of our system. If they were visitors instead, the orbits of many comets would be markedly hyperbolic, as Schiaparelli pointed out in 1871, owing to the rapid motion of the solar system as a whole (8.17). In order to have a parabolic orbit, a comet falling toward the sun from outside the system must start at rest relative to the sun; in other words, it must be moving with the sun. Only a few of the many orbits that have been computed are certainly hyperbolas, and none of these differs much from a parabola.

Strömgren has shown that eight comets up to 1914 were without doubt moving in hyperbolas *when they were observed;* but in every case the comet's velocity had been increased by the attractions of

Jupiter and Saturn, and that previous to these disturbances it was, or may have been, an ellipse. It is not known whether these fast-moving comets are eventually retarded, or whether they escape from the solar system. Nor does this evidence prevent us from supposing, if we like, that the present comets were recruited long ago from interstellar space.

6.12. Changing Appearance and Dimensions of Comets.

Characteristic of all comets is the coma, the foggy disk, often nearly circular, that distinguishes the distant comet from a star or asteroid. As the

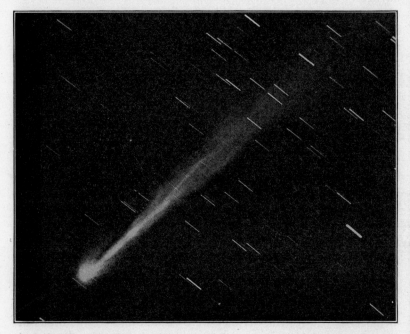

FIG. 6.12. Morehouse's Comet, September 29, 1908. A comet's tail is directed away from the sun. Here its direction is nearly at right angles to the direction of the comet's motion indicated by the star trails. (From a photograph at the Royal Observatory, Greenwich)

comet approaches the sun, the coma at first expands, but nearer perihelion it becomes smaller again. The diameter of the coma averages 80,000 miles, according to Holetschek, or nearly that of the planet Jupiter. In the great comet of 1811, the coma reached the maximum of a million miles, or greater than the sun's diameter.

　　The star-like nucleus, near the center of the coma, usually appears, if at all, when the comet is near the sun. It is relatively small, even in the largest comets. The nucleus of the great comet of 1882, before it divided, was 1800 miles across — somewhat less than the moon's diameter. The path of the nucleus, when it is present, is considered to be the orbit of the comet.

Many comets never develop tails. In large comets the tail begins to form when the comet is about twice our distance from the sun. At or after perihelion passage the tail attains the maximum length, which varies from 5 to 100 million miles, or somewhat more than the distance from the earth to the sun. Rapid development of the tail is often accompanied by signs of great activity within the head of the comet. Brilliant *jets* issue from the nucleus, usually on the sunward side, and *envelopes* form concentric rings in the coma, and sweep back into the tail, which always points away from the sun.

6.13. Masses and Densities of Comets. Comets are not important disturbing elements in the solar system. Whenever they pass near a planet or satellite, the only perceptible effect is upon the comet. Since the mass of a celestial body is measured by its attraction for other bodies, all that can be learned from such encounters is how massive the comet is *not*. Lexell's comet at its record approach, in 1770, within one and a half million miles of the earth, would have altered the length of the year by more than a second, if its mass had been as much as 1/10,000 of the earth's mass. But no change at all in the year could be observed. Photometric considerations appear to reduce the *upper limit* of a comet's mass to one millionth of the earth's mass, according to Orlow's study of the light reflected by Halley's comet, or to that of an asteroid of moderate size.

This upper limit is equal to the mass of the earth's atmosphere. Imagine this thin shell of our air diffused throughout a sphere 100,000 miles in diameter, and we have the order of the mean density of the comet's head. This must not, however, be taken to mean that the comet is composed only of very rare gas; in fact, an entirely gaseous comet would have little stability. Very small average density may be attained by an aggregation of solid pieces, if the pieces are far apart compared with their diameters. It has been estimated that the brightness of Halley's comet in 1909, assuming that its light was then reflected sunlight only, can be accounted for by supposing that every cubic mile of its volume contained nothing more than a dozen bodies no larger than small marbles.

An aggregation of solid pieces so widely separated would offer very little obstruction to the view of anything behind it. The heads of comets are highly transparent. They have passed over stars without affecting their light appreciably; and when Halley's comet crossed the sun's disk in 1910, careful watching failed to detect a trace of it.

6.14. The Light of a Comet. As a comet approaches the sun, its brightness usually increases more rapidly than would be the case if the comet shone only by reflected sunlight. Analysis of the light with the spectroscope leads to the same conclusion. Part of it is sunlight,

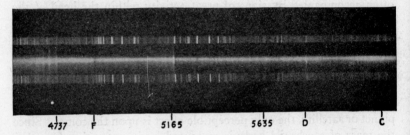

| 4737 | F | 5165 | 5635 | D | C |

FIG. 6.14. Spectrum of Halley's Comet. The bright-line spectrum shows the hydrocarbon bands, indicated by their wave-lengths, and the D line of sodium, which lasted only a few days. In the spectrum of sunlight reflected by the comet's head the dark Fraunhofer lines C and F are prominent. A comparison spectrum appears above and below. (From a photograph by V. M. Slipher, Lowell Observatory)

especially from the vicinity of the nucleus; but *the light of the coma and tail is to a large extent that of a glowing gas,* in which different compounds of carbon are recognized. Close approaches to the sun sometimes reveal sodium, iron, and other luminous metallic gases — the ones that might be expected, if the heads of comets are aggregations of meteors.

The quantity and quality of the light varies greatly from one comet to another, and in the same comet rapid fluctuations occur. Often the maximum brightness is attained after perihelion passage. The conspicuous comets are in general those that pass close to the sun or earth.

Since the glowing gas brightens as the comet's distance from the sun diminishes, it is natural to hold the sun responsible for this part of the illumination as well. But the heating effect of the sunlight at the great distances of most comets is inadequate to explain it. The problem may well be similar to that of the auroral glow in the earth's atmosphere (3.21). Something coming from the sun stimulates the gases to luminosity; perhaps, as Zanstra's investigations suggest, it is sunlight itself which the gases absorb and emit again selectively.

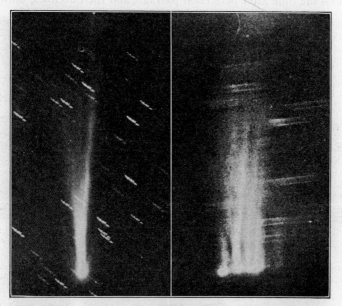

FIG. 6.14A.   Direct and Objective Prism Photographs of Morehouse's Comet. In the photograph with the objective prism (right), separate images of the comet are formed by the light of the different wave-lengths which it emits. (From photographs by E. B. Frost and J. A. Parkhurst, Yerkes Observatory)

6.15. The Nature of a Comet. What, then, is a comet? Superficially, it is a hazy object in the sky, which sometimes develops a brilliant nucleus and a tail of enormous length. But what underlies these transitory phenomena? It is generally believed that a comet is a swarm of relatively small bodies, held together loosely by their mutual attractions, and more concentrated toward the center of the swarm, although even here they are widely separated. This construction is consistent with the low average density and the high transparency we have already noted, the frequent disruptions of comets (6.17), and the association of some comets with meteor swarms (6.24).

This describes the comet completely, when it is far from the sun. As it draws nearer the sun, gas and fine dust issue from the solid

pieces and spread by diffusion, forming a coma. The gas glows because of some stimulation from the sun, and is swept away by the
pressure of the sun's radiation to form the tail. The activity increases
up to some time after perihelion passage, and then declines, until the

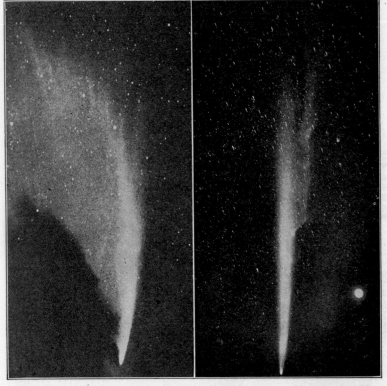

FIG. 6.15. Comet 1910a. Photographed January 26, 1910. Part of
the comet is hidden by the pine trees in
the lower left corner. (From a photograph by C. O. Lampland, Lowell Observatory)

Halley's Comet. Photographed May
13, 1910, when the comet was visible
in the east before dawn. The bright
object at the right is the planet Venus.
(From a photograph by C. O. Lampland, Lowell Observatory)

gas ceases to form and has streamed away. The comet departs as it
approaches us — an aggregation of small solid bodies, but with somewhat diminished mass, because the material that formed the tail is
not retrieved.

The degree of a comet's activity as it rounds the sun, and the resulting
splendor of the comet, depends on its distance from the sun at perihelion.

But some comets are decidedly less active than others at the same distance. The comets of Jupiter's family are never brilliant objects, either because their masses are small, or because their supplies of gas are nearly exhausted, or for some other reason. Many of the phenomena of comets are not yet fully explained; in particular, the manner of liberation of the gases and the precise cause of their shining require further study.

The damage that might result, if we should collide with the head of a comet, would depend on the masses of the bodies of which it is composed. If they are like pinheads, or no larger than marbles, the result would be simply a fine display of meteors. If, however, the separate pieces weigh tons, instead of grains or ounces, a severe bombardment might occur.

6.16. Formation of Comets' Tails.

The material of which a comet's tail is composed has three distinct motions: (1) It is expelled from the nucleus, sometimes as fast as several miles a second, as indicated by the jets and expanding envelopes. (2) It is repelled from the sun's direction; the material is driven away from the comet's head to form the tail. Since the first motion is still in progress, the tail increases in breadth as the distance from the head increases, often taking the form of a hollow cone, or horn.

FIG. 6.16. Tail of a Comet Directed Away from the Sun. The tail is usually curved, and is longest and brightest near perihelion.

(3) It is revolving meanwhile around the sun. By the law of areas, the material revolves less rapidly as it moves outward through the tail, falling more and more behind the nucleus, so that the tail is curved.

It is well known that radiation exerts pressure on anything that obstructs it. For large bodies the pressure of the sun's radiation is insignificant in comparison with its powerful attraction. For very small bodies radiation pressure becomes important, since the area on which the light falls decreases as the square of the radius, while the mass to be moved decreases as its cube. The pressure on a dust particle $1/100,000$ inch in diameter may be more than ten times the sun's attraction; and upon a molecule of gas which absorbs the radiation the pressure may exceed the attraction as much as 150 times.

In a large comet the material moves in something like a week from the coma to the end of the tail, where it becomes too much scattered to be visible. The outward progress of distinctive condensations is often readily observed by comparing successive photographs. At times, comets have lost their tails, and have formed new ones. Evidently this can happen, if the supply of gas and dust is not renewed as fast as it is swept away.

The tail of a comet is a highly tenuous haze of gas and dust. If the tail of Halley's comet was composed entirely of gas, its mass may not have exceeded 100 tons, according to Schwarzschild's calculations. It is not surprising, therefore, that nothing unusual can be observed when the earth passes through the tail of a comet, an event which certainly occurred in 1861, and perhaps again in 1910, in the case of Halley's comet.

FIG. 6.17. Brooks' Comet, October 23, 1911. One of the finest of recent comets. It was visible to the naked eye for four months. Perihelion passage occurred on October 27. (From a photograph by E. E. Barnard, Yerkes Observatory)

6.17. Disintegration of Comets; Biela's Comet.

The breaking up of the great comet of 1882 (6.10) is not an isolated case. As many as a dozen other cases are on record. Brooks' comet of 1889 is an example; it developed four companion comets, one of which for a time outshone the original comet. Taylor's comet of 1916 broke in two while under observation. But in this respect Biela's comet gave the most dramatic performance.

Biela's comet was a member of Jupiter's family, having a period of 6½ years. At its return in 1846 the comet became elongated and finally divided, each part becoming a separate comet with a nucleus and short tail. In 1852, the two comets again came into view, traveling side by side, but now separated 1½ million miles. First one and then the other became the brighter. *The twin comet has never since been seen,* although there has now been time for a dozen returns. The Andromedes, or Bielid meteors (6.23), moving in the path of the lost comet, which then crossed the earth's orbit, gave brilliant showers of shooting stars in 1872 and 1885.

A reason for the disintegration of some comets is found in the tidal forces which the sun and planets exert upon them. Assuming that comets are aggregations of meteors, Schiaparelli concluded that a comet can be broken up if it passes within 90 million miles of the sun, 9 million miles of Jupiter, or 1¾ million miles of the earth. Disruptions of comets have occurred, however, for which the sun and planets can hardly be held responsible.

The amount of material that streams away in the tail of the comet at every approach to the sun must be very small compared with the total mass. There is no theoretical evidence as to the effect on the cohesion of the remaining material, or of its ability to renew the tail indefinitely.

Leuschner has definitely raised the question of a close relationship between comets and asteroids. Formerly, comets were distinguished from asteroids by the greater eccentricities of their orbits, and in the telescope by the presence of the coma. The first difference no longer holds in all cases. Some asteroids are known to have more eccentric orbits than several comets. On the other hand, the Schwassmann-Wachmann comet, 1925 II, appears to have a nearly circular orbit. It is interesting to recall that Leuschner, in 1921, insisted that there must be comets of this description.

Telescopically the distinction vanishes, if comets eventually cease to be active, but continue to make their presence known by reflected sunlight. It is sometimes not easy to decide whether the coma is observed or not. The well-known asteroid Amherstia was " discovered " and listed as comet 1917 VI before the mistake was recognized.

Meteors and Meteor Streams

Meteors are in general small, solid, swiftly moving celestial bodies. Ordinarily they are invisible; but those that enter the earth's atmosphere are heated by impact of air molecules. Then they appear momentarily as *shooting stars,* the familiar star-like objects that occasionally dart across the sky at night, vanishing when they are consumed. Bright ones often leave luminous trains, which fade away gradually, sometimes remaining visible for several minutes, and even as long as half an hour after the meteor itself has disappeared. Unusually brilliant ones, as bright as the brighter planets and sometimes even as the full moon, are *fireballs;* they are *bolides,* if they explode at the ends of their paths. *Meteorites* are those that partly survive the flight through the air, and fall to the ground.

The word "meteor" is derived from the Greek word pertaining to anything in the air. Meteorology, the science of atmospheric phenomena, is not concerned with meteors, except as they provide information about the upper levels of the air.

6.18. Frequency of Meteors. Aside from infrequent copious showers, the number of meteors visible to the unaided eye at any one place is rather small. The average for a single observer under the

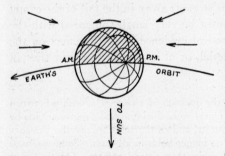

FIG. 6.18. Meteors More Numerous After Midnight. In the morning we are on the forward side of the earth.

best conditions varies from one meteor every 15 minutes in the early evening in the spring to one every 4 minutes before dawn in the autumn, say ten an hour throughout the year. A single observer can see only those meteors above 1/100,000 of the earth's surface. Over all the earth's surface, therefore, meteors visible to the naked eye fall at the rate of a million an hour, or 24 millions a day. Those visible with the telescope are doubtless several times more numerous.

The frequency of the meteors increases through the night, until before dawn twice as many can be seen as at nightfall. The reason is that at 6 o'clock in the evening we are on the following side of the earth with respect to its revolution, and are protected except from meteors that overtake us. In the morning we are on the forward side, fully exposed to the bombardment. There is an annual as well as a daily variation in the number, the maximum in the northern hemisphere coming in the autumn; for at this season the point toward which the earth is revolving is highest above the horizon at night.

6.19. Paths of Meteors. The observation of a meteor consists in locating the trail among the stars, in estimating the interval of time from the beginning to the end of the flight, and of course in noting the time of the appearance. Amateurs have as much opportunity as professional astronomers for making these observations. The results are especially valuable when two observers a few miles apart are watching the sky at the same time; for the trails they record of the same meteors have different locations among the stars, owing to the

FIG. 6.19. A Brilliant Meteor. (From a photograph, August 13, 1928, by M. de Kerolyr at Digne, France)

effect of parallax. On comparing the records they can easily calculate the heights of the trails. Photography is more accurate, but it can record only bright and slow-moving fireballs.

On the average, the small meteors appear and disappear at heights of 68 and 54 miles respectively, according to von Niessl; the trails are 36 miles in length, and the durations of the flights vary from one third to one half of a second. But the observed heights differ greatly, depending on the masses and relative speeds of the meteors. Those that we see before sunrise appear at average heights of nearly 100 miles. The trails of fireballs are 87 miles high at the beginning, and 31 miles at the end; they average 200 miles in length, and the durations of the flights are several seconds. Simultaneous observations of meteors from two stations were first made systematically in 1798, by two students in Göttingen.

6.20. Velocities of Meteors. The velocities of meteors relative to the revolving earth increase from nightfall to dawn. If we suppose that the meteors are moving in parabolic orbits, and therefore at the rate of 26 miles a second when they cross the earth's orbit, their speeds, as they enter the atmosphere, must vary from 26 *minus* 18½, or 7½ miles a second for one that overtakes us, to 26 *plus* 18½, or 44½ miles a second for a head-on collision, with the addition of from 0.5 to 2.7 miles a second in each case for the earth's attraction. From a study of many observations Hoffmeister concludes that the majority of the fireballs, and smaller meteors as well, have greater speeds than these; thus they are moving in hyperbolic paths with respect to the sun. But Fisher has pointed out that the published velocities of many *periodic* meteors are hyperbolic, showing that observers have overestimated the velocities of meteors.

Whatever the true velocities may turn out to be, they are very great indeed. Since the production of heat and light in the flight through the air depends on the kinetic energy (4.30) of the meteor, that is, on its mass and the *square* of its velocity, calculations indicate that a body no larger than a pinhead may produce the effect of the average shooting star, while one as large as a golf ball can appear as bright as the full moon. The phenomena attending the flights of fireballs and meteorites will be described later (6.27).

6.21. Radiants. The trails of meteors are not entirely random in direction. Careful watching of the sky for two or three hours in the evening, in which the trails are recorded on a constellation map, sometimes shows that several have diverged from the same spot, although they usually do not start there. If the number so diverging is greater than may be ascribed to chance, a *meteoric shower* is in progress, that is to say, the earth has encountered a *swarm of meteors*. The meteors in the swarm, or *stream*, are moving together around the sun in nearly parallel paths; their luminous trails through the air are therefore nearly parallel, and like the rails of a track they seem to diverge from a point in the distance. *The radiant of a meteoric shower is the vanishing point* in the perspective of the parallel trails. It is located by extending the streaks backward until they meet.

Usually the radiant is a small area instead of a point, because the members of the swarm have slightly different directions and speeds, and may also be diverted in their flight through the air. In a shower of considerable duration, the position of the radiant point shifts appreciably, for it depends not only on the direction of the meteor

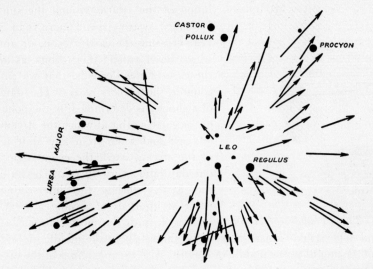

Fig. 6.21. Leonids Charted November 15, 1901. The trails were observed by W. Upton, F. Slocum, and others at Brown University during a watch of five hours. With three or four exceptions, the trails apparently diverge from the radiant point in Leo.

stream, but also on the direction of the earth's revolution, which changes from day to day. When the position of the radiant and the speed of the meteors have been observed, and when allowance for the effects of the earth has been made, the orbit of the swarm around the sun can be calculated.

Meteoric showers and the streams that produce them are named from the positions of the radiants among the constellations. The Perseids and Leonids are examples.

6.22. Showers and Streams of Meteors.

The number of meteoric showers is very large, although the majority can be detected only by careful watching. Valuable contributions in this field are being made by associations of amateurs, such as the American Meteor Society. Olivier's list, up to 1920, contains at least 600 radiants representing real streams.

A meteoric shower can occur only when the stream crosses the earth's orbit, and when the swarm and earth arrive together at the point of intersection. If the swarm is a small one, the interval between showers depends on the period of revolution of the swarm around the sun. Extended swarms spend more than a year crossing the earth's orbit, or are so scattered around their orbits, as in the case of the Perseids, that we encounter them every year. The date of a shower is determined by the point of the earth's orbit at which the stream crosses; and aside from any shifting of the stream itself, the event occurs one day later every 70 years, because the earth reaches the intersecting point at intervals of a sidereal year.

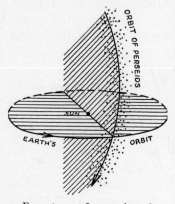

FIG. 6.22. Intersecting Orbits of the Perseids and the Earth.

The Perseids, or August meteors, furnish the most conspicuous and dependable annual showers, beginning about the middle of July and lasting until the middle of August, with the maximum of the display on August 11. Many Perseids leave bright trains which fade away slowly. Next in order of reliability and numbers are the *Orionids,* whose maximum occurs on October 20, and the *Geminids,* on December 10.

6.23. Remarkable Meteoric Showers.

Spectacular displays of meteors are less frequent than are brilliant comets. In the past hundred years a dozen comets were bright enough to be really conspicuous objects; but in that interval only four or five meteoric showers can be described as remarkable. The reason for the difference is that comets can be seen many millions of miles away, while meteor swarms are quite invisible, unless they enter our atmosphere. Three streams have provided the most brilliant meteoric showers on record:

The Lyrids (April 20). Showers from this stream are recorded as early as 687 B.C. In the year 15 B.C. the "stars fell like rain," and as late as 1803 the display as observed in Virginia was "alarming." Since the period of the main swarm is not known, it is uncertain when, if ever, it will return, according to Olivier. A few Lyrids are to be seen every year.

The Leonids (November 14). The period of the swarm is 33¼ years. Showers in 1833 and 1866–1867 were so brilliant as to terrify superstitious people. The failure of the Leonids to return in 1899 or 1900 in great numbers was a severe disappointment, although calculations by Stoney had already given warning of the probable diversion of the main stream by Jupiter and other planets. The first appearance of the Leonids was recorded in 902 A.D.

The Andromedes, or Bielids (November 24). They move in the path of Biela's comet, which disintegrated (6.17) and was last seen in 1852. Remarkable showers were observed in 1872 and 1885, as many as a thousand meteors a minute being estimated to have appeared at one place. Since 1899 only a few Bielids have been seen. Perturbations have shifted this narrow stream away from the earth's orbit.

Disturbing effects of the planets, which diverted the streams of the Leonids and Bielids, might conceivably shift them back again into view, or they may bring to intersection with the earth's orbit other great streams we have never seen. A remarkable meteoric shower, like a brilliant comet, may make its appearance at any time unheralded.

6.24. Association of Comets and Meteor Streams. That meteor swarms travel around the sun in elongated orbits, like those of comets, was not definitely known until about the time of the shower of Leonids in 1866. When the orbits of this and other swarms were calculated, it was further discovered that some of them are practically identical with the orbits of comets. Schiaparelli, in that year, was the first to demonstrate this interesting relation in the case of the Perseids and Tuttle's comet; and five other convincing coincidences were subsequently found.

METEOR SWARMS AND COMETS
HAVING NEARLY IDENTICAL ORBITS

Meteor Swarm	Date of Maximum	Associated Comet	Comet's Period
Lyrids	April 20	1861 I	415 years
η Aquarids	May 6	Halley	76
Meteors of 1916	June 28	Pons-Winnecke	6
Perseids	August 11	Tuttle, 1862	123
Leonids	November 14	Tempel, 1866	33
Andromedes	November 24	Biela	6½

The orbits of the η Aquarids and of Halley's comet are four million miles apart in the vicinity of the earth, but they appear to be parallel. The Andromedes and the swarm associated with the Pons-Winnecke comet are now practically lost, owing to perturbations of their orbits.

6.25. Relation Between Comets and Meteors.   The supposition that meteor swarms are the remains of disrupted comets is based on the

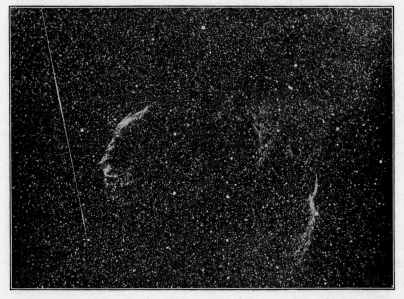

FIG. 6.25.   Meteor Trail.   In the region of the great loop of nebulosity in Cygnus.   The network nebula N. G. C. 6992 appears on a larger scale in Fig. 11.29.   (From a photograph by E. E. Barnard, Yerkes Observatory)

following evidence: (1) The meteoric constitution of comets best explains some of their phenomena (6.15). (2) A number of comets have broken up (6.17). (3) Comets and meteor swarms pursue nearly identical orbits in six known cases. The brilliant showers of Andromedes soon after the division and disappearance of Biela's comet may be construed either as striking evidence in support of the assumption, or simply as an interesting coincidence, owing to the shifting of the meteor stream.

It would be unwarranted at present to assume that all meteors have sprung from comets. The majority of the meteors, that we see, are *sporadic,* that is, they are not known to belong to any stream.

Moreover, Hoffmeister and others conclude that the greater number of meteors come from outside the solar system (6.20), while comets are known to be, at present, members of our system. In addition, there is the possibility that comets are formed in meteor streams. Under what conditions a discrete aggregation of solid matter exhibits cometary phenomena is a problem requiring further study.

6.26. The Zodiacal Light. The faint glow of the *zodiacal light* is best seen, in northern latitudes, in the west after nightfall in the spring, and in the east before dawn in the autumn, in a clear, moonless sky. It is broadest and brightest near the horizon, and tapers upward, following the course of the ecliptic to a distance of about 90° from the sun; it reaches a greater altitude and is therefore easier to observe when the ecliptic is most nearly perpendicular to the horizon (1.20). In the tropics the zodiacal light is visible throughout the year, both morning and evening, and in especially clear skies it has been traced, as a narrow *zodiacal band* completely around the ecliptic. Opposite the sun this band widens into an elliptical spot, known as the *gegenschein*, or counterglow. But these extensions are ordinarily not easy to see. The photo-electric cell can readily detect the brightening of the sky across the region of the gegenschein, as Elvey has demonstrated at Yerkes Observatory.

The zodiacal light is believed to be sunlight reflected by many small bodies, or perhaps by widely dispersed molecules of gas, which extend outward considerably beyond the earth's orbit, and which have a strong preference for a plane not much inclined to the ecliptic. This scattered medium can not appreciably retard the motions of planets and comets. It is only because of the great extension of this medium that the glow is visible at all.

According to van Rhijn, the zodiacal light spreads faintly over the whole heavens, and contributes altogether nearly 60 per cent of the light of the sky on a moonless night. An additional 15 per cent is furnished by permanent auroral light, and the remaining 25 per cent is starlight.

METEORITES

6.27. The Fall of Meteorites. Startling phenomena of light and sound often accompany the fall of meteorites. Preceding the fall at Homestead, Iowa, in 1875, according to an observer, a body was seen moving across the sky, which seemed as bright as the sun; it emitted sparks and puffs of smoke, and was followed by a brilliant train ten miles long. A minute or two after the dazzling mass of light had extinguished itself in five sharp flashes, five quickly recurring reports were heard, which seemed to shake the earth to its very foundations; and blending with the explosions there was a roar that rolled southward, as if a tornado of fearful power were retreating upon the meteor's path.

Such phenomena are caused by the resistance of the air to the swiftly moving masses, which heats and fuses their exteriors; the fused material forms a luminous envelope, and is swept back into the train. The sounds, resembling the crashes and rumblings of thunder, are produced by the violent disturbance of the air as the meteors rush through. The resistance of the air so reduces the speed of the meteorites that they rarely penetrate into the ground more than a few feet. With the reduction in speed the intense heat ceases, and the meteorites quickly cool, because the heat has not had time to affect their cold interiors.

6.28. Groups of Meteorites.
The fall of many meteorites, perhaps thousands, at one time and place is not uncommon. Either they entered the atmosphere in a compact swarm, or they entered as a single body which was shattered by the shock of the sudden reduction in speed, as effectively as if they had been struck with a great hammer.

That meteors sometimes travel in groups was abundantly verified by the remarkable " meteor procession " of February 9, 1913. According to Chant, there were ten or more groups, each containing from thirty to forty meteors, all following the same path. This procession, which occupied more than three minutes in passing above an observer, was visible from western Canada to beyond Bermuda, a distance of 6000 miles. The meteors had long trains; and rumbling sounds, like distant thunder, were heard as they passed.

When a group of meteorites falls, the individuals are distributed over an elliptical area, whose major axis lies in the direction of the flight. The largest individuals are found near the farther end of the ellipse, evidently because their greater momentum carried them farther. In the Khairpur, India, fall (1873) the meteorites were scattered over an area 16 miles long and 3 miles wide, the widest known distribution. The fall at Pultusk, Poland, in 1868 is estimated to have scattered 100,000 meteorites, most of them very small, over an area five miles in length.

6.29. External Appearance of Meteorites. Characteristic of most meteorites is a thin black crust which oxidizes to a reddish brown. It is formed from the fused material which was not swept away, and which hardened quickly near the end of the flight through the air. Veins of similar appearance often strike deep into the meteorite, owing to penetration of the heat through fissures. The surface is often irregular, having depressions where softer materials have melted away.

If the meteorite was shattered shortly before reaching the ground, the fragments are of irregular shape. If the individual had a longer flight through the air, it was shaped by the intensely heated air, depending on its original form, composition, and other factors. One of the more common forms is that of a cone, showing that the body kept the same orientation in its flight; the front side was worn away to a point by the parting of the air. The large iron meteorites which have this form were perhaps cones originally. Pear shaped, jaw shaped, and ring shaped meteorites are examples of other forms exhibited.

FIG. 6.30. Etched Section of the Knowles (Oklahoma) Meteorite. The pattern of bands is characteristic of the iron meteorites. (By courtesy of the American Museum of Natural History, New York)

6.30. Structure and Composition. Meteorites are of two kinds, the *irons* and the *stones*. There are all gradations between the two, from meteorites that are mostly metallic to stones in which a few particles of metal are scattered.

Iron meteorites have a uniform structure. They are composed chiefly of iron alloyed with from five to twenty-five per cent of nickel. A freshly exposed surface beneath the crust has a silvery appearance; when this is etched by heating or by treatment with dilute acid, a pattern of parallel bands intersecting in two or more directions is often revealed.

Stone meteorites are likely to have a grayish color beneath a black crust, and, in the majority of cases, have a granular structure. The rounded granules are crystals, or combinations of crystals, of chrysolite, enstatite, and other minerals. About thirty of the familiar chemical elements have been identified in the composition of meteorites and of the gases occluded in them; and no new element has been found, although the combinations are somewhat different from those in the native rocks. In most cases the differences are sufficiently marked to establish the celestial origin of meteorites which have not been seen to fall.

Up to the middle of 1927, according to Fisher's tabulation, 980 falls of meteorites were recognized, of which slightly more than half had been seen to fall, and of these less than seven per cent are irons. Among the "finds," however, the irons predominate, doubtless because they are more likely to attract attention, and also to resist disintegration by weathering for a longer time. On the average, five new "falls" are recovered yearly. For the whole earth, including the oceans and the large sparsely populated areas of land, one fall a day is believed to be a conservative estimate.

6.31. Collections of Meteorites.

Until the beginning of the nineteenth century it was not generally believed, even by scientists, that stones fall from the sky. With the recognition of this fact, as the result of notable falls of meteorites at L'Aigle, France, in 1803, and at Weston, Connecticut, in 1807, the collection of meteorites began in earnest, not only of these and subsequent falls, but of earlier falls as well.

The most representative collection of meteorites is that of the Field Museum in Chicago, which contains individuals from the majority of known falls. Other large collections are possessed by the natural history museums of New York, Washington, Paris, Berlin,

Vienna, and the British Museum. Smaller collections are to be found
in many parts of the world.

Meteorites are designated by the locality in which the fall occurred, for example, the Canyon Diablo meteorites.

FIG. 6.31. Willamette Meteorite. The weathered base of this conical iron
meteorite is shown in the photograph. (By courtesy of the American Museum of
Natural History, New York)

6.32. The Largest Meteorites. The largest known meteorite lies
where it fell, in the Grootfontein district, South West Africa. It is a
mass of nickel-iron whose estimated weight, according to Luyten, is
between 50 and 70 tons. Its rectangular upper surface measures
about 9 x 8 feet.

Next in order is one of a group of three, which Peary found in
1895, near Cape York, Greenland, and brought to the American Museum of Natural History in New York. The Cape York meteorite
weighs 36½ tons; it is a compact mass of iron nearly 11 feet long,
5 feet wide, and 7 feet high. The Willamette meteorite, in the same
museum, is a conical mass of iron weighing 15½ tons. Large cavities
in its base were formed by weathering after the fall of the meteorite;
for an unknown length of time it remained, base uppermost, exposed
to the moisture of an Oregon forest.

Three other iron meteorites, each weighing more than ten tons,
were found in Mexico, namely, the Bacubirito (27 tons), the Chupa-

deros (26 tons, in two pieces that fit together), and the El Morito (11 tons). Six other iron meteorites weigh between one and ten tons. None of these was seen to fall. The largest observed fall of iron occurred at Boguslava, 140 miles north of Vladivostok, in 1916. Two masses weigh 440 and 125 pounds.

FIG. 6.32. Cape York Meteorite. Until recently, the largest and heaviest known meteorite. It is a mass of nickel-iron weighing $36\frac{1}{2}$ tons. (By courtesy of the American Museum of Natural History, New York)

Stone meteorites do not have the large dimensions of the irons, evidently because they offer less resistance to fracture and erosion. The largest stone meteorite is the Long Island meteorite, which weighs, all together, more than half a ton; it was broken by the fall. The largest unbroken stone meteorite, now in the Field Museum, fell at Paragould, Arkansas, on February 17, 1930. It weighs 750 pounds.

6.33. The Siberian Meteorite. The most destructive of known meteorites fell on June 30, 1908, in a densely forested region of north central Siberia. According to the report of an expedition sent out, in 1927, to this region by the Russian Academy of Sciences, an area twenty or thirty miles in radius is completely devastated. The trees, without bark or branches, lie with their tops pointing away from the center of the area. Near the center many craters were found, the largest being 150 feet wide.

In the settlement of Vanovara, fifty miles south of the place of the fall, a very hot wave of air had hurled a man several feet from the

FIG. 6.32A. Great Meteorite, Grootfontein, South Africa. The largest known meteorite, weighing more than 50 tons. The exposed surface measures about 9 x 8 feet. (By courtesy of W. J. Luyten, Harvard College Observatory)

steps of his house, which was badly damaged by the wave. The air wave was felt, and a roaring was heard 400 miles from the place of the fall.

This is the only known case of a fall of meteorites which caused serious destruction. Apparently there was no human being in the devastated area at the time of the fall, but a large herd of reindeer was completely annihilated. The spreading of the great bubble of intensely heated air brought down by the meteorite caused the destruction.

6.34. Meteor Crater in Arizona. Near Canyon Diablo in northeast Arizona there is a circular depression in the desert 4200 feet in diameter and 570 feet in depth, measured from the rim which is about 130 feet above the surrounding country. It is known as Meteor

Crater, and is believed to have been caused by the fall of a meteorite. Although drillings have not yet certainly located this meteorite, which may well have been almost completely vaporized by the impact, several tons of smaller pieces of meteoric iron have been picked up within a radius of six miles around it, which were evidently the companions of its flight. The largest individual, weighing half a ton, is preserved in the Field Museum in Chicago.

FIG. 6.34. Meteor Crater, Arizona. A great hole in the desert twenty miles west of Winslow, Arizona. (From an official photograph of the United States Army Air Corps)

The rocks below the crater floor are crushed to a depth of several hundred feet, and give evidence of having been highly heated. Millions of tons of rock — limestone and sandstone — were displaced outward, forming the wall of the crater, while loose blocks of rock lie around the rim, the largest weighing 7000 tons. The weathering of the rocks indicates that the meteorite fell not more than 5000 years ago; the fall was certainly not less than 700 years ago, because cedar trees of this age are growing on the rim.

6.35. Other Meteor Craters are being recognized. Barringer describes a circular pit 530 feet in diameter near Odessa, Texas, which appears to have been caused by a fall of meteors. Fragments of meteoric iron were found in the vicinity. There is a crater of presumably meteoric origin, now partly filled with water, on the island of Oesel, in Esthonia; the depression is about 300 feet across, and within the distance of half a mile around it there are twelve or more smaller craters ranging from 100 to 15 feet in diameter.

A group of fifteen craters has been discovered near Henbury, in Central Australia. The main crater is oval, 650 feet long and 350 feet wide. The others are nearly circular, ranging from 250 to 30 feet in diameter. They were evidently formed long ago, for the walls are washed down, and the interiors are largely filled in.

Twin craters at Wabar, Arabia, are described by H. St. John Philby who visited the region in 1932. There is a legend among the Arabs that a great city on this site was destroyed by fire from heaven and buried in the desert sands. A mysterious block of iron " as large as a camel " is said to have been seen in the neighborhood. Philby identified the " buried ruins " as two large meteor craters. His search for the great meteorite was unsuccessful, but he picked up what seemed to be a fragment of meteoric iron.

F. A. Melton and William Schriever of the University of Oklahoma have photographed (1932) from an airplane large numbers of elliptical rings which are unnoticed from the ground, near the Atlantic Coast between Savannah and Norfolk. The rings are crossed by roads and paths, and many are parts of cultivated fields. Some of them are fully 8000 feet long. Their major axes lie in the same direction, from northwest to southeast.

ORIGIN OF THE SOLAR SYSTEM

6.36. Kant's Speculations. The first notable hypothesis of the origin of the solar system was proposed by the philosopher Kant in his *Theory of the Heavens*, published in 1755. Kant supposed that the material of the solar system was once spread uniformly through all the space it now occupies, an arrangement that seemed to him " the simplest that can follow on nothing." The heavy elements began to draw in from the regions around them the less heavy ones. He postulated repulsive forces at work as well as attractions, so that the material, as it was drawn into the nuclei, was thereby deflected a little, which set the nuclei into rotation.

At first, there were many nuclei moving in various directions, but collisions eventually reduced them to a smaller number of larger bodies all moving in the same direction in nearly circular orbits around the greatest mass of all which had accumulated in the center. Thus, by this account, the planetary system grew.

Kant's hypothesis was probably as consistent with the contemporary understanding of physics as any of the theories that have followed. Parts of the process which he briefly sketched reappear in some of the subsequent theories. For a long time it received very little attention. Laplace seems to have been unaware of Kant's contribution, and to have formulated his nebular hypothesis entirely independently.

6.37. The Nebular Hypothesis. In the *Exposition du Système du Monde* (1796) the mathematician Laplace presented a theory of the early history of the solar system, " with that diffidence which ought always to attach to whatever is not the result of observation and computation."

The account begins with the sun already formed and surrounded by an extensive nebulous atmosphere, which was hot, and in slow rotation. As this atmosphere cooled, it contracted, and therefore (4.32) rotated faster. The increasing speed of rotation caused a greater flattening at the poles and bulging at the equator, until a critical stage was reached at which the centrifugal force at the equator of the rotating mass became equal to the force of gravity. The equatorial ring of gas was then abandoned, and the remainder went on contracting, leaving behind other rings whenever the critical stage was repeated. Each ring gradually assembled into a gaseous planet whose orbit around the sun was the same as the ring from which it was formed, and whose rotation was also from west to east. Most of the planets, as they condensed further, left behind rings from which the satellites were formed. The rings of Saturn seemed to have remained to support the theory.

Laplace supposed that the sun and its atmosphere had been formed by the concentration of very diffuse nebulosity, and that the stars were formed in the same way. Double stars and groups of stars, such as the Pleiades, were formed by the condensation of the nebula around two or more nuclei.

6.38. Value of the Nebular Hypothesis. The simplicity of the nebular hypothesis and the weight of its distinguished authorship combined to elevate it to a leading place among astronomical theories throughout the nineteenth century. For more than a century it served as a powerful stimulus to scientific thought, not only in astronomy, but in allied sciences as well; and it led the way to considerations of orderly development in other fields. Although astronomers now regard it as untenable, the nebular hypothesis of Laplace remains the most successful theory of the origin of the solar system, in the sense of the confidence it inspired. No preceding theory had received much attention, and no subsequent one has yet met with such general approval.

The process of development, which has been outlined, led to the simple plan of the solar system, as it was understood when the theory was proposed, namely: (1) the nearly circular orbits of the planets and their satellites; (2) the approximate coincidence of the planes of all the orbits and equators; (3) the common direction, from west to east, of the revolutions and rotations. These characteristics were accordant with the theory and, in fact, suggested it; for Laplace argued that so simple an organization could not have arisen by chance. The failure of comets to abide by these rules was not embarrassing to the theory, because comets were believed at that time to have originated independently.

Before the newer theories are described, it will be profitable to review some of the developments which have caused astronomers to abandon the nebular hypothesis, and to search for a substitute.

6.39. Progress Since Laplace's Time. Since the formulation of the nebular hypothesis, the advance of knowledge in two directions has served to show its shortcomings, and to guide the hypotheses that follow it.

(1) The process of the development of the solar system, as Laplace outlined it, is in serious conflict with well-established physical principles, in particular, the law of the conservation of moment of momentum (4.32), and the kinetic theory of gases (3.13). It can be shown that in order to have abandoned the material from which Neptune was formed, the system must have possessed at that time a total moment of momentum exceeding the present total more than two hundred times. No reason can be assigned for so great a decrease.

It does not seem possible that rings of gas could have been abandoned at intervals by the shrinking mass; it seems more likely that the equatorial region, once having become unstable owing to its rapid rotation, would remain unstable, and that the gas would stream continuously from this region and disperse. If, however, the gaseous rings were formed in some manner, it is improbable that they could ever begin to assemble into planets. It has been pointed out that gravity at the surface of a body as large and dense as the moon is powerless to prevent the escape of gases.

(2) The organization of the solar system is more complex than it was believed to be in Laplace's time. Exceptions have been discovered to the regularities which suggested the nebular hypothesis. The asteroids present a tangle of orbits, some of which have high eccentricities and inclinations. Some of the satellites of the major planets have retrograde revolutions. The inner satellite of Mars has a shorter period of revolution than the planet's period of rotation. These are instances of details of the solar system which are not in harmony with the nebular hypothesis.

6.40. The Planetesimal Hypothesis.

In 1900 and the following years, Chamberlin and Moulton at the University of Chicago developed a different theory of the growth of the solar system, which has found favor with many geologists and astronomers.

According to the planetesimal hypothesis, the sun was long ago surrounded by a vast swarm of planetesimals (tiny planets) which revolved around it in intersecting elliptical orbits approximately in the same plane. The organization of the swarm bore some resemblance to the arms of a spiral nebula (12.5), but everything was on a very much smaller scale. There were local centers of condensation which in their revolutions swept up individual planetesimals, and slowly grew into planets and satellites. At the same time, many members of the swarm fell into the sun, increasing its mass and accelerating its rotation, especially in the equatorial regions. As the planets grew by accretion, their orbits became more nearly circular, and more nearly in the same plane.

By the substitution of a swarm of solid bodies for the gaseous atmosphere of the nebular hypothesis, difficulties of cohesion, arising from the kinetic theory of gases, are avoided. The postulation of spiral structure was contemporaneous with Keeler's discovery at the Lick Observatory that spiral nebulae are very numerous; it does not require an excessive total moment of momentum to bring about the formation of the planets. The lack of symmetry in the spiral organization gives opportunity for the development of a more complex planetary system than Laplace knew.

The theory requires that the large planets, having been formed as the result of many collisions, must have nearly circular orbits, and must move in nearly the average plane of the original swarm. The smaller planets and especially the asteroids, resulting from fewer collisions, may have orbits of considerable eccentricity and inclination. This is consistent with the observed motions. Mercury, the least massive of the principal planets, has a more eccentric and inclined orbit than most of them; and the orbits of some of the tiny asteroids have far greater eccentricities and inclinations.

6.41. Origin of the Planetesimals. The original statement of the planetesimal hypothesis began with the spiral structure already formed. It was accompanied by a suggestion that the spiral might have originated as the result of great tides raised in the sun by a passing star, and the process was explained in detail. At present, less emphasis is laid on the spiral, and considerably more on the dynamic encounter which is now definitely incorporated in the theory.

According to the present planetesimal hypothesis, the tides raised in the sun by the disturbing star attained such heights that large quantities of gas broke loose from the sun and streamed away in opposite directions, toward and away from the star. As the star advanced in its hyperbolic orbit with respect to the sun, this material moved forward, as well as outward, under the star's attraction. Much of the material fell back into the sun, thereby increasing the speed of the solar rotation. A considerable part of the remainder solidified into planetesimals, which from the start were crowded together in places, forming the nuclei of the future planets and satellites.

6.42. Tidal Theories. The original suggestion of Chamberlin and Moulton, that the planetary system was formed from material torn from the sun by the action of a passing star, is developed in a somewhat different way in the tidal theories of Jeans and Jeffreys at Cambridge. According to these two theories, which differ only slightly, the ejected material, as it moved outward from the sun and also forward under the attraction of the passing star, gradually cooled and *liquefied*. It separated into *large* portions which became the planets. In the meantime a part of the gas was lost by diffusion.

At the outset, the planets revolved in eccentric orbits which passed near the sun. When the larger planets came to perihelion for the first time, they were disrupted by the tidal action of the sun, just as the sun had been disrupted by the passing star; the systems of satellites developed out of the material thus torn from the planets by the same process that had formed the planets themselves.

When the smaller planets came to perihelion for the first time, they were sufficiently condensed to resist disruption to any great extent. Thus Mercury and Venus have no satellites, and Mars has two very small ones. The origin of the moon presents a special problem, for the moon is one of the more massive satellites, while the earth is among the less massive planets. It is believed that the solar tides alone could not have formed the earth-moon system from a single body; but Darwin suggested that these tides could have been amplified to enormous heights, if the period of rotation of this body became twice as great as its natural period of vibration.

The eccentric orbits of the planets and satellites were in time made more nearly circular, according to the tidal theory, by the resistance of the diffused gases; this medium would eventually be cleared away from the paths of the planets, either by being swept up, or by settling back into the sun.

The tidal theories and the planetesimal hypothesis in its present form shift the responsibility for the large angular momentum associated with the outer planets from the sun to the disturbing star. The plane of the orbit of this star becomes the plane with which the orbits and equators of the planets and satellites in general approximately coincide. The direction of the star's motion with respect to the sun becomes the common west to east direction of most revolutions and rotations in the solar system.

6.43. Frequency of Planetary Systems. Since the sun is only one of the multitude of stars, the question arises as to whether other stars are attended by planetary systems. The question can not be answered at present by direct observation, because a system like ours associated with even the nearest star would be invisible with the greatest telescope.

No way has been discovered whereby the sun or any other star by itself, by virtue of its rotation, can develop a planetary system. To produce this result the close approach of another star seems to be required, and the encounter must be almost close enough to be an actual collision. Owing to the vast distances that separate the stars, the probability of such close encounters between two stars is very small. Jeans concludes that in our entire stellar system a new planetary system can be developed, on the average, only once in 5000 million years, and that for stars spaced like those around us, not more than one star in 100,000 can have a planetary system at present.

If the encounter theory is correct, systems of planets are probably rare. But in the whole physical universe their number could still be very great, and the number of planets capable of supporting life might be very great also.

REFERENCES

C. P. Olivier, *Comets* (Williams and Wilkins, 1930).

C. P. Olivier, *Meteors* (Williams and Wilkins, 1925).

O. C. Farrington, *Meteorites* (1915).

F. R. Moulton, *Astronomy* (Macmillan, 1931). A chapter is devoted to the evolution of the solar system.

T. C. Chamberlin, *The Two Solar Families* (University of Chicago Press, 1928).

J. H. Jeans, *Astronomy and Cosmogony* (Cambridge University Press, 1928).

Yerkes Observatory, Williams Bay, Wisconsin.

CHAPTER VII

THE SUN

ANALYSIS OF SUNLIGHT — THE SURFACE OF THE SUN — THE CHROMO-
SPHERE AND CORONA — RADIATION OF THE SUN

7.1. The Sun as a Star. We have dealt at considerable length with the characteristics of the solar system, because this system occupies the foreground in our picture of the physical universe. As the dominant member of the system the sun has an important part in the picture, especially because its radiation is the source of practically all the various forms of energy manifested on the earth.

Viewed from another part of the stellar system, however, the sun would appear as only one of many stars, having no outstanding characteristics to distinguish it from the others. From the viewpoint of astronomy the sun is important because it is the only star near enough to be observed in detail. No other star shows more than a point of light in the most powerful telescope. In the study of the sun we are learning about a star.

It will not be sufficient simply to examine the face of the sun, and to describe what appears upon it. Much information is contained in the sunlight itself about the source from which it came. We begin, therefore, with the analysis of sunlight, and with its uses in promoting our knowledge of the sun.

ANALYSIS OF SUNLIGHT

7.2. Wave Theory of Light. Light, to the psychologist, is the sensation produced when something enters the eye and stimulates the retina; or it is the group of sensations which we designate as the different colors. To the physicist, light is that something — a form of energy (4.30) that comes to us always with the velocity of 186,284 miles a second (2.12) in empty space.

Huyghens, about 1678, formulated the *wave theory* of light. Newton proposed the rival *corpuscular theory*, namely, that light consists of material particles emitted by the source. The wave theory is useful in interpreting many phenomena of light. It supposes that light spreads out in waves from a source, in something like the way that ripples spread over the surface of a pond, when a stone is thrown into the water. According to the *quantum theory* proposed by Planck, in 1900, energy is emitted and absorbed discontinuously, in definite units, or quanta, $h\nu$, where h is a constant and ν is the frequency. The quantum theory inaugurated the present era of great activity in theoretical physics.

The *wave-length* of light is the distance between successive waves, say from crest to crest, which varies from 4×10^{-5} centimeter for violet light to twice that length for the reddest light we can see. It is often more convenient to employ the *frequency* of the light, which means the number of waves or vibrations emitted or received in one second; it is equal to the velocity of light divided by the wave-length. The frequency of violet light is 7.5×10^{14} cycles.

Like most receiving apparatus the eye is sensitive to a limited band of wave-lengths. Light is only a small part of the energy that is transferred from one place to another. *Radiation* goes on in waves of a great variety of length, from Hertzian or radio waves, as much as 15 miles long, to the minute "cosmic rays," whose wave-lengths are as small as 4×10^{-12} centimeter. All radiation has the constant "velocity of light" in empty space.

7.3. Analysis of Sunlight. When a ray of white light passes obliquely from one medium to another, as from air into glass, it is re-

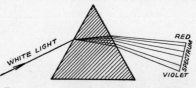

FIG. 7.3. Formation of a Spectrum
by a Prism.

fracted, or changed in direction, and also dispersed into a spectrum having the colors of the rainbow. Newton, in 1666, was the first to show that the spectrum is formed because the different colors of which white light is composed are refracted different amounts, the violet most, the red least. He admitted sunlight into a darkened room through a rather narrow slit, placed a glass prism in the path of the light, and studied the spectrum which appeared on the wall. In 1802, Wollaston repeated Newton's experiment, and saw three indefinite shadings across the spectrum, which he supposed were the boundaries between the colors.

In 1814, Fraunhofer examined the sun's spectrum, using a better prism and a small telescope for observing the spectrum, instead of allowing it to fall on a screen. He counted as many as 750 parallel

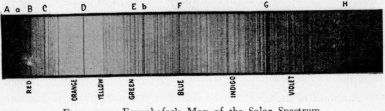

FIG. 7.3A. Fraunhofer's Map of the Solar Spectrum.

dark lines across the spectrum, and mapped 350 of them with considerable accuracy. On this map the prominent dark lines are designated by letters of the alphabet, starting at the red end of the spectrum. Thus the pair close together in the yellow region are the D lines. Not only are these designations still in use, but all the dark lines in the solar spectrum are known as the *Fraunhofer lines* in honor of their discoverer.

Although the dark lines were often studied thereafter, their significance remained unknown until 1859, when Kirchhoff explained that they denote colors abstracted from sunlight by a layer of gases surrounding the sun, whose chemical composition determines the particular pattern of lines that is shown.

FIG. 7.4. The Spectroscope. (By courtesy of Adam Hilger, Ltd.)

7.4. The Spectroscope. A familiar type of spectroscope consists of a prism of glass, quartz, or other transparent material, toward which two small telescopes are directed. The light enters the first telescope through a narrow *slit*, between the sharpened parallel edges of two metal plates. It then diverges to the objective of this telescope, the _collimator_, which makes the rays parallel before they enter the _prism_. The light is refracted by the prism, and dispersed into a spectrum, which is observed with the second telescope, the _view telescope_. Often the eyepiece of this telescope is replaced by a plate holder, so that the spectrum can be photographed.

If the light is monochromatic, the spectrum is simply the image of the slit in that particular color; if it is white light, composed of all colors, the spectrum is a band, violet at one end and red at the other, which is formed by overlapping images of the slit in the different colors. The absence of any color in the light can be detected in the spectrum most easily when the separate images are so narrow that they overlap as little as possible. This is the reason for the narrow slit.

The lines in the spectrum have nearly the same shape as the slit. They represent the presence or absence of particular colors in the light, which ordinarily might entirely escape notice. Integrated sunlight is like a set of books in many volumes piled in disorder. But the spectrum of the light is like the set arranged in order on a shelf; if a volume is withdrawn, the vacant space bears witness to the fact. The spectroscope is then an instrument for analyzing light into its constituent colors. It has great importance in astronomical investigations.

When the light is bright enough to be spread further, the scale of the spectrum can be increased by substituting for the single prism a train of prisms, or else a _grating_; this is a plate of speculum metal or transparent substance, on which many fine parallel grooves are ruled, perhaps 10,000 or more to the inch. The grating forms the spectrum by the diffraction of light. Its greatest use in astronomy has been in the study of the sun, where its wastefulness of the light, as compared with the prism, is of no consequence.

7.5. Three Kinds of Spectra. The spectra of all luminous bodies are of three kinds:

The bright-line spectrum is a succession of colored lines on a dark background. The source of the light is a glowing gas, which broadcasts on series of wave-lengths characteristic of the chemical element of which the gas is composed. Each gaseous element under the same conditions emits its particular selection of wave-lengths, and gives, therefore, its own pattern of lines in the spectrum.

The continuous spectrum is a continuous band of colored light, from violet to red. The source is a luminous solid, or liquid; or it may be a gas under special conditions, such that it can not emit light selectively. Regardless of its chemical composition, it sends out light of all wave-lengths, so that all colors are present in the spectrum.

The dark-line, or *reversed spectrum* is a continuous spectrum, except where it is crossed by dark lines. Cooler gas intervenes between the source of the continuous spectrum and the observer. This intervening gas is opaque to precisely the wave-lengths it emits. The

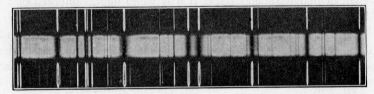

FIG. 7.5. Bright and Dark-Line Spectrum. A portion of the spectrum of an exploding iron wire. (From a photograph by J. A. Anderson, Mount Wilson Observatory)

spectrum is therefore the reverse of that of the gas itself; it is a pattern of dark lines characteristic of the chemical element of which the gas is composed.

When the continuous spectrum is observed, the composition of the luminous body remains undetermined, and we have three guesses as to its physical condition. The spectra of the sun and stars are chiefly dark-line, or *absorption spectra.* Some of the nebulae give bright-line, or *emission spectra.* The moon, shining by reflected sunlight, gives the solar spectrum.

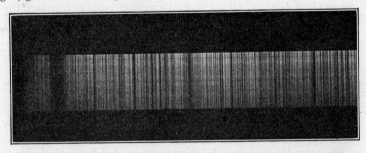

FIG. 7.6. Part of the Solar Spectrum. The spectrum in the violet. The broad lines at the left are the H and K lines of calcium. (From a photograph at the Allegheny Observatory)

7.6. The Solar Spectrum.
The visible solar spectrum is a band of colors from violet to red interrupted by thousands of dark lines. These lines are designated by their wave-lengths expressed in *angstroms,*

and preceded by the prefix λ. One angstrom is 10^{-8} centimeter. Thus λ4000 denotes a wave-length of 4000 angstroms, or 4×10^{-5} cm. The visible part of the spectrum lies between λ3900 and λ8000. In the ultra-violet the solar spectrum can be photographed as far as λ2900, beyond which it is cut off by the absorption of the earth's atmosphere. In the infra-red the spectrum has been photographed with specially stained plates as far as λ11,900; and it has been observed with the bolometer to λ20,000.

Rowland's *Preliminary Tables of Solar Spectrum Wave-Lengths,* since their publication in 1893, have served as the basis of studies of the solar spectrum. Revised and extended at Mount Wilson (1928), the tables now contain the wave-lengths of nearly 22,000 lines. The wave-lengths are given in international angstroms; the unit, differing very slightly from the angstrom defined above, is based on the adopted value of λ6438.4696 for the red line of cadmium.

Some of the most conspicuous lines and bands in the visible part of the solar spectrum are:

Fraunhofer letter	Wave-length	Identification
B	λ6867	oxygen (telluric)
C	6563	hydrogen, $H\alpha$
D	5893	sodium (double)
E	5270	iron
F	4861	hydrogen, $H\beta$
H	3969	calcium
K	3934	calcium

By far the strongest lines are the Fraunhofer H and K of calcium near the termination of the visible spectrum in the violet.

Some of the lines in the sun's spectrum are not of solar origin. There are *telluric lines* and bands produced by absorption of sunlight in the earth's atmosphere. The Fraunhofer lines A and B are identified with terrestrial oxygen, and *a* with water vapor. The abrupt termination of the spectrum at λ2950 is ascribed to ozone, while great gaps in the infra-red beyond λ10,000 are caused by water vapor and carbon dioxide in our atmosphere. Telluric lines are distinguished from solar lines by their greater strength when the sun is near the horizon, and in other ways.

7.7. The Doppler Effect.

When the source of light is relatively approaching or receding from the observer, the lines in its spectrum are displaced respectively toward the violet or red end by an amount proportional to the speed of approach or recession.

This principle, first announced by Doppler, in 1843, with respect to change of color of the light, was applied to the spectrum by Fizeau, in 1848. The approach of the source of light, no matter how fast, can not alter the speed of the light as we observe it (4.33). What happens is the increased frequency of the light. A familiar example of this effect in sound is the abrupt lowering of the pitch of the bell of a passing engine.

The Doppler effect has important applications in astronomy. It was this effect in the spectrum of Saturn's rings that gave the first observational evidence of their meteoric constitution (5.38). It is the only means of observing the motions of stars in the line of sight; and it is of great value in studying the rotations of the sun, the planets, and other celestial bodies. The application to the sun's rotation will be the next consideration.

7.8. The Sun's Rotation. The speed of the sun's rotation in any latitude can be determined by photographing on the same plate the spectra of the east (approaching) and west (receding) limbs, and comparing the two (Fig. 7.8). The lines in the first spectrum are displaced toward the violet by the Doppler effect; in the second spec-

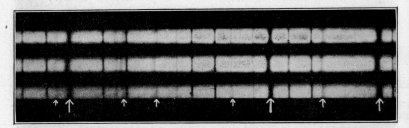

FIG. 7.8. Effect of the Sun's Rotation on Its Spectrum. In the upper and lower spectra, of the sun's west limb, the solar lines are displaced to the right (red). In the middle spectrum, of the east limb, the lines are displaced to the left (violet). Solar lines are indicated by the arrows. Telluric lines, which are not marked, are not affected by the sun's rotation. Only a small part of the spectrum is shown. (From a photograph at the Mount Wilson Observatory)

trum they are displaced toward the red. Half the difference denotes the speed of the rotation in that latitude, and from it the period can be derived.

Adams found (1908) in this way that the period of the sun's rotation is 24.7 days at the equator, 28.2 days in latitude 45°, 30.9 days in latitude 60°, 33.2 days in latitude 75°, and about 34 days nearer the poles. Thus *the period is shortest at the sun's equator and steadily increases toward its poles.* But the periods of the sun's rotation as determined by the spectroscope are changing. During the twenty years following 1908, the period at the equator increased as much as two days; afterwards, it diminished. The change may be caused, as St. John suggests, by the variable flow of the gases which produce the dark lines in the solar spectrum.

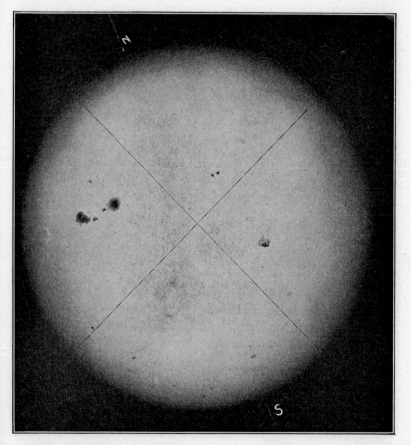

FIG. 7.8A. The Sun, September 17, 1926. The appearance of the sun's disk five days later is shown in Fig. 7.8B. (Both Figures are reproduced from photographs at the Royal Observatory, Greenwich)

The retardation of the sun's rotation toward the poles was first made known by Carrington, in 1860, from his observations of sunspots. At the sun's equator the period of the rotation is 25¼ days.

In latitude 35°, beyond which the spots rarely appear, the period is around 27 days. These periods have remained unchanged, in the average, though individual spots show unmistakable drifts relative to others.

These dark spots move across the sun's disk from east to west, with respect to positions in the sky; which shows that the sun's rota-

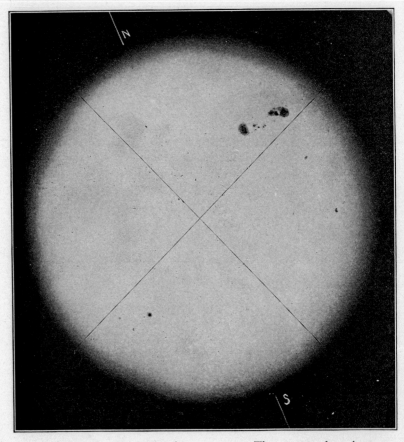

FIG. 7.8B. The Sun, September 22, 1926. The sun-spots have been carried to the right by the sun's rotation. One small group has disappeared beyond the right limb, while another has come into view at the left.

tion, like the earth's, is from west to east. The sun's equator is inclined 7° to the ecliptic. The paths of the spots across its disk are, therefore, usually curved.

7.9. The Einstein Shift. One of the few available physical tests of the theory of relativity is the slight displacement toward the red of the lines in the spectrum of a massive body. This effect is easily understood in terms of the quantum theory (7.2). An element of energy, $h\nu$, in the sunlight has to use up some of its energy in escaping from the sun's attraction. If it were a material particle, its speed would be retarded; but the speed of light in empty space can not be altered, according to the theory of relativity. Since h is constant under all conditions, the only factor that can become smaller is the frequency ν. Thus the wave-lengths of the light are increased, and the lines in its spectrum are shifted toward the red by amounts directly proportional to the mass of the source, and inversely as its radius.

A shift in the lines of the solar spectrum has been observed by Evershed and by St. John, in agreement with the values predicted by the theory of relativity. The determination is a delicate one, because the displacements are of the order of 0.01 angstrom; moreover, they are confused with Doppler effects produced by convection currents, which have the same character as the Einstein shift. Much larger displacements have been observed in the spectrum of the faint companion of Sirius (10.12), as the theory requires in the case of this remarkable star.

7.10. Contributions of Spectrum Analysis to Knowledge of the Sun. The spectroscope is responsible in a large measure for the rapid advance in the knowledge of the sun during the past quarter of a century. The solar spectrum shows the influence of almost every physical condition of the sun in which we are interested.

(1) *Chemical composition.* The patterns of lines in the spectrum are identified with chemical elements present in the sun (7.28).

(2) *Motions.* Doppler effects (7.7) in the spectrum indicate the sun's rotation (7.8), and also local movements of the gases in different parts of the sun.

(3) *Magnetic conditions.* The splitting of the spectrum lines (Zeeman effect) shows that sun-spots are magnets (7.22), and that the sun as a whole is magnetic (7.23).

(4) *Temperatures.* The distribution of intensities in the continuous spectrum (7.38) and the strengths of certain lines (10.18) permit determinations of temperatures in different parts of the sun.

(5) *Densities.* Absence of pressure effects in the solar spectrum, corresponding to those observed in laboratory spectra, namely, the widening and displacement toward the red of most lines, shows that densities in the outer parts of the sun are very small. The density of the gases in the reversing layer immediately above the photosphere is probably less than 10^{-4} times the density of the air around us.

In addition, the spectroheliograph (7.29) and spectrohelioscope make it possible to observe through the lines of the spectrum the arrangements and motions of gases at different levels in the sun's atmosphere, which otherwise could not be seen at all.

The Surface of the Sun

7.11. The Sun's Constitution. The sun is a great ball of intensely hot gas, whose visible surface is 864,100 miles in diameter. In volume it is $1\frac{1}{3}$ million times greater than the earth; in mass it is one third of a million times greater, so that its average density is one fourth the earth's density, or 1.41 times the density of water. Let us begin the description of the sun with an outline of its different parts.

The interior of the sun, lying below the visible surface, is known to us only indirectly from theoretical researches. Its temperature increases from 6000° K at the lowest visible level probably to many millions of degrees at the center.

The photosphere, or "light sphere," is the visible surface; it is the region of dark *sun-spots* and bright *faculae.* The more nearly transparent gases above the photosphere constitute the sun's *atmosphere.*

The reversing layer extends immediately above the photosphere, merging into the chromosphere at a height of a few hundred miles. It is the densest, and chemically the most complex layer of the atmosphere, whose absorption of the light from the photosphere forms the dark lines in the solar spectrum.

The chromosphere, or "color sphere," so named because of its scarlet color, is composed chiefly of highly rarefied hydrogen, helium, and calcium. It is several thousand miles in height, and from it the scarlet *prominences* rise at times to heights of hundreds of thousands of miles; they are visible to the naked eye during total eclipses, and with special apparatus at other times.

The corona, the outermost solar envelope, appears at the time of a total eclipse as a filmy, pearly halo of intricate structure.

7.12. Observing the Sun's Surface. It is unsafe to look very long at the sun on a clear day even without the telescope; to look at it *with* the telescope, without special precaution, invites immediate and serious injury to the eye, for the objective acts as a burning-glass. The

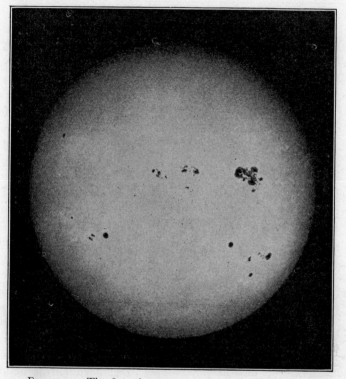

FIG. 7.12. The Sun, August 12, 1917. The photograph was taken near the time of sun-spot maximum. Faculae are visible near the limb, where the photosphere is less bright. (From a photograph at the Mount Wilson Observatory)

most convenient way to observe the sun with the telescope is to hold a sheet of smooth white cardboard back of the eyepiece, racking the eyepiece out beyond the usual position of focus until the sun's image is sharply defined on the card. In this way many can observe at once.

For studying the finer details of the solar surface the direct view is better. Special solar eyepieces admit to the eye only enough light to form a clear image of the sun. Langley's drawings of sun-spots, made by this means in Pittsburgh, about 1870, are unequaled in the delineation of detail by any projected view, or in fact by any photograph. But photography has supplanted the drawing as a means of recording the appearance of the solar surface accurately and rapidly. Photographs of the sun on every clear day have been made for many years at a number of observatories.

FIG. 7.13. The 150-foot Tower Telescope of the Mount Wilson Observatory.

7.13. The Tower Telescope. Fixed telescopes are of great value in solar investigations. They permit the use of long-focus objectives that are needed to form large images of the sun, with the minimum of mechanical construction. The largest of the fixed telescopes is the 150-foot tower telescope of the Mount Wilson Observatory.

The tower telescope has at its summit a little dome which contains a coelostat, a plane mirror equatorially mounted and driven by clockwork. This and a second fixed mirror beside it reflect the sunlight downward to a 12-inch objective of 150-foot focus just below them, which forms an image of the sun 16½ inches in diameter in the laboratory at the base of the tower. Under the laboratory is a well 80 feet deep, into which the sunlight can be directed upon a grating which returns it to the laboratory dispersed into spectra.

There are two other fixed solar telescopes on Mount Wilson, a tower 60 feet in height and the Snow telescope, which is horizontal. The 80-foot tower telescope of the Astrophysical Observatory at Arcetri (Florence), Italy, is employed by Abetti and his associates in studies of the solar atmosphere. The 50-foot Einstein tower (Fig. 4.34) of the Astrophysical Observatory in Potsdam, Germany, is another telescope of this type.

7.14. The Photosphere. The sun's visible surface presents in the telescope a mottled appearance, which is resolved under good conditions into many brilliant "rice grains," averaging 500 miles across, on a less luminous and by contrast grayish background. The brightness of the disk diminishes from the center to the edge, where it is only a third as bright to the eye, and even less in the photographs, showing that the light at the edge is redder as well as fainter. At the limb, as Abbot has explained, we are viewing the sun obliquely, through a greater thickness of its atmosphere, and therefore to a smaller vertical depth. The light at the edge of the sun is fainter and redder, because it comes from a higher and cooler level.

With the telescope, as without it, the photosphere appears as sharply defined as the surface of a ball. Until recently, it was supposed to be an actual surface formed by the tops of brilliant clouds at the distance from the sun's center where lowered temperature would allow some of the gases to condense into droplets. The presence of this cloud-shell would account also for the continuous spectrum. But at the high temperature of the photosphere (5750° K) everything must be gaseous. Moreover, it is believed that the density of the photosphere can scarcely exceed 1/10,000 of the density of air at sea level.

The present view is that the photosphere is opaque, despite its low density, because many free electrons are present at this high temperature. Anderson, at Pasadena, has demonstrated that the exceedingly hot gas around an exploding wire is opaque to light behind it, and that it gives a continuous spectrum. He has produced the same effects in rarefied gas in a vacuum tube by passing through it a heavily condensed charge of electricity.

Large bright spots, the *faculae,* are usually visible on the photosphere, especially in the vicinity of *sun-spots,* the dark spots on the sun whose description will follow. In the ordinary view, the faculae are most conspicuous near the limb, where the background is less bright. They are actually above the photosphere and are probably a little hotter.

7.15. Sun-Spots. The dark spots on the sun are sometimes large enough to be seen with the naked eye, when the glare of the sun is reduced by a dark glass, or by a hazy sky. Although accounts of such appearances are found in earlier records, the study of sun-spots really begins with their observation with the telescope, in 1610, by Galileo and others.

A sun-spot consists of two distinct parts: the *umbra*, or central dark part, and the *penumbra*, the lighter border whose outer edge is sharply defined and somewhat darker than the rest. The penumbra is composed of filaments arranged radially with respect to the center

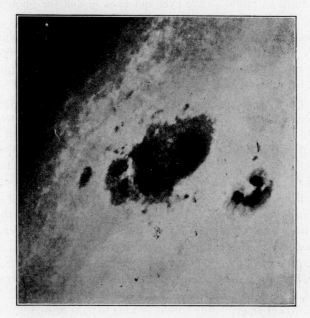

Fig. 7.15. Sun-Spot Group and Faculae, January 20, 1926. (From a photograph at the Royal Observatory, Greenwich)

of the spot, and not very clearly delineated in the photographs. While the more stable spots are roughly circular, sun-spots exhibit great variety and rapid changes of form, giving the impression of great turmoil. They occur usually in groups. Single spots vary in size from the smallest ones that can be seen, a few hundred miles in diameter, to great spots 50,000 miles across. Exceptionally large groups of spots spread over as much as one sixth of the diameter of the sun's disk.

Sun-spots are dark by contrast with their more brilliant surroundings. The umbra is less than one tenth as bright as the photosphere visually, and still less on the photographs, which shows that it is redder than the photosphere. The spots are, however, hotter and brighter than most artificial sources of light.

7.16. The Life of a Sun-Spot Group. Sun-spots generally occur in extended groups, or streams. Single spots are the survivors of groups. Rapid development and slow decline characterize the life of the average group, as Nicholson describes it.

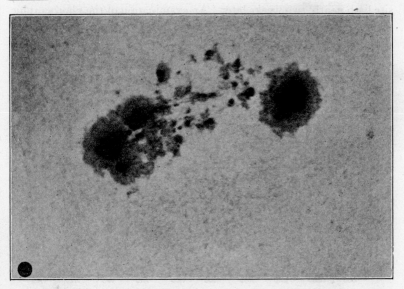

FIG. 7.16. Great Sun-Spot Group, February 8, 1917. The group is extended in the direction of the sun's rotation, which is toward the right. The follower spot is breaking up. The black disk in the corner represents the relative size of the earth. (From a photograph at the Mount Wilson Observatory)

The group is inaugurated by the appearance of two small spots in the same latitude, and three or four degrees apart in longitude. While these *principal spots* are rapidly growing, they draw apart to a difference of 10° or more in longitude; and in the meantime many smaller spots form in their vicinities. The leader spot, in the direction of the sun's rotation, becomes slightly the larger; it is also the more symmetrical, and is subject to less rapid changes. At the end of a week the group attains its maximum area, and the decline sets in.

Of the principal spots the follower spot is the first to disappear,

usually by repeated subdivision by brilliant " bridges." The smaller
spots vanish, and in a week or more after the maximum only the
leader spot remains; it may last several weeks or months. Finally,
all that remain to mark the region are bright calcium flocculi, whose
appearance was in fact the first indication of the disturbance which
produced the group of spots.

During its lifetime the group is carried slowly across the sun's disk
by the rotation of the sun; at length it disappears beyond the limb,
if it lasts long enough, and it may come into view again at the opposite limb nearly two weeks later. An examination of the photographic
records of the sun at Greenwich over a period of many years shows
that out of every hundred groups eight returned to view once, and
only two groups returned a second time. The record for observed
duration is held by a spot which lasted 18 months in 1840–41.

7.17. The Sun-Spot Cycle.

In some years sun-spots are numerous,
while in other years the sun may remain spotless for many days or
even weeks at a time. From the records of his daily counts of sun-

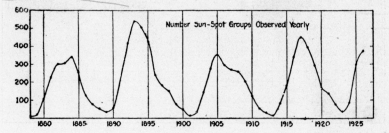

Fig. 7.17. The Sun-Spot Number Cycle. The point for each year represents the number of sun-spot groups observed during that year. The
curve shows the roughly periodic variation in the numbers. (From a
diagram by Nicholson)

spots, which extended over nearly twenty years, Schwabe, in 1843,
discovered that the variation in the number of spots is roughly periodic, in cycles of about eleven years.

Wolf, at Zurich, and his successors, Wolfer and Brunner have assembled the data concerning the daily number of spots, from 1610 to
the present time. The result is a curve which exhibits the variations
in the area of the sun's disk covered by spots. The average of the
intervals between successive maxima is 11.2 years; the observed
periods are mostly between 8 and 14 years, but extreme values of 7.3

and 17.1 years are noted. The rise from minimum to maximum spottedness is more rapid than the decline. Not only is the period variable, but the average number of spots varies from one maximum to another. It is possible, therefore, to predict only approximately the date of the next maximum, and the intensity of the outburst. Sun-spot minimum occurred in the summer of 1923, and the following maximum was reached in the spring of 1928.

7.18. The Shifting of Sun-Spot Zones. The sun-spot cycle is characterized also by the shifting equatorward of the two rather narrow zones in which the spots appear. The beginning of each new cycle is announced by the breaking out of small spots in the neighborhood of heliographic latitudes 30°, north and south. As these spots vanish and others appear, the disturbance draws in steadily toward the sun's equator. At the times of maximum number of spots, the zones of the activity are around latitudes 16°; and when the minimum is reached, the fading disturbance is marked by a few spots near the sun's equator, while the first members of the new cycle are making their appearance in the higher latitudes.

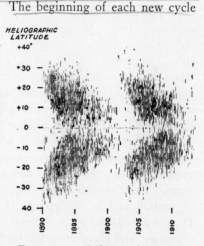

FIG. 7.18. Shifting of Sun-Spot Zones. The disturbed areas gradually draw in toward the sun's equator. As the disturbance dies out near the equator, a new cycle of spots begins at higher latitudes. (From a diagram by E. W. Maunder)

This one-way shifting of the sun-spot zones was first described by Spoerer. The details are now well known from the studies of this effect by Maunder at Greenwich. The explanation, however, like that of the number cycle itself, is unknown. Nor is it clearly understood why the spots are restricted, for the most part, to the belts between heliographic latitudes 5° and 30°, and why almost none are seen beyond 45°. It seems probable that the source of these effects is within the sun, and not outside it.

7.19. Associated Solar and Terrestrial Phenomena. Sun-spots are the most obvious manifestations of solar disturbances whose influence extends to all the levels of the sun that come under observation, from the photosphere to the outer corona. The faculae and prominences (7.32) vary in number and distribution with the sun-spots; the corona (7.34) undergoes marked changes of form as the spots vary in number; the total radiation (7.36) of the sun increases as the spots increase.

On the earth, magnetic storms and displays of aurora (3.21) are more frequent and intense near the times of sun-spot maxima. A *magnetic storm* is a disturbance of the earth's magnetic field, as indicated by erratic variations of the compass needle, and often by strong earth-currents of electricity, which seriously interfere with telegraphic communication. Maunder and others find many striking cases of individual connections between great magnetic storms and large sun-spots, the storms coming, on the average, a day later than the times when the spots are nearest the center of the sun's disk. The maxima and minima of the aurora are likely to occur later than sun-spot maxima and minima; the unusually brilliant auroras in the summer of 1928 followed the spot maximum in the spring of that year.

It is believed that the mean temperature of the air at the earth's surface is about a degree centigrade lower when spots are most numerous, despite the greater output of the sun's radiation at those times. There is some evidence also of slight variations in the amount of rainfall and in the growth of vegetation in the 11-year cycle. Douglass finds the cycle definitely recorded in tree rings over many centuries; and there are other interesting cases.

7.20. Explanation of Sun-Spots. Our acquaintance with sun-spots has been greatly advanced in recent years by the researches of Hale and his associates at the Mount Wilson Observatory. It is believed that a sun-spot is produced by a whirling storm in the outer part of the sun. Hot gases are carried upward in the vortex to a region near the photosphere, where the pressure is so much reduced that they expand and flow out over the surface. By expansion the gas is cooled and therefore darkened; thus the dark sun-spot.

From the studies of the magnetic properties (7.22) of the vortices underlying the spots, from which the existence and direction of rotation of the vortices are inferred, it appears that the preceding principal spots of the groups whirl in opposite directions in the sun's northern and southern hemispheres, and that *these directions are both reversed with the beginning of each new cycle.* It appears also from the magnetic effects observed that *the follower spot of each group whirls in the opposite direction from that of the leader spot.* Neither of these effects is completely understood. With reference to the latter, Hale offers the tentative suggestion that the two principal spots may be the two ends

Fig. 7.20. Vortices Above Sun-Spots North and South of the Sun's Equator. A portion of the sun photographed in the light of Hα line. The regions above the two spots are whirling in opposite directions. (From a photograph at the Mount Wilson Observatory)

of a single U-shaped vortex, while the smaller spots of the group are subordinate vortices arising from the main disturbance and whirling in either direction.

A compensating inward and downward flow of the overlying gases of the chromosphere, several thousand miles above the spot, is represented by the vortex structure of the hydrogen flocculi (Fig. 7.20), first observed in 1908 with the spectroheliograph (7.30). *These upper vortices do not reverse direction at sun-spot minimum.* The majority, according to Hale, whirl counter-clockwise in the sun's northern hemisphere and clockwise in the southern hemisphere, like cyclones in the earth's atmosphere (2.4), and are evidently produced by the deflection of the inflowing gases by the sun's rotation.

7.21. The Sun-Spot Spectrum. The spectrum of a sun-spot resembles, in general, the normal solar spectrum; but there are differences which arise from and give important evidence regarding three notable characteristics of the spots:

(1) *Lower temperature of sun-spots.* As compared with the normal solar spectrum: (a) Some lines are weakened in the sun-spot spectrum. They are "enhanced lines" which are conspicuous in the spectra of gases at high temperatures. (b) Some lines are strengthened. These are conspicuous in laboratory spectra of sources at lower temperatures. (c) Other lines appear only in the sun-spot spectrum. They belong to bands in the spectra of chemical compounds, especially titanium oxide and the hydrides of calcium and magnesium, which can not form at the high temperatures above the undisturbed surface of the sun. Pettit and Nicholson conclude that the temperature of the spot umbra is probably near 4800° K, or possibly a little less.

(2) *Radial movements of gases.* In the spectra of regions around sun-spots near the edge of the sun Evershed discovered Doppler effects, which St. John has studied also. They arise from the rapid flow of gases toward and away from the axes of the vortices, as the theory requires. Faint low-lying lines show an outflow at the rate of 1 km. a second; while lines originating at higher levels show an inflow, which increases upward to 2 km./sec.

(3) *Magnetic fields in sun-spots.* Many lines in sun-spot spectra are widened, and some are plainly split. This effect has been known for a long time; but Hale, in 1908, was the first to demonstrate its association with the magnetism of sun-spots.

7.22. Sun-Spots as Magnets. *The Zeeman effect,* known by the name of the physicist who discovered it, is the splitting of the lines in the spectrum when the source of light is in a strong magnetic field. The lines are divided into pairs or triplets, depending on whether the light that is analyzed has come out along or across the field. The amount of the separation of any line is proportional to the strength of the field, but it is not the same for all lines. Since the light of the components of a divided line is polarized in different ways, it is possible by means of an interposed Nicol prism to suppress one component and transmit another, a device that is especially useful when the separation is so small as to be hard to detect otherwise.

In the spectra of spots near the center of the sun's disk the lines are double; for spots near the limb they are triple. This shows that the line joining the magnetic poles of the spot has the same direction as the axis of the vortex. The *polarity* of the spot, that is to say, whether the positive or negative magnetic pole is at the top, is determined by observing whether the violet or red component of the divided line is transmitted by the analyzing Nicol prism. The direction of rotation of the vortex is inferred from the polarity of the spot. A daily polarity record of sun-spots is kept at Mount Wilson.

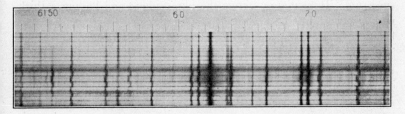

FIG. 7.22. Zeeman Effect in the Sun-Spot Spectrum. A small part of the Mount Wilson photographic map of the sun-spot spectrum. A Nicol prism and compound quarter-wave plate over the slit of the spectrograph divides the spectrum lengthwise into several strips in which the violet and red components of a line are alternately suppressed. Thus the lines widened by the Zeeman effect have a zigzag appearance.

7.23. The Sun's Magnetic Field. If the whirling of a sun-spot produces a local magnetic field, the rotation of the sun should make the entire sun a magnet. But the smaller speed of the sun's rotation produces a field of much less intensity, and therefore only very slight broadening of the lines of the normal solar spectrum. By this reasoning and by measurements of remarkable precision, the general magnetic field of the sun was discovered and studied at Mount Wilson. Its intensity just above the photosphere is 50 gausses; and it falls off so rapidly with increasing elevation that it can not be measured more than 200 miles above this level.

A *magnetic field* is the region around a magnet in which its influence is felt. *Lines of force* show the direction in which a magnetized needle will point at different places in the field; they converge toward the two *magnetic poles*. On the sun, except near a sun-spot, a needle would point nearly north, as it does on the earth. The sun's magnetic poles are 4° from its poles of rotation, and revolve around them in a period of 31.8 days.

The Chromosphere and Corona

7.24. The Sun's Atmosphere. It is the custom to speak of the photosphere as the surface of the sun, and of the more nearly transparent gases above it as constituting the sun's atmosphere. But all these parts of the sun are gaseous, and they merge one into another. The photosphere, as it has already been noted, is the region from which most of the sunlight emerges, and below which we can not see. Its thickness is estimated in tens of miles.

The reversing layer produces most of the dark lines in the solar spectrum. Immediately above the photosphere and having a thickness of several hundred miles, it may be regarded either as a separate layer, or else as the lowest and densest part of the chromosphere. The thickness of the chromosphere is measured in thousands of miles; above it the prominences rise to heights of many tens of thousands of miles. The corona, above all, is hundreds of thousands of miles in depth, and less dense than the best vacuum ever produced in the laboratory.

7.25. The Flash Spectrum. Since the dark lines of the solar spectrum, with the exception of the telluric lines (7.6), are produced by selective absorption and scattering of the light from the photosphere in the gases which lie about it, it is evident (7.5) that these gases alone

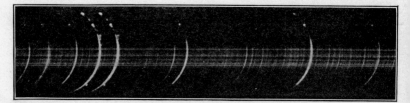

Fig. 7.25. The Flash Spectrum. Photographed by J. A. Anderson near the end of the total eclipse of January 24, 1925. The pair of long crescents at the left are the H and K lines of calcium. Projections to the right of these lines are prominences. Breaks in the crescents are caused by irregularities in the moon's surface. (By courtesy of the Mount Wilson Observatory)

must give a bright-line spectrum; and this spectrum must match approximately the dark-line pattern of the solar spectrum. The bright-line spectrum of the reversing layer and chromosphere was first observed during the total solar eclipse of 1870 by Young who named it the *flash spectrum,* because it flashes into view in the spectroscope near the beginning of totality, and disappears soon after the end of the total phase of the eclipse.

As the moon advances across the sun's disk, the dark-line spectrum persists as long as any part of the photosphere remains visible. At the instant when the photosphere becomes entirely hidden, the dark lines are completely replaced by the bright-line spectrum of the light from the narrow crescent of the chromosphere, still uncovered by the advancing moon. Many excellent photographs of the flash spectrum have been secured during total solar eclipse. Slitless spectrographs can be employed; for the source of the light is itself very narrow. With this procedure the bright lines are images of the crescent in the different colors of the chromospheric light.

7.26. Heights of Elements in the Chromosphere. The different lengths of the bright crescents in the flash spectrum (Fig. 7.25), with the slitless spectroscope, show that some elements rise higher than others in the chromosphere. Mitchell, of Virginia, has determined the heights by measuring the lengths of the crescents. Menzel has employed photographs of the flash secured in a different way by Lick eclipse expeditions. Hydrogen, helium, and ionized calcium, which produce the longest crescents, ascend to elevations of 6000 miles or more. A few other elements appear at lower levels in the chromosphere proper; but, for the most part, both the emission and absorption of light by the elements in the sun's atmosphere are confined to the reversing layer.

With some notable exceptions, the bright crescents match in position, though not always in relative intensity, the dark lines of the solar spectrum. The most conspicuous differences are found in the hydrogen and helium lines. All the hydrogen lines of the Balmer series are present in the flash spectrum, but only the first four, from $H\alpha$ to $H\delta$, have been observed in the dark-line spectrum of the sun. Helium lines, which are prominent in the spectra of the chromosphere and prominences, are almost entirely absent in the dark-line solar spectrum. Helium was discovered in the spectrum of the prominences during the total solar eclipse of 1868; its presence on the earth was not detected until 1895.

7.27. Constitution of the Chromosphere. From the evidence of the flash spectrum the chromosphere rises to a height of five or six thousand miles. Its temperature is about 5000° K and, above the reversing layer, its density is of the order of 10^{-10} times the density of air at sea level, diminishing very gradually with increasing elevation. If the gases above the photosphere were affected only by gravity and temperature, their density would diminish about ten times for every five miles of vertical ascent, so that not much material would be left above a height of a hundred miles. Milne has explained that the gases rise to much greater heights because the outward pressure of the sun's radiation nearly neutralizes gravity.

This equilibrium between gravity and radiation pressure occurs only when the density is very low. If the gases flow upward too abundantly, gravity gets the upper hand and they fall again until the equilibrium is restored. Thus the greater part of the material in the sun's atmosphere is kept in the reversing layer; and only those gases which are most strongly repelled by radiation pressure are maintained at higher levels.

The chromosphere is composed chiefly of hydrogen, helium, and calcium. The first two elements, the lightest of all elements, might be expected to rise to great heights; but it is surprising, at first, to find calcium, whose atomic weight is 40, associated with them. The explanation is that the construction of the singly ionized calcium atom, which is responsible for the Fraunhofer H and K lines, makes it exceptionally expert at "riding the sunbeams," in Eddington's words.

When an atom in the sun's atmosphere absorbs radiation flowing outward from the sun, it acquires the momentum of this radiation, and is carried upward. Straightway it falls again under gravity. The energy that is absorbed raises an electron in the atom to a higher orbit. The electron at once drops back again with emission of the energy in all directions; and the atom is ready to absorb more energy, and to be boosted again. In the ionized calcium atom this process can occur 20,000 times a second. The upward impulses are frequent enough to keep the atom afloat. It is by no means certain, however, that radiation pressure is the only important factor in maintaining the state of equilibrium in the chromosphere.

7.28. The Sun's Chemical Composition. By comparisons of the solar spectrum, both the dark-line and the flash, with the spectra of the chemical elements in the laboratory, it is possible to identify many elements in the sun's atmosphere. Of the 90 known elements about fifty have been recognized in the sun, and other identifications of more recently discovered elements may be added, when their spectra have been studied more thoroughly in the laboratory. There remain two groups of elements whose lines are not observed in the solar spectrum. Of the first group, which includes chlorine and argon, the strongest lines are far in the ultra-violet, beyond $\lambda 2900$ where the solar spectrum is cut off by absorption in our atmosphere. The second group contains tungsten, platinum, and uranium, and other heavy elements.

It seems probable that all the known elements are present in the sun, but that many of them occur in too small amounts, at least in the sun's atmosphere, to make appreciable contributions to the solar spectrum.

With few exceptions, the elements in the sun's atmosphere do not enter into chemical combinations, because compounds are generally unstable at such high temperatures. In the blue and ultra-violet parts of the solar spectrum there are a few bands which are supposed to arise from compounds of nitrogen and carbon, nitrogen and hydrogen, and one or two other combinations. Bands, which are characteristic of compounds, are conspicuous in the spectra of sun-spots, and of the red stars.

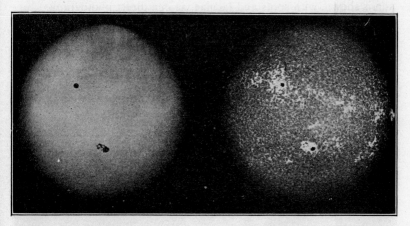

FIG. 7.29. Direct Photograph and Spectroheliogram of the Sun. The spectroheliogram is taken with the H line of calcium. Calcium flocculi are conspicuous in the two sun-spot zones, and especially near the spots. (From photographs at the Mount Wilson Observatory)

7.29. The Spectroheliograph. Since its invention in 1890, independently by Hale in America and Deslandres in France, the spectroheliograph has been one of the most valuable instruments in solar investigations. It is a development of the spectroscope, by means of which the sun can be photographed in the light of a single chemical element. The photograph, or *spectroheliogram*, shows how the gases of this element are distributed above the sun's surface.

The image of the sun is focused by the telescope on the first slit which admits the light from a narrow strip of the image to the grating, or prisms, where its spectrum is formed. A second slit parallel to the first allows only a very limited region of this spectrum to reach the photographic plate. By a slight rotation of the grating, any part of the spectrum can be passed through the second slit, for example, the dark K line of calcium. It must be remembered that the dark lines in the solar spectrum are not devoid of light; their light is fainter because it comes from the cooler gases above the photosphere. While the plate is being exposed, the sun's image is moved across the first slit, and the plate is moved at a corresponding rate, until a complete picture of the sun is obtained by the light of the single dark line. The iron, sodium, and other lines are employed in addition to the H and K lines of calcium and the hydrogen lines. If a portion of the continuous spectrum is set on the second slit, the normal surface of the sun is shown, with spots and faculae, as in a direct photograph.

In 1924, Hale perfected the *spectrohelioscope* which is designed for visual observations of the sun in the light of a single element. Two slits are made to oscillate rapidly enough to give a persistent image of a portion of the sun in the light of a selected wave-length.

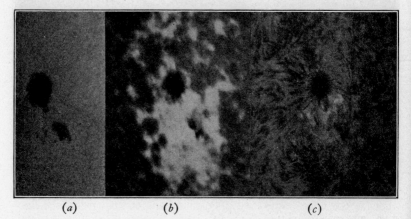

(*a*) (*b*) (*c*)

FIG. 7.30. A Sun-Spot Region at Three Levels. (*a*) Direct photograph. (*b*) Spectroheliogram, with the edge of the K line of calcium. (*c*) Spectroheliogram, in hydrogen light. (From photographs at the Mount Wilson Observatory)

7.30. Spectroheliograms of the Sun.

The value of the spectroheliograph is greatly enhanced by its ability to produce photographs of the sun's atmosphere *at different levels,* depending on the particular line

whose light is admitted through the second slit, and also, in the case
of the broad lines, on the part of the line that is employed. The center of a broad, dark line in the solar spectrum is formed at a higher
level in the sun than are its edges; while in a series of lines of the same
element the one nearest the red end of the spectrum is probably pro-

FIG. 7.30A. Very Bright Solar Eruption. Photographed October 13, 1926,
with the center of the Hα line. (From a photograph at the Astrophysical Observatory, Meudon, France)

duced at the greatest elevation. The centers of the H and K lines and
of the red hydrogen line Hα give the highest level spectroheliograms
of all.

The mottled appearance of the sun, as it is observed directly, is
more pronounced in the spectroheliograms. These patches, both
bright and dark, are the *flocculi,* so named by Hale; they are masses
of gas which are hotter and cooler respectively than those around
them in the photograph. In the calcium spectroheliograms the flocculi are generally bright, and they are especially conspicuous in the
sun-spot zones. At higher levels the calcium flocculi are larger and
brighter, sometimes completely covering the dark spots below them.

Hydrogen flocculi are more often dark, and are more elongated.
In the vicinity of sun-spots they are drawn out and curved, as they
whirl in the vortices overlying the spots. Large dark and bright
patches, which characterize the Hα spectroheliograms, are promi-

nences seen in projection against the sun's disk. When they are carried by the sun's rotation beyond the edge of the disk, they appear as bright prominences, and can be photographed in either hydrogen or calcium light when the bright disk is hidden behind a circular screen.

7.31. The Prominences are projections from the chromosphere, sometimes rising to very great heights. Their color is scarlet like that of the upper chromosphere, owing to the predominance of the light of the

FIG. 7.31. Prominence Observed at the Total Eclipse of May 29, 1919. At this eclipse the displacement of stars near the sun's limb, predicted by Einstein, was observed (4.36). (From a photograph by A. S. Eddington)

red Hα line of hydrogen. This vivid color, contrasting with the pearly glow of the corona, contributes to the splendor of the total eclipse of the sun. Prominences are not visible ordinarily without an eclipse, for the same reason that the stars are not seen in the daytime, owing to the glare of the atmosphere which strongly diffuses the sunlight, especially near the sun's limb.

Until 1868, the prominences were observed only during total solar eclipses. In that year Lockyer and Janssen independently discovered an easy way to see them at other times. With a spectroscope of high dispersion the diffused sunlight is diluted, because its spectrum is mainly continuous; but the light of the prominences is concentrated in a few bright lines which are spread farther apart but are not much weakened by dispersion. When the slit of the spectroscope is opened rather wide and set tangent to the sun's limb where a prominence is projecting, the prominence can be seen through the widened red hydrogen line.

In recent years, prominences have been photographed regularly with the spectroheliograph, and they can now be studied visually with the spectrohelioscope, both beyond the limb and as hydrogen flocculi in projection against the sun's disk.

7.32. Quiescent and Eruptive Prominences. *Quiescent prominences* bear some resemblance to clouds in our atmosphere, so far as their appearance is concerned. They attain heights of the order of 50,000 miles above the chromosphere, and are often connected with it by numerous columns. Like the upper chromosphere they are composed chiefly of hydrogen, helium, and singly ionized calcium. They persist for many days with very gradual changes in form. Quiescent prominences occur at all parts of the sun's limb. Their number is somewhat greater when sun-spots are more numerous.

Eruptive prominences are generally smaller, brighter, and very much more active. The speed of their ascent from the chromosphere may exceed 200 miles a second; some of them have swift horizontal motions also. A remarkable eruption

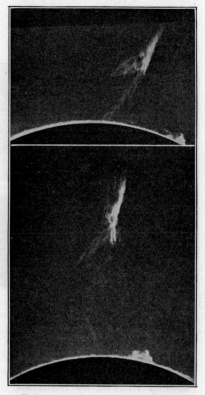

FIG. 7.32. Very High Prominence, November 19, 1928. The lower spectroheliogram was taken 53 minutes later than the upper one. Half an hour later, at the height of 567,000 miles and still ascending, the prominence was hidden by clouds. (From photographs by T. Royds, Kodaikanal Observatory, India)

(Fig. 7.32) was photographed by Royds at Kodaikanal at intervals during the rapid rise, on November 19, 1928. It had reached a height of 567,000 miles above the solar surface, about two thirds of the sun's diameter, when clouds intervened. Eruptive prominences appear usually in the vicinities of active spots, and therefore vary in number with the spots in the 11-year cycle. They exhibit great variety in their forms. In addition to those which rise more or less vertically, Pettit recognizes three classes: (1) *active* prominences, which appear to be torn apart; (2) *spot* prominences which resemble fountains; (3) *tornado* prominences which have the appearance of vertical spirals or tightly twisted ropes.

FIG. 7.32A. Prominence Observed at the Total Eclipse of May 9, 1929. (From a photograph by R. W. Marriott at the Swarthmore College Eclipse Station in Sumatra)

7.33. Light of the Corona. The total light of the corona is one half that of the full moon. Measurements by Stebbins and Kunz with the photo-electric cell, by Pettit and Nicholson with the thermocouple, and by other observers at recent eclipses agree closely as to its value. Stetson's measurements, however, suggest that the corona is somewhat brighter at the times of sun-spot maximum.

The light falls off so rapidly with increasing height that it is impossible to photograph the whole corona satisfactorily with a single exposure. Half the light comes from within 3', or less than 100,000 miles of the sun's surface; this is the *inner corona*, whose color is yellowish. The *outer corona* is pearly white, and its delicate streamers can sometimes be traced visually to heights exceeding a million miles; but the duration of a total eclipse is not long enough to allow the outermost extensions to be recorded on the photograph.

Until recently, the corona was observed only during total solar eclipse. There seemed to be no prospect of studying it, at least satisfactorily, at any other time, because the sunlight scattered by the atmosphere makes the sky just beyond the sun's limb thousands of times brighter than the inner corona. Lyot, of Meudon, succeeded in observing the inner corona and its spectrum outside eclipse, from the Pic du Midi, in 1930–31.

The light of the corona is mostly scattered sunlight, but its spectrum contains many bright lines also, of which the strongest is usually in the green at $\lambda 5303$, showing that the corona is partly self-luminous. Since none of these bright lines has ever been observed in the laboratory, it was formerly considered among the possibilities that they might belong to the spectrum of an otherwise unknown element "coronium." The recent identification of "nebulium" lines as unusual manifestations of oxygen and nitrogen (11.29) makes it seem probable that the bright lines in the spectrum of the corona are unusual lines of a familiar element, or elements, under the peculiar conditions of the corona, namely, the very low density and great volume of its gases.

7.34. Changing Form of the Corona.

It has been known for the past fifty years that the form of the corona undergoes a cycle of changes in the 11-year period. Near the times of the greatest numbers of spots, the corona is approximately circular; it has been likened to a dahlia because of the petal-like streamers in various directions. Near sun-spot minimum the corona is considerably flattened at the poles where short, curved streamers bear some resemblance to the lines of force around the poles of a bar magnet; they are symmetrical with the sun's rotation axis. Long equatorial extensions also characterize the corona near sun-spot minimum. Ludendorff (1928) finds that the form of the corona at a given eclipse depends considerably on the distribution of spots on the sun's disk at that time. It seems certain that the structure of the outer corona is determined by influences from lower levels.

A solar disturbance can be studied at five different levels: (1) The whirling vortex below the photosphere gives rise to the strong magnetic field of the sun-spot, made known by the Zeeman effect in the spectrum of the spot. (2) The dark spot which is seen and photographed directly. (3) The bright flocculi above the region of the spot, observed with the spectroheliograph through the edges of the

H and K lines of calcium. (4) The still higher and very active region observed through the Hα line; here the hydrogen flocculi are whirling, and great dark patches are being sucked into this upper vortex. (5) The eruptive prominence rising to a great height above the

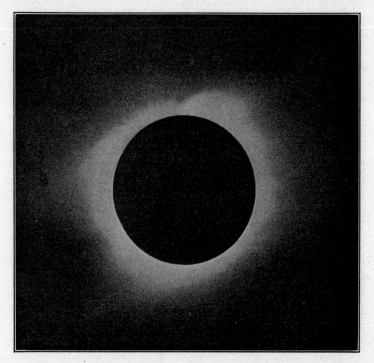

FIG. 7.34. Photograph of the Corona, September 21, 1922. Near the time of sun-spot minimum. Short curved polar streamers and long equatorial extensions characterize the corona at this phase of the sun-spot cycle. (From a photograph by the Lick Observatory Eclipse Expedition to Australia)

disturbed area, and the petal structure of the corona built up in the same region.

RADIATION OF THE SUN

7.35. Intensity of the Sun's Radiation; the Solar Constant. In order to measure the rate at which we receive energy from the sun it is necessary to employ a device that is sensitive to all wave-lengths. Neither the eye nor the photographic plate serves this purpose, for they are sensitive to only very limited ranges of wave-length. All radiation, when it is absorbed, produces heat. Thus the heating effect of the sun's radiation is a measure of its intensity. The *pyrheliometer* is an instrument designed for observations of this kind; it

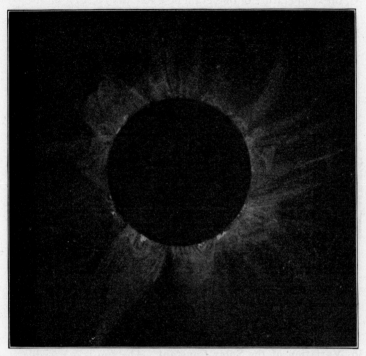

FIG. 7.34A. Drawing of the Corona, January 14, 1926. Approaching the time of sun-spot maximum. At this phase the corona is approximately circular. The petals and the arches over the prominences are more clearly shown than is possible in printed reproductions from the negatives. (Composite drawing by Emma T. R. Williams from photographs by the Swarthmore College Expedition to Sumatra)

contains a thermometer for measuring the rate at which the sun's radiation raises the temperature of a small quantity of water or mercury, or of a metallic disk. Instruments of this type are in continuous use at the stations of the Astrophysical Observatory of the Smithsonian Institution.

The *solar constant* is a measure of the rate at which energy is received by a surface exposed at right angles to the sun's radiation just outside the atmosphere, when the earth is at its mean distance from the sun. It is expressed in terms of the heat produced at this surface by complete absorption of the radiation. The average value of the solar constant, according to Abbot, is 1.94 calories a minute per square centimeter. A *calorie* is the quantity of heat required to increase by 1° C. the temperature of one gram of water (at 15° C.).

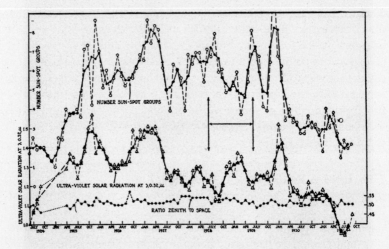

FIG. 7.36. Variations in Number of Sun-Spot Groups and in Intensity of Solar Ultra-Violet Radiation, 1924–1931. Open dots represent monthly averages; full dots, three-month running averages. The lowest curve shows the slight variation in atmospheric transmission of the ultra-violet radiation. (From a diagram by Edison Pettit)

7.36. Variation of the Solar Constant. The sun is a variable star. Abbot and his associates have shown that the value of the solar constant fluctuates in the period of the sun-spot cycle; it is two or three per cent higher when the spots are most numerous than at sun-spot minimum. The variation is almost entirely in the ultra-violet and violet radiations.

Systematic studies of this variation have been conducted, since 1924, by Pettit at Mount Wilson. His solar radiometer permits accurate comparisons of the sun's ultra-violet radiation (λ3200), transmitted by a silvered lens, with its green light (λ5000) transmitted by a gilded lens. Pettit finds that the ratio, ultra-violet to green, is fully 50 per cent greater at spot maximum. This change is too great, as he clearly points out, to be ascribed entirely to a variation in the sun's temperature.

7.37. Energy Radiated by the Sun. The value of the solar constant, 1.94 calories a minute for a square centimeter at the earth's distance, can be easily transformed to other units; it is equal, for example, to 1½ horsepower for a square yard at right angles to the sun's direction outside the atmosphere. Multiplying by the number of square yards in the surface of a sphere whose radius is the earth's distance from the sun, we have a measure of the sun's total radiation. Since the space between the sun and the earth is practically transparent, the total energy intercepted by the surface of the sphere is identical in amount with that which leaves the sun's surface. It is equal to 5.08×10^{23} horsepower. This enormous output of energy suggests that the sun must be very hot. Dividing this total radiation by the number of square yards in the sun's surface, we find that each square yard emits continually an amount of energy equivalent to 70,000 horsepower.

7.38. Laws of Radiation. As the temperature of a body, say a piece of metal, is raised, the amount of its radiation increases, and the quality of the radiation is altered. With increasing temperature the metal begins to glow with a red light which brightens and changes to a bluish white. The *laws of radiation* are relations between the temperature of a body and the quantity or quality, or both, of the radiation it emits. These relations apply to a *perfect radiator* which has the greatest possible efficiency as a radiator, and which is also a perfect absorber of radiation, or a *black body*. This ideal body, when cold, would be absolutely black.

Stefan's law states that the total energy, E ergs, emitted in one second by a square centimeter of a perfect radiator is directly proportional to the fourth power of its absolute temperature, T. The relation is: $E = aT^4$. The value of the constant, $a = 5.72 \times 10^{-5}$, is known from experiments with bodies whose total radiations and temperatures can be determined separately. Thus, if the temperature of the body is doubled, its total radiation becomes sixteen times more intense.

Wien's law states that the wave-length, λ_m, for which the radiation is the most intense, is inversely proportional to the absolute temperature. The relation is: $\lambda_m = 0.289/T$. Thus, if the temperature is 4000° K, the brightest part of the spectrum has a wave-length of 7200 angstroms, in the red; if the temperature is raised to

8000°, the greatest intensity is shifted to 3600 angstroms, in the ultra-violet.

7.39. The Energy Curve.

The most general law of radiation is the formula derived from theoretical considerations by Planck. By means of this formula, which may be found in treatises on physics, it is possible to calculate for a black body at a given temperature the relative intensities of its radiations in various wave-lengths. The *energy curve* so calculated shows the variation in the intensity of the radiation throughout the spectrum.

For a higher temperature the curve is higher at all points, showing that the output of energy is greater in all wave-lengths; but up to a certain point the increase is greater for the shorter wave-lengths, so that the peak of the curve is shifted toward the violet end of the spectrum. Stefan's law and Wien's law can be derived from Planck's general formula. The former relates to the area under the curve, which represents the total energy radiated at a given temperature; the latter gives the wave-length of the peak of the curve for that temperature.

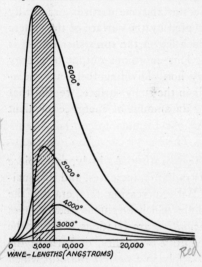

FIG. 7.39. Energy Curves of a Perfect Radiator. The heights are proportional to the intensity of the radiation. As the temperature is increased, the total radiation, represented by the area under the curve, increases (Stefan's law); and the peak of the curve is shifted to shorter wave-lengths (Wien's law). The shape of the curve for each temperature is calculated by Planck's formula. The shaded area represents the radiation to which the eye is sensitive.

By the use of these radiation laws the sun's *effective temperature* can be determined, that is to say, the temperature that the sun's surface must have, if it is a perfect radiator, in order to radiate as it does. On the supposition that the sun's photosphere is not a perfect radiator, its actual temperature must be higher than that calculated by the radiation laws; but the difference in this case can not be very great.

7.40. The Sun's Temperature. *The effective temperature of the sun is about 5750° K.* It must be nearly the mean temperature of the photosphere. This value of the temperature is determined by Stefan's law from the solar constant. At the center of the sun's disk the effective temperature is about 6000°, as determined:

(1) *By Stefan's law.* The rate at which radiation of all wave-lengths is emitted by the sun is calculated from the observed value of the solar constant (7.35). The resulting temperature is 5950° K.

(2) *By Wien's law.* The wave-length of the most intense radiation is found by precise observations of the solar spectrum. The resulting temperature is 6150° K.

(3) *By Planck's formula.* The intensities of the solar spectrum at the different wave-lengths are measured by means of a special instrument, the spectrobolometer. This observed energy curve is compared with curves calculated by the formula for different temperatures, until the best fit is found. The energy curve for a temperature of about 6000° K is in fair agreement with the observed curve.

7.41. Temperatures in Different Parts of the Sun. The sun's effective temperature of 5750° K is the average for all parts of the disk. Near the middle of the disk, where the light comes from a greater depth, the temperature is somewhat higher; close to the limb, where the line of sight makes a small angle with the surface, the light comes from a higher level whose temperature is not much above 5000°. In sun-spots the temperature is reduced to 4800°.

In general, the sun's temperature rises with increasing depth. Below the photosphere the temperature increases rapidly, until at the center of the sun it presumably reaches a value of many million degrees. The temperature of the chromosphere is about 5000°; and even in the outer corona it is as much as 3000°. These are the temperatures that would be attained by black bodies in these regions. Throughout the sun, the heat is sufficient to vaporize all known materials, where they are likely to be. It is almost certain, therefore, that all parts of the sun are gaseous./

7.42. Problems of the Sun's Radiation. The enormous outflow of energy from the sun, whose value in horsepower has been given (7.37), has continued at about the present rate for hundreds of millions of years, according to geological records. It is a problem of the greatest importance to determine the source of this energy. A prominent theory, at present, is that the sun continues to shine at the expense of the vast store of energy possessed by its mass, in accordance with the theory of relativity (4.33). If this is true, it is easy to show that the mass of the sun must be diminishing at the rate of 4,200,000 tons a second in order to supply the energy necessary for radiation.

Another problem relates to the apparent lavish expenditure of this radiation. Of all the energy that pours forth from the sun, less than one part in 200 million is intercepted by the planets and their satellites. The remainder spreads through interstellar space with little chance, so far as we know, of being recovered. The suggestion that the sun shines only in the directions of material that can intercept it makes an appeal from the point of view of economy, but appears to have little else to recommend it. It would seem that nature is squandering its resources of energy so prodigally that it must end in bankruptcy; but we doubtless have at present an imperfect account of the situation.

The study of the sun's radiation by itself gives information concerning the energy that leaks through the insulation, but it does not tell us much directly about what is going on inside the furnace. A complete account of the radiation demands an investigation of the sun's interior. These and other problems of the sun's radiation are among the fundamental problems of physical science. They arise in connection with the radiations of the stars in general. These considerations are resumed in Chapter X.

7.43. The Contraction Theory. Among the theories which were proposed, and which finally proved insufficient to account for the maintenance of the sun's radiation, the contraction theory is the most notable because of the confidence it inspired. In this respect the contraction theory resembles the nebular hypothesis (6.37) of the origin of the solar system; and it is closely related to this hypothesis.

In 1854, Helmholtz proposed the theory that the sun continues to shine because it is steadily shrinking as the result of gravitational attraction toward its center. It can be shown that a contraction in the sun's radius of 140 feet yearly would produce as much heat as the sun loses by radiation in a year. This process could not continue indefinitely. With increasing density and consequently diminishing rate of contraction the sun would grow cooler, until it could no longer supply the earth with heat enough to support life.

This would come about in the course of a few million years. Eventually the sun would solidify and cease to shine at all.

In contracting to its present size from very much greater dimensions, the sun would have gained enough heat to keep it shining at the present rate for at least 22 million years, according to Helmholtz's calculations. This, at the time, seemed to provide the sun with a past history of adequate duration. But the current conclusion from the study of fossils is that the sun has been warming the earth at about the present rate for hundreds of millions of years. Thus the sun's contraction becomes a minor factor in the maintenance of its radiation.

REFERENCES

For supplementary reading and reference in connection with this and the remaining chapters the following books are suggested. See also the list of general references at the end of Chapter I.

C. G. Abbot, *The Sun* (Appleton, 1929).
C. G. Abbot, *The Earth and the Stars* (Van Nostrand, 1925).
H. F. Newall, *The Spectroscope and its Work* (1910).
G. E. Hale, *The New Heavens* (Scribners, 1922); *The Depths of the Universe* (1924); *Signals from the Stars* (1931).
F. J. M. Stratton, *Astronomical Physics* (Methuen, 1925).
Herbert Dingle, *Modern Astrophysics* (Macmillan, 1924).
J. H. Jeans, *The Universe Around Us* (Macmillan, 1929).
A. S. Eddington, *The Nature of the Physical World* (Macmillan, 1928). " It treats of the philosophical outcome of the great changes of scientific thought which have recently come about."
H. T. Stetson, *Man and the Stars* (McGraw-Hill, 1930).

Authoritative articles by H. N. Russell on astronomical subjects of current interest appear monthly in *Scientific American*.

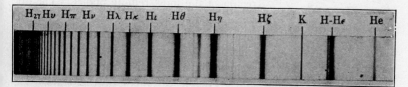

Hydrogen Lines in the Spectrum of ζ Tauri. Ultra-violet portion of the spectrum, showing the Balmer series of hydrogen lines from Hε to the limit of the series, at the left. (From a photograph by R. H. Curtiss, Observatory of the University of Michigan)

CHAPTER VIII

STELLAR MOTIONS AND DISTANCES

DISTANCES OF THE STARS — STELLAR MOTIONS RELATIVE TO THE SUN — THE PECULIAR MOTIONS OF THE STARS — BINARY STARS — ECLIPSING STARS

DISTANCES OF THE STARS

8.1. Stellar Parallax. In consequence of the earth's revolution around the sun, the nearer stars seem to describe little orbits annually with respect to the more distant stars. These apparent orbits

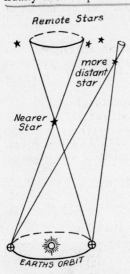

FIG. 8.1. Parallaxes of the Stars. Owing to the earth's revolution the nearer stars describe parallax orbits annually with respect to the remote stars.

are similar in form to the aberration orbits (2.10), varying from circles at the ecliptic poles to straight lines for stars on the ecliptic. They are much smaller, however, even for the nearest stars, and shrink to imperceptible size for the more distant ones.

The heliocentric or annual parallax of a star is the semi-major axis of its parallax orbit. It is the maximum difference between the directions of the star as seen from the earth and sun during the year. We shall refer to it as the *parallax* of the star.

In early times, the stars were generally supposed to be only a little way beyond the region of the most remote planet. The absence of perceptible parallaxes was taken to mean that the earth is stationary. Aristarchus of Samos was one of the very few who seem to have had some appreciation of the much greater distances of the stars. He argued rightly that stellar parallaxes must be very small indeed, and that the failure to observe them did not disprove the earth's revolution. When the Ptolemaic theory of the stationary earth was definitely challenged by Kepler's laws, it became important to ob-

302

serve the parallaxes of the stars, not only to establish the Copernican theory conclusively, but also to demonstrate the vast distances of the stars. It was not until 1838, however, that the many attempts to observe this effect finally met with success; in this year, Bessel in Germany measured the parallax of 61 Cygni, and soon afterward Struve in Russia, and Henderson at the Cape of Good Hope announced the parallaxes of α Lyrae and α Centauri respectively.

8.2. Photographic Determination of Parallax. The early observations of parallax were visual, usually with the meridian circle or with the heliometer, a telescope having its objective cut in two. Photography was tried without much success, until Kapteyn in 1900 demonstrated that photographic parallaxes could be obtained with as much accuracy as the visual ones, and more expeditiously. At this time the parallaxes of scarcely sixty stars had been measured, and not more than half of them could be relied upon within $0''.05$.

Beginning in 1903 with the Yerkes refractor Schlesinger, now director of the Yale Observatory, laid the foundations on which the modern photographic determinations of stellar parallaxes are based. The methods of observation and reduction which he developed gave such greatly increased accuracy that many astronomers were encouraged to enter this important and exacting field. Direct measurements of parallaxes are being carried on at the Allegheny, Dearborn, McCormick, Greenwich, Sproul, Van Vleck, Yerkes, and Mount Wilson Observatories, and at Johannesburg, South Africa, where the Yale Observatory has instituted a parallax campaign in the southern sky. As a consequence of this concerted effort, direct parallaxes of more than two thousand stars are already available.

8.3. Measurements of Parallax. If the earth's orbit is represented by the circumference of a period on this page, the nearest star on this scale is a microscopic speck a hundred feet away. The parallax problem is to measure the change in the star's direction as viewed first from one edge of the dot, and then from the other. This is, of course, the easiest case of all. It is evident that the greatest care must be taken in parallax measurements.

The method is differential. It consists in observing the changing position of the *parallax star* with respect to apparently neighboring *comparison stars,* but which are really so much farther away that they are not greatly affected by the earth's revolution.

The procedure is to obtain sets of plates of the region, when the star that is under investigation is near the extremities of its tiny parallactic orbit, that is to say, at intervals of about six months. Two

Fig. 8.3. Eye End of the 40-inch Refractor of the Yerkes Observatory Arranged for Photography. Instead of the eyepiece the double-slide plate holder is attached; it carries a small eyepiece (at the upper edge) containing cross wires with which the observer guides on a star near the edge of the field, while the exposure is in progress.

sets are not enough, however, for the nearer star has a proper motion (8.7) as well, in a straight line with respect to the distant stars; it therefore advances among them in a series of loops. Five sets or more are needed in order to extricate the parallax effect precisely.

It will be noted that the result obtained is the *relative parallax;* for the comparison stars themselves are shifted slightly in the same directions as the parallax star. The *absolute parallax* is obtained by adding a correction not exceeding a few thousandths of a second of arc, depending on the brightness of the comparison stars, and their position in the sky (8.21). Even after the correction is made, the parallax of a distant star often comes out negative, indicating that the unavoidable errors of observation are larger in this case than the parallax itself, and happen to take this direction, or that the mean distance of the comparison stars is less than that of the parallax star.

8.4. Units of Distance: the Parsec and the Light-Year. When the star's parallax, p, has been measured, its distance is found by the relation (Fig. 8.4):

$$\text{Distance (in astronomical units)} = 206{,}265''/p''.$$

Since one astronomical unit, the earth's mean distance from the sun, equals 149,450,000 km., or 92,870,000 miles (4.25), we have:

$$\text{Distance (in kilometers)} = 206{,}265''/p'' \times 1.495 \times 10^8.$$
$$\text{Distance (in miles)} \quad = 206{,}265''/p'' \times 9.287 \times 10^7.$$

But the distance of a star expressed in miles, or even astronomical units, is an inconveniently large number. It is better to use larger units, either the *parsec,* or the *light-year.*

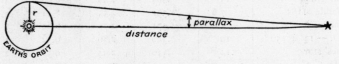

FIG. 8.4. The Heliocentric Parallax of a Star.

The parsec is the distance at which a star would have a parallax of one second of arc. This distance, by the above relations, is 206,-265 astronomical units, or 3.083×10^{13} km., or 1.92×10^{13} miles. The advantage of the parsec is its simple relation to the parallax:

$$\text{Distance (in parsecs)} = 1''/p''.$$

The light-year is the distance traversed by light in one year; it is equal to the velocity of light, 2.998×10^5 km./sec., multiplied by 3.156×10^7, the number of seconds in a year. The light-year is therefore 9.461×10^{12} km., or 5.88×10^{12} miles (nearly six million million miles). One parsec equals 3.258 light-years. Thus the

$$\text{Distance (in light-years)} = 3.258/p''.$$

As an example, consider the brightest star, Sirius, also one of the nearest, whose parallax is $0''.371$. The distance of Sirius in astronomical units is $206,265''/0''.371$, or a little more than half a million astronomical units, which amounts to about 50 million million miles. The distance in parsecs is $1/0.371$, or 2.70 parsecs. The distance in light-years is $3.258/0.371$, or 8.80 light-years.

8.5. The Nearest Stars. There are 14 known stars, counting a double star as one system, within the distance of $3\frac{1}{3}$ parsecs, or eleven light-years from the sun. If the apparent brightness of a star depended simply on its distance from us, the nearest stars would be the brightest ones. Although Sirius, the brightest star of all, is included among the fourteen, the Table shows that more than one half

TABLE 8.I. THE NEAREST STARS

Name	Magnitude (m)	Parallax (p)	Distance		Annual Proper Motion (μ)
			Parsecs	Light-Years	
Proxima Centauri	10.5	$0''.783$	1.28	4.16	$3''.85$
* α Centauri	0.1	.757	1.32	4.30	3 .68
Barnard's star	9.7	.538	1.86	6.06	10 .25
Wolf 359	13	.404	2.48	8.08	4 .84
Lalande 21185	7.6	.392	2.55	8.31	4 .78
* Sirius	− 1.6	.371	2.70	8.80	1 .32
B.D. − 12° 4523	10	.350	2.86	9.32	1 .24
Innes' star	12	.340	2.94	9.58	2 .69
B. D. − 7° 4003	9.2	.331	3.02	9.8	1 .33
Kapteyn's star	9.2	.317	3.16	10.3	8 .76
τ Ceti	3.6	.315	3.17	10.3	1 .92
* Procyon	0.5	.312	3.21	10.4	1 .24
ε Eridani	3.8	.310	3.23	10.5	0 .97
* 61 Cygni	5.0	.300	3.33	10.9	5 .20

* Double stars

of the nearest stars are invisible to the naked eye, since their magnitudes (1.25) are numbers greater than 6; and further discoveries of large parallaxes among the telescopic stars are to be expected. On the other hand, some of the brightest stars have very small parallaxes, as Table 9.I shows. The conclusion is that the stars differ widely in actual brightness.

For a long time α Centauri was supposed to be the nearest star. This distinction is now held by a telescopic star, a little more than two degrees from this bright star, and slightly nearer the sun, which bears the appropriate name " Proxima." The large parallax of this star was announced, in 1915, by Innes at Johannesburg. It is to be noticed that the annual proper motions of the nearest stars exceed their parallax displacements.

8.6. Limitations of the Direct Method. The direct, or *trigonometric* method of determining stellar parallaxes diminishes in accuracy as more distant stars are observed. The probable error of the best parallaxes, in which several independent determinations are averaged, is of the order of $0''.005$. For the very nearest stars the error is only about one per cent of the parallax. The percentage of error increases as the parallax decreases; it is ten per cent for a parallax of $0''.05$. If the parallax is as small as $0''.01 \pm 0''.005$, it follows from the definition of the probable error (2.13) that the chance is one half that the true value lies between $0''.015$ and $0''.005$, and that the distance is between 67 and 200 parsecs. It is equally probable that the true values are outside these limits. Thus the distance is very uncertain. For stars whose distances exceed 50 parsecs (about 160 light-years) the direct method fails; the great majority of the stars are excluded.

Since the success of many investigations of the stars depends on the knowledge of their distances, astronomers have sought for and discovered indirect ways of determining stellar parallaxes. These will be considered in appropriate places as we proceed. Among the indirect means of deriving the distances of the stars are mean parallaxes (8.21), dynamical parallaxes of double stars (8.36), spectroscopic parallaxes (9.27), and variable star parallaxes (9.35).

STELLAR MOTIONS RELATIVE TO THE SUN

8.7. Proper Motions and Radial Velocities. As we have seen, the positions of the stars are continually changing because of the effects, such as precession (2.32), aberration (2.10), and parallax (8.1), which arise from motions of the earth. After allowance has been

made for all such displacements, the motion of any star with respect
to the sun can be studied in two projections: (1) *Proper motion* is the
rate of change in the star's direction, or position on the celestial
sphere. (2) *Radial
velocity* is the speed
with which the star is
approaching or reced-
ing from the sun.

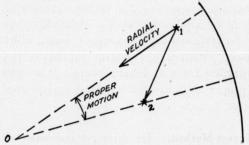

These two, and the
distance of the star,
constitute the principal
data in the studies of
stellar motions.

FIG. 8.7. Proper Motion and Radial Velocity.
As the star moves from *1* to *2*, the radial velocity
is the rate at which its distance changes; the
proper motion is the angular rate of its change
in direction.

8.8. Proper Motions of the Stars.

Halley,
in 1718, was the first to
demonstrate that the stars are not "fixed." He showed that the
stars Sirius, Betelgeuse, Aldebaran, and Arcturus had moved from
the places assigned them by Ptolemy by amounts comparable with
the moon's apparent diameter.

With the accumulation of more accurate catalogues of star positions, separated by considerable intervals of time, the proper motions
of the majority of the naked-eye stars have become known, and of
many telescopic stars as well. The *Preliminary General Catalogue*
by Lewis Boss (1910) contains the proper motions of more than six
thousand stars; it is being extended by Benjamin Boss at Albany to
include all stars brighter than magnitude 7.1, and some fainter stars
as well.

In the determinations of proper motions, the procedure is to
compare the right ascensions and declinations of each star, as
they have been recorded at different times. After the effects of
the earth's motions have been eliminated, and any systematic
errors peculiar to the different catalogues, the proper motion is
obtained.

The value of a star catalogue for use in determinations of proper
motions increases with its age, and depends also, of course, on the
accuracy of its positions. A very ambitious photographic project,
known as the *Astrographic Catalogue*, will, when it is completed,
give the positions of three or four million stars. The work was

planned in 1887, and divided among 18 observatories in different parts of the world. It is now about half done.

8.9. Proper Motions by Photography.   Proper motions can be detected and measured with high accuracy by the direct comparison of two photographs of a region taken several years apart. Indeed, the largest known proper motions have been found in this way. The direct comparison is effective because precession, aberration, and other apparent displacements of the stars, with the exception of parallax, are nearly the same over a small area of the sky.

Two devices have been especially useful for the rapid comparison of photographs: the stereo comparator and the blink microscope. The *stereo comparator* consists of a frame for holding two plates side by side, and a movable viewing apparatus with two eyepieces, one for each eye, so arranged that all parts of the two plates can be examined. When the plates are adjusted so that the majority of the images combine stereoscopically, an image that is present on only one of the plates stands out from the rest.

The original purpose of the stereo comparator was the detection of stars that vary in brightness, and of false images which might be mistaken for celestial objects. It proved to be useful also for detecting proper motions of stars.

The *blink microscope* has a single eyepiece, and the principle employed is the persistence of vision rather than stereoscopy. By mechanical means the two plates are alternately hidden automatically at the rate of 3 or 4 blinks a second. If any of the stars are displaced on one plate relative to the other, the result is a jumping effect which at once attracts the observer's attention to these stars.

8.10. Amounts of Proper Motions.   The largest known proper motion was discovered by Barnard, in 1916, in the case of a tenth magnitude star. The position of this star with respect to its neighbors is changing at the rate of 10''.25 a year, so that in 180 years it moves through an angle equal to the moon's apparent diameter. Kapteyn's star is next in order, having an annual proper motion of 8''.76. If all the stars were moving as fast as this, and at random, the forms of the constellations would be altered noticeably in the course of a lifetime. But these are exceptions. About fifty stars have proper motions exceeding 2'' a year, and not more than seven or eight hundred are known to exceed half a second a year. The probable errors of the best determinations are less than 0''.005 a year.

It is to be noticed that the proper motion is angular. A star having a large proper motion may be actually in rapid motion, or it may be nearer than most stars, or both, which is true of Barnard's star. The speed in miles, or kilometers, a second becomes known only when the distance is known. It is also to be noticed that the proper

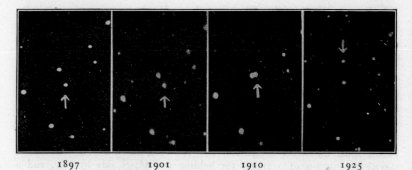

1897   1901   1910   1925

Fig. 8.10. Proper Motion of Proxima Centauri. Proxima is marked by an arrow on each photograph. Its motion is shown relative to apparently neighboring but much more distant stars. (From photographs at Harvard College Observatory)

motion relates only to that part of the motion that is transverse to the line of sight; it gives no evidence concerning the motion of the star toward or away from us.

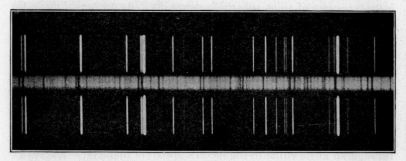

Fig. 8.11. Doppler Shift in the Spectrum of Procyon. The dark lines in the star's spectrum are displaced to the violet (left) with respect to corresponding bright lines in the comparison spectrum of iron and vanadium, above and below. At the time the spectrogram was taken, this star and the earth were approaching at the rate of 30 km./sec. (From a photograph by V. M. Slipher, Lowell Observatory)

8.11. Radial Velocities. The motion of a star in the line of sight, or its radial velocity, is observed with the spectroscope. By the Doppler principle (7.7), if the star is approaching, the lines in its spectrum are displaced to the violet; if it is receding, the lines are displaced toward the red end of the spectrum. For a line of a given wave-length the relation is:

$$\text{Radial velocity} = \frac{\text{change of wave-length}}{\text{wave-length}} \times \text{velocity of light.}$$

If, for example, a line whose wave-length is 4000 angstroms is displaced one angstrom toward the violet, the star is approaching us with the velocity of 1/4000 of 186,284 miles a second, or about 46.5 miles a second.

Among the neighboring stars, radial velocities up to 30 km./sec. (about 20 miles a second) are usual. Those exceeding 100 km./sec. are rare. The globular clusters have velocities around 300 km./sec. The spectra of systems beyond the Milky Way exhibit displacements, chiefly to the red, corresponding to higher radial velocities.

FIG. 8.11A. Micrometer for Measuring Stellar Spectra. The slide to which the spectrogram is fastened is moved horizontally by a fine screw with a large divided head, at the right. The field of the microscope contains a vertical "wire" with which the spectrum lines are bisected. (By courtesy of the Observatory of the University of Michigan)

In order to determine the radial velocity of a star, the spectrum of the star is photographed in conjunction with the comparison spectrum of a laboratory source, often luminous iron or titanium vapor near the slit of the spectrograph. The spectrogram is then observed under the microscope, and the displacements of the star lines are measured micrometrically with respect to the comparison lines which are not displaced. Since the shifts of the lines on the plates are minute, great care must be exercised in securing and measuring the spectrograms.

In this way the radial velocities of more than 5000 stars have already been determined, notably at the Lick, Mount Wilson, Yerkes, Bonn, Victoria, and Cape of Good Hope Observatories. The application of the method is limited to stars whose light is bright enough to be photographed after it is spread out into a spectrum. All the naked-eye stars are easily observed with present spectrographs and telescopes. The spectra of fainter stars can be obtained by lengthening the exposures and by using prisms of smaller dispersion, with loss of accuracy in the measurements corresponding to the diminished scale of the spectra. Moore's *General Catalogue of the Radial Velocities of Stars, Nebulae, and Clusters* gives the radial velocities of 6739 stars which were available at the beginning of 1932.

8.12. Annual Variation in the Radial Velocities of the Stars.

As a consequence of the earth's revolution around the sun, the observed radial velocities of the stars, with the exception of stars near the ecliptic poles, exhibit annual fluctuations. When the earth is approaching a star, the lines in the star's spectrum are displaced to the violet; and when it is receding, the lines are displaced toward the red end of the spectrum. In practice the observed radial velocity of the star is *reduced to the sun,* by correcting for this effect, and for the slight daily fluctuation due to the earth's rotation as well.

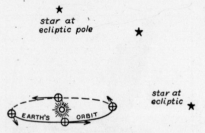

FIG. 8.12. Annual Variation in the Radial Velocity of a Star. Owing to the earth's revolution the lines in the spectrum of a star oscillate in a period of a year. The effect is greatest for stars at the ecliptic, and diminishes to zero at the ecliptic poles.

This annually periodic effect on the radial velocities of the stars constitutes a proof of the earth's revolution around the sun (2.8). It also affords a rather precise means of determining the earth's distance from the sun. As the simplest case, consider a star on the ecliptic, and at rest with respect to the sun. Once during the year the earth will be moving directly toward the star; six months later it will be moving directly away. On either occasion the observed radial velocity of the star is numerically equal to the speed of the earth's revolution, in miles or kilometers a second. The earth's distance from the sun can then be calculated by the procedure already described (2.10). If the star is not on the ecliptic, nor at rest relative to the sun, appropriate corrections must be made.

From the radial velocities of bright stars observed at the Cape of Good Hope, Jones derives (1927) for the solar parallax the value $8''.803 \pm 0''.004$, in agreement with the value adopted in this book.

8.13. Space Velocity.

When the annual proper motion, μ, of a star and its parallax, p, are known, the tangential velocity, T, can be calculated. The *tangential velocity* is the star's velocity with respect to the sun, at right angles to the line of sight. It can be easily shown that the relation is:

$$\text{Tangential velocity} = 4.74\mu/p \text{ km./sec.}$$

When the star's radial velocity is known as well, in kilometers a second, the *space velocity, v,* which is the star's true velocity with respect to the sun, is simply the diagonal of the right triangle (Fig. 8.13), given by the relation: $v^2 = V^2 + T^2$; and the direction of the motion is denoted by the angle, θ, that it makes with the line of sight.

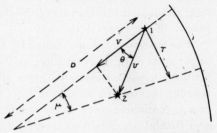

The space velocities of the stars are generally of the same order as the velocities of the planets in their revolutions around the sun. Among the brightest stars, Arcturus has the highest space velocity,

FIG. 8.13. Relation between Space Velocity (v), Tangential Velocity (T), Radial Velocity (V), Proper Motion (μ), and Distance (D) of a Star.

which is directed nearly at right angles to the line of sight ($\theta = 87° 50'$). The tangential velocity is 135 km./sec. The radial velocity is -5 km./sec. The space velocity of Arcturus is therefore the square root of $135^2 + 5^2$, or 135.1 km./sec.

8.14. Moving Clusters; Ursa Major and Scorpio Groups. A number of stars moving in the same direction constitute a *moving cluster.*

Such stars have nearly the same proper motions and radial velocities, and are often alike in color. They are not, as a rule, unusually close together, being separated by ordinary interstellar distances, so that they are likely to encompass at any time stars not belonging to the cluster; the non-cluster, or *field stars,* can

FIG. 8.14. Common Motion of Stars in Ursa Major. The stars of the Great Dipper, with two exceptions, have a common motion. The lengths of the arrows show the amount of the proper motion in 50,000 years.

be identified by their discordant motions. There are many known examples of moving clusters, differing greatly in the area of the sky that they cover. The widest dispersion is found in the *Ursa Major group.*

It has long been known that the stars of the Great Dipper, with the exceptions of the end stars, α and η Ursae Majoris, are moving together. Hertzsprung showed that other stars, widely scattered over the sky, belong to this group; among them are Sirius, α Coronae, and β Aurigae. The thirty or more stars in the group form a large flat disk as much as 50 parsecs across. The sun's presence within this disk, although it is not a part of the cluster, accounts for the wide dispersion of the group in the sky.

The Scorpio group, discovered by Kapteyn, comprises many of the bright stars in this constellation, and spreads into Centaurus and the Southern Cross. Despite its great apparent size, this group is very remote; it does not include α Centauri and Proxima. *The Orion group,* containing most of the bright stars of this constellation, except Betelgeuse, is moving directly away from us. Like the Scorpio group it is remote, and made up, for the most part, of blue (class B) stars.

8.15. The Taurus Cluster. Just as the paths of meteors in a shower seem to diverge from the radiant point, so the parallel paths of the

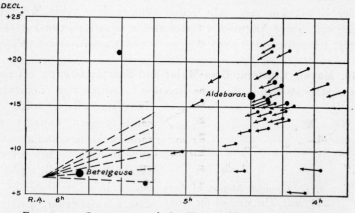

FIG. 8.15. Convergence of the Taurus Cluster. The V-shaped Hyades and neighboring stars in Taurus are converging toward a point in the sky east of Betelgeuse, in Orion. Aldebaran, the brightest of the Hyades stars, is not a member of the moving cluster. The lengths of the arrows represent the proper motions of the stars of the moving cluster in an interval of 50,000 years. (Adapted from a diagram by Lewis Boss)

stars in a moving cluster must be directed away from a point on the celestial sphere, if the cluster is approaching us, and toward a point, if it is receding. This effect of perspective is especially noticeable in the proper motions of the members of the Taurus cluster, as Boss was the first to point out.

The Taurus cluster comprises stars of the Hyades (Aldebaran is not included) and the surrounding region. About 80 stars form a

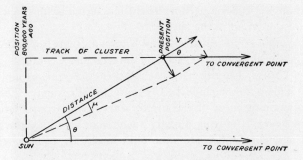

FIG. 8.15A. Track of the Taurus Cluster. The present distance of the cluster can be found when the proper motion, μ, radial velocity, V, and angular distance, θ, from the convergent point, have been determined.

spheroidal cluster, most of them within five parsecs of the center whose present distance from the sun is about 40 parsecs (130 light-years). The *convergent point* of their paths lies a little way east of Betelgeuse in Orion. In 65 million years the cluster will have shrunk in the distance into a telescopic cluster.

When the convergent point of a moving cluster is known, and the proper motion, μ, and radial velocity, V, of one of the stars have been measured, the distance of the cluster can be calculated. The space velocity is $v = V/\cos\theta$, where θ (Fig. 8.15A) is the star's angular distance from the convergent point. The tangential velocity is $T = v\sin\theta$. The parallax can now be found from the relation (8.13): $p = 4.74\mu/T$.

As an example, the observed values for δ Tauri in the Taurus cluster are: $\mu = 0''.115$, $V = +38.6$ km./sec., and $\theta = 29°.1$. The space velocity is found to be 44.0 km./sec., and the parallax is $0''.025$. The distance of the cluster is therefore 40 parsecs.

The space velocity and θ define the track of the star with respect to the sun. By means of relations that can be easily worked out from the figure, Boss showed that the Taurus cluster was nearest the sun 800,000 years ago, at the distance of 20 parsecs.

8.16. Significance of Moving Clusters. This preference of the stars to move in companies is a pronounced characteristic. It is manifested in the very numerous double and multiple stars, in moving clusters, and probably in the great local system of stars, and in similar star-clouds.

Moving clusters differ greatly in the number of stars they contain; but in general their areas in the sky must diminish as the dis-

FIG. 8.16.   The Pleiades.   (From a photograph by E. E. Barnard at the Lick Observatory)

tances become greater. Thus we pass from neighboring, widely dispersed clusters, such as the Ursa Major group, to the more distant and restricted aggregations, of which the Pleiades and Coma Berenices clusters are examples; and finally to the telescopic open clusters (11.18). Shapley's studies of the Harvard photographs indicate that the stars generally, at least as far as the fifteenth magnitude, have a more clustered distribution than would have been expected on the basis of chance alone.

There is no evidence that the sun belongs to a moving cluster. If there were stars moving with the sun, they would have large parallaxes, but their proper motions and radial velocities would be zero. Such stars have not been found.

The common motion of the stars in a moving cluster suggests common origin. The maintenance of this parallelism, despite the fact that the cluster moves through regions occupied by other stars, shows that the movement of a star is not often greatly altered by collisions with, or even by the attractions of its neighbors. Nevertheless, these factors must eventually disintegrate the cluster, in Jeans' opinion; and on this basis he estimates the life of a moving cluster as of the order of 10^{12} years.

THE PECULIAR MOTIONS OF THE STARS

8.17. The Solar Motion. For the description of motions within the solar system, the transfer of the standard of rest from the earth to the sun, inaugurated by Copernicus, was a noteworthy advance. Since the sun has by far the greatest mass in this system, its position represents very nearly the average of the system. Thus far we have referred the motions of the stars also to the sun. But this is not the best procedure for most purposes; for in the system of the stars the sun is only one of the multitude. It is necessary, therefore, to correct the space velocities of the stars for the effect of the sun's motion with respect to them. This consideration is the principal reason for determining the solar motion.

The *solar apex* is the point on the celestial sphere toward which the solar motion (motion of the solar system as a whole) is directed. It is located in right ascension $18^h 3^m$, declination $+28°$, in the constellation Hercules, not far from the fourth magnitude star o Herculis. The *antapex* is the opposite point in the sky.

In consequence of the motion of the solar system, the stars seem to us to be moving in the opposite direction, from the apex toward the antapex. This effect can be observed both in the proper motions and in the radial velocities. Thus two ways are open of determining the direction of the solar motion.

8.18. Solar Motion from Proper Motions. The stars in the part of the sky toward which the solar motion is directed seem to be opening out from the apex; those in the region behind us seem to close in toward the antapex, while the stars that are in between appear to be passing by. These secular *parallactic motions* are nothing more than the apparent backward shifting of the celestial scenery, as we move along with the sun. But each star has, in addition, its own *peculiar* *motion* with respect to the others; its observed proper motion is the resultant of the two motions. If, however, the peculiar motions are at random, the average proper motion will be away from the apex.

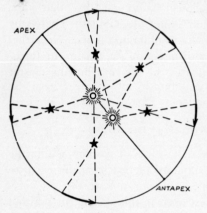

Sir William Herschel, in 1783, was the first to determine the position of the solar apex by means of proper motions. Although there were then available the proper motions of only 13 stars, he located the apex near λ Herculis, within 10° of the place now assigned to it. This result was confirmed, in 1837, by Argelander, who could employ the proper motions of many more stars. As the number of proper motions increased, the position of the apex was often calculated, always in about the same region.

FIG. 8.18. Parallactic Motions of the Stars. The stars are apparently drifting away from the point on the celestial sphere toward which the sun is moving. For an individual star, this effect is confused with the peculiar motion of the star.

The solar apex, as determined by Wilson in 1926 from 2748 revised proper motions of the Boss catalogue, is in right ascension 270°.8, declination +27°.0.

8.19. Solar Motion from Radial Velocities.

An independent means of locating the solar apex is found in the radial velocities of the stars. This method is probably the more reliable. It consists in photographing the spectra of many stars in all parts of the sky, and in measuring the Doppler effect in each one. In the spectra of the stars near the apex the lines have the greatest displacement to the violet, on the average; near the antapex there is the greatest displacement toward the red. These two points are located finally by a mathematical treatment of all the observed radial velocities. The maximum radial velocity thus calculated, of approach or recession, is the velocity of the solar motion, which can not be readily determined from the proper motions.

The most extensive investigation of the radial velocities of the stars for this purpose was conducted by the Lick Observatory over a period of more than thirty years at Mount Hamilton, and at a southern station in Chile. The final results of this program are given by Campbell and Moore (1928) as follows:

Solar apex from radial velocities $\begin{cases} \text{right ascension} = 270°.6 \\ \text{declination} = +29°.2 \end{cases}$

Velocity of solar motion = 19.65 km./sec. (12.3 miles a second).

It will be noticed that this position differs by two degrees from the one determined from the proper motions. Part of this difference may well arise from the use of different stars in the two determinations; for the sun's motion that is derived in each case is relative to the average of the group of stars employed in the determination. At the same time, the fair agreement of the two results makes it reasonable to adopt a compromise between the two (8.17) as representing the sun's motion with respect to the stars in our part of the stellar system.

The solar motion in one year is about four times the distance from the earth to the sun. The combined effect of the earth's revolution around the sun and the solar motion is evidently a helical course of the earth relative to the stars.

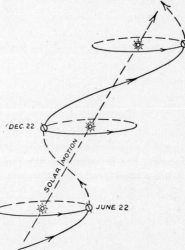

FIG. 8.19. The Earth's Motion in a Helix. The combined effect of the earth's revolution and the solar motion is the helical course of the earth relative to the stars. In one year, the earth moves forward with the sun four times its mean distance from the sun.

8.20. Stellar Distances from the Solar Motion.

As we have already noticed, the determinations of the distances of the stars by the direct parallax method is limited to the nearest stars. For the more distant ones the diameter of the earth's orbit is inadequate as a base line, because of its relative shortness. At first sight it would seem that the solar motion might provide the ideal base line for stellar parallax determinations. In one year it takes us a distance twice as great as the diameter of the earth's orbit. If this longer base line is still too short to produce appreciable parallax displacements of the distant stars, we could wait two years, or perhaps a hundred, until the distances of all the stars would finally become known.

If the stars were really " fixed," so that the annual proper motion of a star would be only its parallactic motion, the distances of individual stars could be measured by means of the solar motion. But since the stars have peculiar motions of their own, it is impossible to say, unless the distance is already known, what part of the star's proper motion is parallactic, and what part is peculiar. Thus the longer base line provided by the solar motion can not be used for determining the distances of individual stars.

8.21. Mean Parallaxes of the Stars. The only use that can be made of the solar motion in determining the distances of the stars is a statistical one. For any group of stars having random peculiar motions, and numerous enough so that these motions are likely to cancel in the mean, the distance can be measured from the drift of the whole aggregation toward the antapex. These are *mean parallaxes*. For stars of different apparent visual magnitudes, Seares derives the following mean parallaxes (the base line is the earth's distance from the sun), on the assumption that the solar motion is the same with respect to both faint and bright stars:

TABLE 8.II. MEAN PARALLAXES OF STARS OF
DIFFERENT MAGNITUDES

Magnitude	Mean Parallax	Magnitude	Mean Parallax
1	0″.060	7	0″.0090
2	0 .044	8	0 .0065
3	0 .032	9	0 .0047
4	0 .023	10	0 .0034
5	0 .017	11	0 .0025
6	0 .012	12	0 .0018

These are average values for the whole sky. They vary somewhat, as determined by different investigators, depending on the particular data and methods employed in deriving them. It must be understood that the mean distance of stars of a given magnitude is considerably greater than the distance derived from the mean parallax for that magnitude, as one can readily see by means of a numerical example.

An important use of a table of mean parallaxes is in correcting relative parallaxes of the stars to absolute parallaxes (8.3). Although they are derived on the assumption of random motion, these corrections are not invalidated by the preferential motions of the stars.

8.22. Preferential Motions of the Stars.

Up to the beginning of the present century, no evidence of systematic motions of the stars had been presented, aside from the community of motion of double stars and clusters of stars. It was generally assumed that the motions of the stars are at random. If this were true, the description of stellar motions in any part of the sky would serve for all other parts; the subject of star motions would then be completed and closed. But the matter is not so simple and uninteresting as this.

In 1904, Kapteyn announced that the peculiar motions of the stars are not at random; they show a marked preference for two directions. This characteristic is well exhibited by a graphical construction (Fig. 8.22), based on a catalogue of proper motions. It consists in counting the number of stars in a limited area of the sky, that are moving in different directions, within five degrees, for example, of north, 10° east of north, 20° east of north, and so on around; and of plotting the numbers on a convenient scale with respect to these directions.

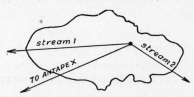

FIG. 8.22. The Two Star Streams. The frequency curve of proper motions in a selected region of the sky shows the effect of the two star streams, and of the solar motion. (From a diagram by Eddington)

If the stars were moving at random, the points so plotted would fall near the circumference of a circle having the origin at its center. Owing to the solar motion, and the consequent apparent drift of the stars toward the antapex, the points might be expected to form an ellipse, supposing that their peculiar motions are at random, whose major axis is directed toward the solar antapex. But the observed frequency curve for a given region exhibits two additional extensions. These preferential motions are parallel in all parts of the sky; for when the effect of the solar motion is allowed for, and when the preferential motions are extended along the celestial sphere from the various regions, they appear to intersect at two opposite points.

8.23. Star Streaming. The two opposite convergent points of the preferential motions are the *vertices*. One is located in right ascension $6^h\ 15^m$, declination $+12°$, between Orion and Gemini; the other is in right ascension $18^h\ 15^m$, declination $-12°$, in the little constellation Scutum, near the northern border of Sagittarius. These vertices are near the central line of the Milky Way. The straight line joining them, which represents the direction of the preferential motion, is therefore almost exactly in the plane of the Milky Way.

Confirmatory evidence is found in the radial velocities of the stars. When these are freed from the effect of the solar motion, it is found that they are greater, on the average, near the vertices.

It is as though two clouds of stars in our neighborhood were passing, and for the present intermingling. This is the *two-stream hypothesis* of Kapteyn. The stream moving toward Orion contains fifty per cent more stars than the other stream, and its speed is twice as great. The relative velocity of the two streams is about 40 km./sec. The two-stream hypothesis is one way of interpreting the observations. The ellipsoidal hypothesis of Schwarzschild is another way, involving only one aggregation of stars. The significance of the star streaming is not completely understood at present. But this stream motion is not far from perpendicular to another stellar drift, with which it is doubtless associated.

8.24. Solar Motion Relative to High Velocity Stars. A remarkable preferential characteristic of stellar motions was made known by Strömberg at Mount Wilson, in 1923, from his analysis of the radial velocities. As we have seen (8.19), the sun is moving relative to the brighter stars at the rate of about 20 km./sec. toward the constellation Hercules. But with reference to stars whose velocities exceed 80 km./sec., the solar motion is much swifter, and is directed toward the southwest corner of the constellation Cepheus. Relative to different classes of high velocity objects, it is greater as the spread of the individual velocities within the class is greater. As an extreme case, the sun's speed with respect to the system of the globular clusters is 286 km./sec.

In the mean, the point in the heavens toward which the sun is speeding, and from which the high velocity stars seem, therefore, to be withdrawing, is in right ascension $20^h\ 40^m$, declination $+57°$, according to Strömberg; it lies in the Milky Way, in galactic longitude

62° (11.4). Wilson and Raymond, at the Dudley Observatory, confirm the position of the point closely from their studies of the proper motions. In his preliminary determination of the solar motion relative to the extra-galactic nebulae, Hubble adopts 280 km./sec. as the velocity, in good accord with that for the globular clusters, although the direction is in less satisfactory agreement.

It is significant that the direction of the solar motion toward Cepheus is nearly in the plane of the Milky Way, and nearly at right angles to the direction of the point in Sagittarius, in galactic longitude 327°, where Shapley's researches have placed the center of the galactic system.

8.25. Evidence of Galactic Rotation.

If our great stellar system is rotating around a massive nucleus, then the stars which are nearer than the sun to the center overtake and pass by it. The stars which are farther away from the center fall steadily behind the sun. Consequently, as viewed from the sun, or the earth, stars whose galactic longitudes (11.4) differ by 45° and 225° from the longitude of the center (toward the left from the direction of the center in Fig. 8.25) are receding with the greatest speed; stars whose longitudes differ by 135° and 315° have the maximum velocity of approach, while those in the direction of the center, and 90°, 180°, and 270° from it are neither approaching nor receding. There are accompanying effects of proper motion also.

A proof of the rotation of the galactic system is there-

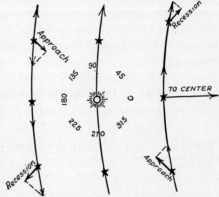

FIG. 8.25. Effect of the Rotation of the Galactic System on the Radial Velocities of the Stars. Stars nearer the center than the sun are revolving faster, and are therefore passing by the sun. Stars farther from the center are revolving slower, and are falling behind the sun. Accordingly, stars whose longitudes differ by 45° and 225° from that of the center are receding from the sun, while stars at 135° and 315° are approaching.

fore to be found in the radial velocities of stars in different galactic longitudes, when these velocities have been freed from other effects, unless, of course, this effect can be attributed equally well to some other cause.

Oort, at Leiden, in 1927, was the first to show that the stars in the sun's neighborhood are moving in accordance with this plan. Plaskett and Pearce, at Victoria, have convincingly confirmed the effect, employing their radial velocities of the hot stars and of the intervening interstellar material (8.41). These results locate the center of the system in the direction previously assigned to it. But the cooler stars indicate a different direction of the " center," as Redman has demonstrated. These stars, the giant red stars in particular, have exhibited pronounced independence in another respect. Dyson at Greenwich, Schilt and Miss Barney at Yale, and others have shown that their proper motions place the ordinary apex of the sun's way north of its accepted position.

The proper motions, in general, give less satisfactory evidence of the galactic rotation effect; indeed, this is not surprising, because the stars whose proper motions are now known are relatively nearby. Schilt, who is responsible for many of the proper motion investigations, concludes that all their differential effects arise from the star streaming.

8.26. Rotation of the Galactic System. The radial velocities of the more distant stars and of the interstellar calcium appear to bear out the assumption that the entire system of the Milky Way is rotating around the center which lies in the direction of Sagittarius. Like the planets in their courses around the sun, the stars farther from the center have smaller linear speeds and longer periods of revolution. This shows that the greater part of the material in the system is near the center. For if the stars were uniformly distributed throughout, all parts of the system would rotate in the same period, as a wheel rotates.

Lindblad, in Sweden (1926), has sought to interpret in terms of the rotation of the galactic system the swift solar motion studied by Strömberg (8.24). Since this motion is directed toward galactic longitude 62°, which is only a little more than 90° removed from the accepted direction of the center of the system, it is reasonable to associate it with the rotation.

According to Lindblad's theory, different classes of objects in our system have different speeds of revolution, and therefore fall into sub-systems having different degrees of flattening. The sun is a member of the most rapidly whirling and flattest of the sub-systems, to which the star-clouds of the Milky Way belong. The globular star-clusters form a more slowly rotating and much less flattened ellipsoid. To us these clusters seem to be moving very fast; but it is our own swift motion that is being observed. The sun is moving around the center of the galactic system at the rate of 286 km./sec., once around in something like 200 million years.

BINARY STARS

8.27. Double Stars, for the most part, appear single to the unaided eye, but are shown by the telescope, or spectroscope, to be two stars close together. Some telescopic double stars are really unrelated, happening to be in nearly the same direction, though one is far behind the other. William Herschel, in 1802, was the first to make clearly

1908   1915   1920

Fig. 8.27. The Binary System Krueger 60. Between 1908 and 1920 the binary star, in the upper left corner, completed about a quarter of a revolution. See Fig. 8.28. (From photographs by E. E. Barnard, Yerkes Observatory)

the distinction between such *optical double stars* and the *binary systems,* which he called "real double stars," that is to say, two stars close together and united by the bond of their mutual gravitation.

Eventually it is possible to decide between the two, for the accidental double will draw apart, because the proper motions of the two stars have different directions. True binary stars move together, and in many instances give evidence of mutual revolution, which is decisive.

Binary stars which can be separated with the telescope alone are known as *visual binaries,* as distinguished from stars that are single with the telescope, and whose binary character is revealed by the periodic oscillations of the lines in their spectra; these are *spectroscopic binaries.* A number of them are so close together, or have orbits so nearly edgewise to the earth that the two members of the revolving system undergo mutual eclipses, and are therefore *eclipsing binaries* as well.

8.28. Discovery of Visual Double Stars.

The fact that certain stars are resolved by the telescope into pairs was recorded casually by earlier astronomers, beginning with Riccioli's discovery, in 1650, of the duplicity of ζ Ursae Majoris (Mizar). In this way a few of the more conspicuous pairs, including Castor, α Centauri, and γ Virginis, became known.

The importance of the study of double stars was recognized by William Herschel who began, in 1779, a systematic search for them;

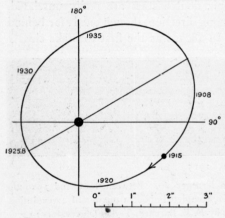

FIG. 8.28. Orbit of Krueger 60. The relative apparent orbit of the fainter star, as determined by Aitken.

he found many new pairs and observed that some of them are mutually revolving. Then followed a succession of distinguished double star observers, among them Wilhelm Struve, Dembowski, and Burnham.

Aitken and Hussey at the Lick Observatory, in 1899, began the systematic examination of every star brighter than the ninth magnitude and north of declination −23° (the limiting southern declination is −14° for the stars that appear in the unfavorable winter months). This program, which was completed in 1915, resulted in the discovery of 4300 new double stars. The program is being rapidly extended in the southern sky by the Lamont-Hussey Observatory of the University of Michigan, at Bloemfontein, South Africa, and by the Union Observatory at Johannesburg.

Astronomers have not been in complete agreement as to the limiting distance, beyond which a pair shall not be called a double star. In modern practice, many very wide doubles in the early catalogues are rejected. Aitken chose (1911) limiting separations progressing from 1″ for very faint stars to 40″ for stars brighter than the second magnitude. Of the stars brighter than the ninth magnitude, at which the limiting separation is set at 5″, he finds that *one star in eighteen* is a visual double; and among the stars brighter than magnitude 6.5 one star in nine is double. Burnham's *General Catalogue* of 13,665 double stars within 121° of the north celestial pole, published in 1906, gives the record of every star in this region that had ever been listed as double. Innes' *Reference Catalogue* of doubles in the southern sky is a useful supplement.

Aitken's *New General Catalogue* (1932) lists 17,180 visual double stars within 120° of the pole. As the limiting separation, ρ'', for any magnitude, m, he adopts the formula: $\log \rho'' = 2.5 - 0.2m$.

8.29. The Micrometer. The position micrometer is attached at the eye end of the telescope, when double stars are to be measured. A rectangular box in front of the eyepiece contains the *fixed thread*, usu-

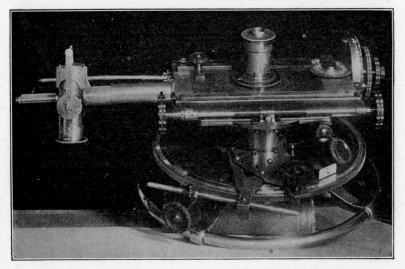

FIG. 8.29. Micrometer of the 36-inch Refractor, Lick Observatory.

ally a spider line, while a sliding frame in the box carries the moving or *micrometer thread;* the latter is moved by a fine screw having a large head outside the box, which is graduated usually into a hundred parts. When the divided head is turned, the micrometer thread moves at right angles to its direction, and is used to measure the angular distances apart of objects in the field of view of the telescope. The micrometer box is attached to a circular plate which can be rotated within a circle graduated in degrees. In this way the threads can be turned into various positions, in order to measure directions in the field.

The *zero point* is the reading of the graduated circle when the threads have the north to south direction. It is determined by taking the reading of the circle when an equatorial star remains bisected by a thread, as it drifts across the field, with the telescope disconnected from the driving clock, and by adding 90° to this reading.

8.30. Measurements of Visual Binaries.

The position of the *companion*, or fainter star of the pair, with respect to the *primary star* is obtained by two measurements: (1) The *position angle* is the angle at the primary star between the direction of the companion and that of the north celestial pole; it is measured counterclockwise, from the north through the east, around the circle. (2) The *distance* is the angular separation of the two stars.

The position angle is determined by rotating the micrometer until the fixed thread bisects the two stars; it is the reading of the thread in this position *minus* the reading on the north point. After this reading is taken, the micrometer is rotated 90° and the two stars are bisected by the two threads. When this is accomplished, the reading of the graduated head of the micrometer screw, reduced to angular value, gives the desired distance. This is the procedure of most double star observers.

With the 36-inch refractor of the Lick Observatory under the best conditions, the least separation of two stars that can be measured is about 0".1. If the separation is much less, the two stars can not be distinguished visually, except by the use of the interferometer (10.6). Photography can be used to advantage for wider pairs; in general for large telescopes 2″ is about the minimum separation for which the position angle and distance can be measured successfully on the plates, though pairs having somewhat smaller separations can be detected. Fox at the Dearborn Observatory has discovered visual binaries photographically where the separation is not much more than one second of arc.

8.31. The Apparent Ellipse and the True Orbit.

The *true orbit* of the companion with respect to the primary star may lie in any plane at all. It follows from the law of gravitation that the true orbit must be a conic, presumably an ellipse, with the primary star at one focus, and that the companion must move in accordance with the law of equal areas (4.10). The observed orbit is the projection of the true orbit on the plane at right angles to the line of sight; it must also be an ellipse (the *apparent ellipse*), and the law of areas must be fulfilled by the apparent motion of the companion relative to the primary, but the primary will not be at the focus of the apparent ellipse.

When the measurements of a double star have been continued through a considerable part of a complete revolution, the observed positions of the companion are plotted on a convenient scale. After a number of trials the apparent ellipse is drawn, that seems best to fit the plotted points; and from it the true orbit can be calculated by any one of several available methods.

The *elements of the double-star orbit* resemble the elements of a planetary orbit (4.28). They are: P, the period of revolution, in mean solar years; a, the semi-major axis of the orbit, or the mean distance between the stars, expressed in seconds of arc; T, the time of *periastron* passage, that is, when the stars are nearest; e, the eccentricity; i, the inclination of the orbit plane to the plane through the primary star at right angles to the line of sight; Ω, the position angle of the node that lies between $0°$ and $180°$; ω, the angle, in the plane of the true orbit, between that node and the periastron point, in the direction of motion.

When the parallax of the binary is known, the linear scale of the orbit can be found by the relation: a (in astronomical units) $= a$ (in seconds of arc)/parallax. Everything is then known about the orbit, except which end is tipped toward us; it remains to be decided by the spectroscope whether the companion is approaching or receding from us when it passes the node.

8.32. Visual Binaries of Special Interest.

More than 1500 visual binaries show some evidence of orbital motion; less than ten per cent of these have progressed far enough in their revolutions since their discovery to exhibit definitely the characteristics of their orbits. The elements of 117 orbits are listed by van den Bos (1926). Some characteristics of a few visual binaries of special interest are given in Table 8.III. The orbits of the first, fourth, and fifth are by Aitken; the second was calculated by Russell, the third by Jones, the sixth by Finsen, and the seventh by Rabe. It will be noticed that the orbits are more eccentric than the planetary orbits, and that the combined masses are of the order of twice the sun's mass.

δ Equulei. This system is notable for its unusually short period of 5.7 years. The semi-major axis of the orbit is 4.5 astronomical units, which is less than that of Jupiter. A system having a still shorter period has been found by Dawson.

42 Comae. The true orbit is almost exactly edgewise to the sun, so that the apparent ellipse is practically a straight line.

Krueger 60. This system (Fig. 8.27) has the smallest mass of any known visual binary. The separate stars are about a fifth as massive as the sun; at the sun's distance these stars would appear only 1/600 and 1/3000 as bright as the sun.

α *Centauri.* The nearest binary system, and one of the first to be discovered. The semi-major axis of the orbit, 23 astronomical units, slightly exceeds that of Uranus. Proxima Centauri, although it is more than 2° removed from α Centauri in the sky, seems to belong to the system; it is 230 times as far from the two bright stars as Neptune is from the sun, and its period of revolution around them must be a third of a million years, if indeed it is revolving.

TABLE 8.III. RELATIVE ORBITS OF VISUAL BINARIES

Name	Magnitudes		Period P	Semi-Major Axis a	Eccentricity e	Parallax p	Combined Mass $m_1 + m_2$
			years				
δ Equulei	5.3	5.4	5.7	0″.27	0.39	0″.060	2.8
42 Comae	5.2	5.2	25.9	0 .66	0.52	0 .063	1.8
Procyon	0.5	13.5	40.2	4 .26	0.31	0 .312	1.6
Krueger 60	9.3	10.8	44.3	2 .46	0.38	0 .257	0.4
Sirius	− 1.6	8.4	50.0	7 .57	0.59	0 .371	3.4
α Centauri	0.3	1.7	80.1	17 .67	0.52	0 .758	2.0
Castor	2.0	2.8	306.3	6 .06	0.56	0 .076	5.5

Castor. The first system whose orbital motion was definitely established, by Herschel. The period exceeds 300 years, and the mean separation of the pair is three times Neptune's distance from the sun.

8.33. Companions of Sirius and Procyon. The discoveries of the faint companions of the Dog Stars, Sirius and Procyon, constitute the first chapter in the " astronomy of the invisible," namely, the detection of invisible celestial bodies by their gravitational effects on the motions of visible bodies. The discovery of Neptune (5.40) is a famous example, and spectroscopic binary stars contribute many others. As in the case of Neptune, the companions of Sirius and Procyon were subsequently viewed with the telescope.

As early as 1834, Bessel noticed that Sirius did not exhibit the uniform proper motion that characterizes the stars in general, but was pursuing a wavy course. Six years later he suspected a smaller oscillation in the case of Procyon; presently he reached the definite conclusion that both stars are attended by invisible companions, and that their revolutions cause the waves in the observed motions. Later, Auwers calculated the orbits for both systems. The companion of Sirius was first observed, in 1862, by Alvan G. Clark, celebrated telescope maker, who was testing the 18-inch refractor now at

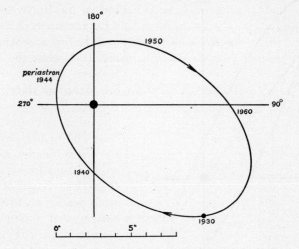

FIG. 8.33. Orbit of Sirius. The relative apparent orbit of the companion, as determined by Aitken. The stars will be closest in 1944. Between 1941 and 1945 the companion will be invisible with present telescopes.

the Dearborn Observatory. The companion of Procyon proved to be more elusive; it was finally observed in 1896, by Schaeberle at the Lick Observatory. These two faint companions are remarkable for their enormous density (10.13).

Interference of a different sort called attention to the faint companion of the variable star Mira (9.38). In the spectrum of this star, as it sank to minimum light, Joy was surprised to find bright lines which were quite inappropriate; he rightly concluded that these lines belong to the spectrum of a faint companion, which becomes visible only when the light of the primary is greatly reduced. Aitken examined Mira near the time of its minimum in 1923, and observed a star of the tenth magnitude nearly a second of arc away.

8.34. Multiple Stars. Many visual binaries are attended by one or more distant companions whose periods of revolution, if they are really revolving, must be reckoned in tens and even hundreds of thousands of years. The visual binary α Centauri with its remote companion Proxima has already been mentioned. Castor, which is a moderately separated double with the telescope, has a faint attendant 73″ distant; and all three are spectroscopic binaries, so that there are six stars in all. The well-known quadruple system of ε Lyrae consists of two pairs, each having a separation of about 3″, while the distance between the pairs is 207″; one of the four stars is a spectroscopic binary.

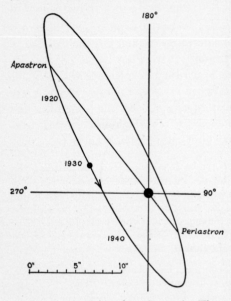

FIG. 8.34. Orbit of α Centauri. The relative apparent orbit, as determined by Finsen.

Aitken estimates that at least four or five per cent of the visual binaries are really triple or quadruple systems. O e p i k ' s recent statistical study leads him to the conclusion that multiple stars seem to be the rule, and that single stars, and even double stars alone, are exceptional. The criterion by which two apparently close stars are known as a binary system, if their revolution has not been observed, is that they have the same proper motion. This is also characteristic of a moving cluster (8.14). It is an interesting question whether a line can be drawn anywhere between the revolving binary and the moving cluster.

8.35. Masses of Binary Systems. The mass of a celestial body is determined by its gravitational effect on the motion of another body a known distance away. This method fails for single stars, which are too far removed from other stars to noticeably alter their paths; it fails also for the majority of visual binary stars which have thus far given no indication of mutual revolution. But for binary systems whose relative orbits have been calculated, and whose distances from us are known, the masses can be evaluated. This is one of the most important products of the study of visual binaries.

By the restatement of Kepler's harmonic law (4.18), the sum of the masses, m_1 and m_2, of the two components, in terms of the sun's mass (the earth's mass is neglected), is given by the relation:

$$m_1 + m_2 = a^3/P^2 p^3,$$

where a is the semi-major axis of the relative orbit in seconds of arc, P is the period of revolution in sidereal years, and p is the parallax.

As the number of well-determined masses has increased, two significant facts have emerged, to which further reference will be made in Chapter X: (1) The stars differ in mass less than in almost every other characteristic, the majority having not less than one fifth, and not more than ten times the sun's mass. (2) There is a marked relation between the mass of a star and its absolute brightness (10.30).

The sum of the masses is all that can be determined from the relative orbit. When, however, the revolutions of the two stars have been observed with reference to neighboring stars, or with the spectroscope, the individual masses become known; for the ratio of the masses is inversely as the ratio of the distances of the two stars from the common focus of their orbits (4.17). The separate masses are known in more than thirty visual binary systems. When the two stars have nearly the same brightness, the masses are nearly the same; when the difference in brightness is considerable, the brighter star is the more massive, with a single doubtful exception.

8.36. Dynamical Parallaxes. The discovery that the masses of the stars are not widely divergent, and that the sun's mass is fairly representative of all, makes it possible to determine the parallaxes of the binary systems, whose orbits are known, by inverting the relation of the previous Section and putting $m_1 + m_2 = 2$; so that $p^3 = a^3/2P^2$. Parallaxes of systems so determined are *dynamical parallaxes*.

Since the luminosity (9.23) of a star bears a definite relation to the mass, increasing as the mass increases, more dependable dynamical parallaxes are derived by choosing a value of the combined mass of each system equal to the average of the observed masses of stars of the same luminosities. Russell has shown that parallaxes derived in this way for binary systems having well-determined orbits have probable errors of only four per cent, and are accordingly more reliable than stellar parallaxes found in any other way, except the trigonometric parallaxes of the very nearest stars.

Russell, Hertzsprung, Jackson, and others have invented useful statistical methods for determining the dynamical parallaxes of slower-moving binary systems in which the portions of the orbits traversed since the discoveries are too small to define the orbits satisfactorily.   About ten times as many systems are available under this heading, although the accuracy of the individual determinations is considerably less.

8.37. Spectroscopic Binaries.

Binary systems in which the separation is less than a tenth of a second of arc are not resolvable with present telescopes.   For the discovery and study of such systems the spectroscope has been used, although some of the wider pairs are

FIG. 8.37.   Spectrum of Mizar (ζ Ursae Majoris).   The first known spectroscopic binary.   The lines of the two components are separated in the upper spectrogram, and superposed in the lower one.   (From photographs at the Yerkes Observatory)

now being observed with the interferometer.   In accordance with the Doppler principle (7.7), as a star revolves, alternately approaching and receding from us, the lines in its spectrum oscillate in the period of the revolution.

All systems of revolving stars exhibit this effect, of course, unless their orbits are exactly perpendicular to the line of sight, so that they neither approach nor recede; but they are classed as spectroscopic binaries, in general, only when the separations are too small to be observed with the telescope.   With the aid of the spectroscope, investigations of binary stars can be extended to the smallest possible separations; in fact, for small separations the revolutions are likely to be more rapid, and the oscillations therefore more conspicuous.

When one star of the pair is much brighter than the other, its spectrum is the only one that can be seen.   When the brighter star is not more than two or three times brighter, the spectrum of the companion is visible also, and the oscillations of the two sets of lines are opposite in phase; for as one star approaches, the other recedes.

When the two spectra are nearly alike, the lines at times appear double, and at other times single (Fig. 8.37).

8.38. Discoveries of Spectroscopic Binaries. The appearance of double lines in the spectrum of Mizar on the objective prism photographs at Harvard, announced by Pickering in 1889, first called attention to spectroscopic binary stars. Many have been discovered in

FIG. 8.38. Single-Prism Spectrograph. Attached to the 37-inch reflecting telescope of the Observatory, University of Michigan. The case is removed to show the prism.

the meantime. Among the brighter stars, and especially among the blue stars, the percentage of these binaries is large. The *Third Catalogue of Spectroscopic Binaries* of the Lick Observatory (1924) lists about one thousand, and gives elements of the orbits of 224 systems that were available at that time. Despite the late beginning, the number of known spectroscopic binaries approaches the number of visual binaries whose orbital motions have been recognized, while the number of orbits is about twice as great. The explanation of this progress is found in the far shorter periods. The periods of spectroscopic binaries range from a few hours to a few years, and are less than ten days for more than half.

A few spectrograms of a star taken at suitable intervals with the slit spectrograph are usually enough to show whether the radial velocity is constant, allowing for the earth's motions, or variable. In the latter case the star is a spectroscopic binary, unless it is of a special type. Some examples of spectroscopic binaries among the bright stars are: Capella, Spica, Castor, β Aurigae, and Algol.

Some, and perhaps all, variable stars (excluding eclipsing binaries) and a few other stars are believed to be single stars, although their radial velocities are variable. The oscillations of the lines in their spectra have been ascribed to some sort of pulsations going on within these stars (9.34).

8.39. The Velocity Curve. The measurement of each spectrogram of a binary gives the displacement of the lines to the violet or red, and from the Doppler formula the velocity of approach or recession of the

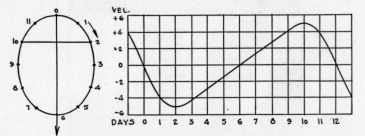

FIG. 8.39. Relation Between the Orbit and Velocity Curve of a Spectroscopic Binary. The period of this binary is 12 days. Only one spectrum appears. From 0 to 6 days the star is approaching the earth; from 6 to 12 days it is receding. The greatest radial velocities occur when the star is crossing the "plane of the sky," at 2 and 10 days.

star, say in kilometers a second, at the time the photograph was taken. If the period of the revolution is known, this time *minus* the preceding zero time, of some particular stage of the oscillation, gives the *phase*. When the observed radial velocities are plotted against the corresponding phases, the smooth curve drawn to represent the course of the plotted points as well as possible is the *velocity curve;* it shows how the radial velocity of the star varies throughout a complete revolution. Whenever the lines of both spectra are clearly visible, a double velocity curve is obtained.

If the orbit of the binary is circular, the velocity curve is a sine curve; if the orbit is elliptical, the shape of the curve depends on the eccentricity and orientation of the orbit. From the velocity curve the elements of the spectroscopic orbit can be calculated by one of several methods that are available.

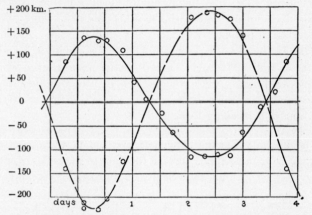

FIG. 8.39A. Velocity Curves of α Virginis. Both spectra are visible, but the lines of the fainter, less massive star are clearly seen only near the times of maximum separation of the lines. (From a diagram in the *Publications of the Allegheny Observatory*)

8.40. Orbits of Spectroscopic Binaries.

The elements of the spectroscopic orbit, which are calculated from the velocity curve, do not completely describe the true orbit of the binary system, unless the plane of this orbit is already known. The eccentricity of the orbit, and the position and time of periastron passage are uniquely determined; but the angle, i, at which the orbit is inclined to the plane of the sky is unknown from the spectroscopic observations. The size of the true orbit, as denoted by the linear value, a, of the semi-major axis, emerges from the calculations entangled in the quantity $a \sin i$. Whether this orbit is relatively small and nearly edgewise ($i = 90°$), or relatively large with a smaller inclination is not revealed by the spectroscopic observations alone. It is only when the binary can be observed visually, or when the two stars of the pair undergo mutual eclipses (8.48) that these two elements can be known separately.

In the majority of spectroscopic binary systems (more than 80 per cent), in which the spectrum of only the brighter star is visible, not much can be learned about the mass of an individual system. When both spectra are seen, the ratio of the masses, m_2/m_1, is easy enough to evaluate; for it is inversely as the ratio of the ranges in velocity of the two stars. The fainter star has the smaller mass, which is the rule for visual binaries also. In this case Kepler's harmonic law permits the calculation of the sum of the masses multiplied by the cube of the sine of the inclination, $(m_1 + m_2) \sin^3 i$. Thus only the lower limiting values of the masses are available, unless the inclination of the orbit can be found independently, as in the case of eclipsing binary stars.

8.41. Interstellar Lines in Stellar Spectra.

Since Hartmann's announcement, in 1904, that the K line of calcium in the spectrum of δ Orionis does not oscillate with the other lines, the same thing has been observed in the spectra of many other binary stars; and in these spectra the H line of calcium and the D line of sodium are found to be stationary as well. Moreover, these lines are narrow, even when the other lines are broad. The problem, at first, was to understand how any lines can be stationary in the spectrum of a star that is alternately approaching and receding from us.

J. S. Plaskett, at the Dominion Astrophysical Observatory in Victoria, has given the problem a wider significance by his discovery that these narrow calcium lines are present in the spectra of practically all of the hottest stars, whether they are binaries or not, and that they do not, in general, show the same Doppler displacements as the other lines.

Eddington, in 1926, presented theoretical evidence for the conclusion that the lines in question are caused by absorption of the starlight in a tenuous medium which is uniformly distributed through interstellar space, except where it condenses into diffuse nebulae. Under the conditions in which this matter exists, its absorption lines of ionized calcium and of sodium are the only ones likely to be seen.

In accordance with this conclusion, the interstellar H and K lines and the D lines of sodium should be present in the spectra of all the stars. The H and K lines are not observed ordinarily in the spectra of stars redder than class B5 (9.5), because they are then hidden by stronger calcium lines originating in the atmospheres of the stars themselves. Struve, at the Yerkes Observatory, observed the interstellar lines of calcium and sodium in the spectrum of the eclipsing binary U Ophiuchi (class B8), on occasions when the oscillating double lines of the binary itself were widely separated. The D lines are being studied by Merrill at Mount Wilson.

If the interstellar matter is uniformly distributed, the intensities of its lines should increase steadily with increasing distance of the stars in whose spectra they appear. Struve has shown that the interstellar lines are, in fact, progressively stronger for groups of stars of increasing faintness and therefore, in the mean, of increasing distance. More recently, Plaskett and Pearce have demonstrated that the radial velocities of groups of stars at different distances from the earth exhibit the effect of galactic rotation (8.25) twice as much as do the velocities of their interstellar lines.

There is, therefore, considerable evidence of the approximately uniform distribution of the interstellar matter. It seems to justify the belief that the strength of the interstellar lines in the spectrum of a star may well provide a reliable criterion of the star's distance.

8.42. Characteristics of Binary Systems. We notice especially:

(1) *The great number of binary systems.* It is believed that at least a quarter of all the stars are double, or multiple. The observed percentage of spectroscopic binaries is greater than that of visual binaries; but in a given volume of space visual binaries are probably by far the more frequent.

(2) *The considerable percentage of these systems containing more than two stars.* Russell's estimate is about ten per cent; some estimates are lower, and others are higher. All authorities agree that the number of multiple stars is large.

(3) *Binaries of longer period have, on the average, more eccentric orbits.* Of all the correlations established by the many statistical investigations, excluding those that relate to the characteristics of stars generally, this relation is the most impressive. There is a fairly steady increase in the average eccentricity, from the nearly circular orbits of binaries having periods up to a few days, to eccentricities averaging around 0.7 for pairs whose periods of revolution are expressed in thousands of years.

(4) *The great variety in the separations of binary stars.* There is a gradation from rapidly revolving pairs practically in contact to pairs so widely separated that the only observed connection between them is their common motion through space.

(5) *The relations between difference in brightness and difference in color* of the two components, established by Leonard's spectroscopic studies of visual binaries. Pairs having equal brightness are likely to have the same color. In pairs that differ considerably in brightness, the fainter star is usually the bluer, if the brighter star is a giant; and the redder, if the brighter star belongs to the main sequence (9.24).

8.43. The Fission Theory. The theory of the formation of double stars by the division, or *fission,* of single stars accounts satisfactorily for binary systems of small separation. As a star having low density and slow rotation shrinks under the action of gravity, it must rotate faster, and accordingly become more and more flattened at the poles. When a certain degree of flattening is reached, it is shown by the mathematical theory based on a conventional model, that the star's equator begins to draw out into an elliptical form. With continued shrinkage and still faster rotation, the elongation of the equator proceeds to the stage where the star becomes unstable. Beyond this stage the theory can not determine what will happen; but Darwin, Jeans, and others have supposed that the star may assume the form of a flattened dumb-bell or pear, and finally divide. The stars of the newly formed pair rotate and mutually revolve in the same period; but their further shrinkage puts the two motions out of step, preparing the way for effects of tidal friction, as outlined by Darwin in the case of the earth-moon system (4.40).

After fission, the separation of the stars increases, the period of revolution increases correspondingly, and the eccentricity of the orbit can increase, but to a limited extent. As Moulton and Russell have clearly demonstrated, the increasing separation of a pair of stars having comparable masses must come to an end; and even when the masses are considerably different, it is improbable that a spectroscopic binary can attain the wide separation and highly eccentric orbit of the visual binary from tidal action alone.

ECLIPSING BINARIES

8.44. Algol. A spectroscopic binary star is also an *eclipsing binary* when its orbit is so nearly edgewise to the earth that the revolving stars undergo mutual eclipses. Since only a single star can be seen with the telescope, what is observed is that the light of the star becomes fainter at regular intervals. Eclipsing binaries are variable stars, only because the planes of their orbits happen to pass nearly through the earth's position. For an observer in another part of the stellar system their light would be constant, and another group of spectroscopic binaries, to us invariable in light, would exhibit eclipse phenomena. Physical variable stars are described in Chapter IX.

Algol (β Persei), the "Demon Star," is the best-known of eclipsing binaries; it was also the first of this type to become known. As early as 1670, its light was observed to be fainter at times than usual; but it was not until 1782 that Goodricke discovered that the light diminishes periodically, and proposed the theory that the bright star is partially eclipsed at intervals of about 2 days and 21 hours by a

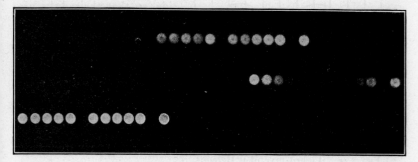

FIG. 8.44. Extra-Focal Images of RZ Cassiopeiae During the Principal Eclipse. The plate was moved horizontally between the exposures which were all of about the same duration. The changing brightness of the variable star is shown by the changing density of its images. (From a photograph by J. A. Parkhurst, Yerkes Observatory)

faint companion which revolves around it. The eclipse theory was definitely established in 1889, by Vogel at Potsdam, whose spectroscopic study of Algol showed that it is a binary, and that the radial velocity of the bright star changes from recession to approach at the time of the primary minimum, as the theory requires.

Extensive investigations of eclipsing binaries, whose known number now exceeds three hundred, have given much information as to their characteristics. The periods vary from 6 hours to 262 days, with one notable exception where it is 27 years.

8.45. The Light Variations. The light curve of an eclipsing binary shows how the light or magnitude of the system varies through a complete revolution. The eclipses occur at intervals of exactly one half of the period, if the orbit is circular; the curve at these times drops to a minimum and rises again. The deeper minimum, when the star having the greater surface brightness is being eclipsed, is the *primary minimum,* and the shallower one is the *secondary minimum.*

Even when the eclipses are not in progress, the light continues to vary appreciably in many of the systems, chiefly because these stars are not spheres, but ellipsoids. They are elongated, each of the pair in the direction of the other, by tidal action, a relation which is maintained by the equality of their periods of rotation and revolution. When the eclipses are occurring, the two stars are seen end on; half-way between the eclipses they are presented broad-side, so that their disks are larger, and the stars are therefore brighter. Thus the light of the system is variable outside the eclipses, rising to maxima midway between them. This effect of the ellipticity of the disks is very conspicuous in the light curves of β Lyrae, and of systems such as W Ursae Majoris, in which the two stars are almost in contact.

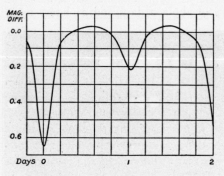

FIG. 8.45. Light Curve of u Herculis. (Determined at the Lick Observatory from photo-electric observations)

In addition, the hemispheres of the two stars that are turned inward are brighter than those turned outward. The difference is greater for the two hemi-spheres of the less luminous star, and on this account the light curve is higher near the secondary minimum. In the more widely separated eclipsing bina-ries, both ellipticity and radia-tion effects are so minute that the light curve outside the eclipses is very nearly a hori-zontal line.

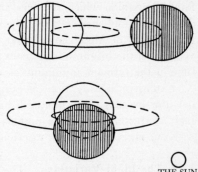

THE SUN

8.46. Light Variations During Eclipses.

The eclipses of binary stars, like eclipses of the sun, may be total, annular, or partial (3.47). In the total eclipse the light curve at the minimum is horizontal; and the duration of this phase is longest, as compared with the whole eclipse, when the orbit is edgewise, and when the two stars differ greatly in size. That the light does not vanish during total-

FIG. 8.46. Eclipsing Binary u Her-culis at Greatest Elongation and Pri-mary Minimum. The eclipses are par-tial. The stars are markedly elongated, one toward the other, by the tidal effect. They are flattened at the poles by their rotations. The hemispheres turned in-ward are somewhat the brighter. The size of the sun on this scale is shown.

ity (the greatest decrease is four magnitudes) shows that the larger star is not dark, although it is usually the fainter of the two, in some cases contributing as little as one per cent to the total light of the system. At the opposite conjunction, when the smaller star is in front, the eclipse is annular. When the eclipse is partial, or total or annular only for an instant, the curve drops to the lowest point, and at once rises again.

In general, the depths and shapes of the light curve during the eclipses depend on the relative size and brightness of the two stars, and on the inclination of the orbit. In some systems the secondary minimum is scarcely discernible; in others it is nearly equal in depth to the primary. The fraction of the period in which the eclipses are occurring depends on the ratio between the sum of the radii of the stars and the radius of the orbit; if the fraction is very large, the stars are revolving almost in contact.

8.47. Bright Eclipsing Binaries. The variability in the light of six eclipsing binaries, including Algol, can be easily observed with the naked eye. The names of these stars, the intervals between the times of primary minimum, and the magnitudes at maximum and minimum light are as follows:

Star	Magnitude		Period		
	Max.	Min.			
β Persei	2.3	3.5	2^d	20^h	49^m
λ Tauri	3.8	4.2	3	22	52
V Puppis	4.1	4.9	1	10	55
δ Librae	5.1	6.3	2	7	51
u Herculis	4.8	5.3	2	1	14
β Lyrae	3.5	4.1	12	21	48

If any one of the stars in the list is compared frequently with a neighboring star, it will eventually be found to be fainter than usual. The times of subsequent minima can then be predicted. There are several other eclipsing binaries that are barely visible to the naked eye. The majority are telescopic objects.

The bright stars δ Orionis, β Aurigae, and α Coronae Borealis are eclipsing binaries, but the eclipses are so slight that the diminution in the light can be observed only with photometers of high precision. By means of the photo-electric cell Stebbins discovered these and a number of other eclipsing binaries of very small range in brightness.

The light of ε Aurigae diminishes nearly a full magnitude once in 27 *years;* the eclipse lasts about two years, with a fairly constant phase at minimum light for nearly a year. The most recent minimum occurred in 1929. Ludendorff at Potsdam finds that the radial velocities conform to the eclipse theory; but there are irregularities in both the light and the velocities which have led him to suppose that the eclipse is caused by a revolving swarm of meteors. Photo-electric studies by Huffer during the recent eclipse confirm the irregular fluctuations in the light.

8.48. The Photometric Orbit. For any model of an eclipsing binary system, in which the inclination of the orbit is specified, it is possible to predict the form of the light curve. Conversely, when the light

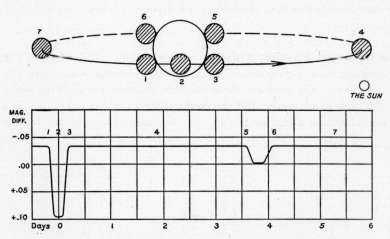

FIG. 8.48. Apparent Relative Orbit and Light Curve of the Eclipsing Binary 1 H. Cassiopeiae. The principal eclipse, of the bright star by its faint and smaller companion, is annular. The secondary eclipse, when the companion is behind the bright star, is total. Tidal and reflection effects are inconspicuous, because of the wider separation of the stars. (Curve and orbit determined by Joel Stebbins from his observations with the photo-electric photometer at the University of Illinois)

curve is determined by photometric observations, it is possible to calculate the elements of the orbit, and the dimensions of the two stars in terms of the radius of the orbit. Russell and Shapley have developed the theory, and have published tables which greatly facilitate the calculations.

One of the elements so determined is the inclination, i, of the orbit. If the spectroscopic orbit is known, we can now return to it and supply the value of i in the expression $a \sin i$ (8.40), thus determining the radius of the orbit in kilometers, or miles, and also the masses of the stars, if the two spectra have been observed. Going back to the photometric orbit, in which the dimensions were derived in terms of the radius of the orbit, we have finally the absolute dimensions of the orbit, and of the stars themselves. Thus the combination of the photometric and spectroscopic orbits permits the evaluation of the sizes and masses, and therefore the densities of the stars — data of the greatest value in studies of the constitution of the stars. At the end of 1927, the photometric orbits of about 120 eclipsing binaries had been determined, and for one third of these systems the spectroscopic orbits were known, of which one half included the orbit of the companion also.

8.49. Dimensions of Eclipsing Stars. In the study of eclipsing systems we have an example of the power of astronomical research. The greatest telescope shows any one of these systems only as a point of light fluctuating periodically in brightness. Yet the observations of this light with the photometer and spectroscope, and the judicious use of analysis lead to fairly complete specifications of the remote binary system.

TABLE 8.IV.   DIMENSIONS OF ECLIPSING BINARIES
(BRIGHTER STAR)

Name	Spec-trum	Period	Radius		Mass	Density
			$a = 1$	$\odot = 1$	$\odot = 1$	$\odot = 1$
		days				
HD 1337	O8	3.52	0.59	23.8	36.3	0.003
V Puppis	B1	1.45	0.42	7.5	19.2	0.04
u Herculis	B3	2.05	0.32	4.6	7.3	0.09
β Persei	B8	2.87	0.21	3.1	4.6	0.16
β Aurigae	A0	3.96	0.16	2.8	2.5	0.11
U Pegasi	F3	0.38	0.40	0.6	0.2	0.88
W Ursae Majoris	G0	0.33	0.32	0.7	0.7	1.9
Castor C	M1	0.81	0.20	0.8	0.6	1.4

The dimensions of the brighter stars of a few eclipsing binaries, in Table 8.IV, are selected from a more complete table by McLaughlin. The stars are listed in order of advancing spectral class

(9.5), or of increasing redness. In most eclipsing systems the stars are blue (classes B and A), but yellow and even red stars are found also, such as the distant red companion, C, of Castor, which has proved to be an eclipsing system. The decreasing radius and mass, and the increasing density with increasing redness of these stars are significant relations which will be considered in Chapter X.

In the fourth column of the Table it is to be noticed that the radius of the brighter star of each pair is a large fraction of the distance, a, between the centers of the two stars. In most eclipsing systems the surfaces of the stars are not far apart; in systems such as β Lyrae and u Herculis, and especially in the group to which W Ursae Majoris belongs, the stars must be almost, if not actually, in contact.

8.50. Rotations of the Stars. The spectroscopic method of studying the sun's rotation, by comparing the Doppler shifts of the lines at opposite edges of the disk, is not applicable ordinarily to the stars which show no disks. It can, however, be applied to some eclipsing binary stars. Preceding the middle of the eclipse of a bright star by a much fainter one, the light comes mostly from the limb of the bright star that is rotating away from us; afterwards, the light comes from the approaching limb. Thus during the beginning of the eclipse the lines of the star's spectrum are displaced farther toward the red, and during the ending they are displaced farther toward the violet end of spectrum than can be ascribed to the revolution of the star.

Since Schlesinger, in 1909, first called attention to the rotation effect in the spectra of eclipsing binaries, it has been observed by others. Rossiter and McLaughlin at the University of Michigan have investigated respectively the rotations of β Lyrae and Algol in this way. Algol rotates at the equator at the rate of 60 km./sec., or thirty times as fast as the sun. Joy, at Mount Wilson, finds that the brighter star of the eclipsing binary U Sagittae rotates at this rate also.

Struve and Elvey at the Yerkes Observatory have determined the rotations of single stars from the contours of the lines in their spectra. The effect of the rotation is to widen the lines, unless the axis of the star is directed toward us. The blue stars which they have studied have equatorial velocities up to 250 km./sec; and the suggestion is made that the most swiftly spinning ones may not be far from the stage where instability sets in. These studies may have a bearing on the fission theory (8.43).

For the blue stars, exceedingly rapid rotation is observed in single stars about as frequently as in members of binary systems. Among the cooler stars, however, rapid rotation occurs only in the close binary systems.

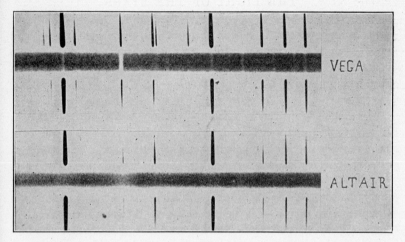

FIG. 8.50. Spectra of Vega and Altair. The widening of the lines in the spectrum of Altair is ascribed to the rapid rotation of this star. (From photographs by Otto Struve, Yerkes Observatory)

REFERENCES

W. W. Campbell, *Stellar Motions* (Yale University Press, 1913).

A. S. Eddington, *Stellar Movements* (Macmillan, 1914).

R. G. Aitken, *The Binary Stars* (McMurtrie, 1918).

Frank Schlesinger, *Catalogue of Bright Stars*, containing all important data known in June, 1930, relating to all stars brighter than 6.5 visual magnitude, and to some fainter ones (Yale Observatory).

CHAPTER IX

THE LIGHT OF THE STARS

In this Chapter we are concerned with the *quality* of starlight, as it is revealed by the spectroscope, and with the *quantity* of the light as it reaches us, from which the quantity that leaves the star can often be determined. A considerable number of the stars vary, periodically or irregularly, in the output of energy. This account of the radiations of the stars leads naturally to the consideration, in Chapter X, of the physical characteristics of the stars themselves.

STELLAR SPECTRA

9.1. Early Studies of Stellar Spectra. Fraunhofer, about 1824, was the first to observe the spectra of the stars. He found that they are *dark-line spectra, like that of the sun,* and that the yellow stars give a pattern of lines resembling the solar spectrum, while the spectra of the blue stars exhibit a simpler pattern. Soon after the fundamental work of Kirchhoff and Bunsen, who identified the spectra of many of the chemical elements, in the laboratory and in the sun, Huggins in England and Secchi at Rome, about 1864, were founders of modern stellar spectroscopy. The former studied intensively the spectra of a few stars, in which he recognized lines of familiar terrestrial elements; the latter examined the spectra of nearly four thousand stars, and found that they could be grouped into four types.

Secchi's classification was the standard for many years. Type I included the blue stars whose spectra are crossed by a few prominent lines, as Fraunhofer had discovered. Type II contained the yellow stars, whose spectra show many fine lines. The red stars were grouped in types III and IV, whose spectra exhibit bands as well

348

as lines; these bands fade out toward the red end of the spectrum in the former type, and toward the violet end in the latter type.

Visual methods were gradually superseded by photographic methods. Huggins, Vogel, Draper, and E. C. Pickering were among the pioneers in the new enterprise. Pickering, in 1891, called attention to the need of an additional compartment in the Secchi classification to include the bright-line nebulae, and a very small percentage of the stars whose spectra exhibit bright lines.

9.2. Stellar Spectrographs.

The term "*spectrograph*" is often used to denote a spectroscope with which spectra are photographed; the photograph is the *spectrogram*.

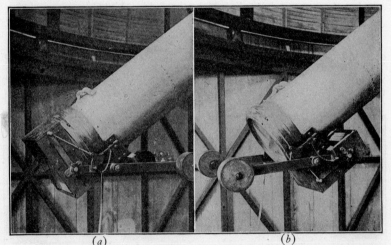

(*a*)   (*b*)

FIG. 9.2. Objective Prism Attached to the 11-inch Telescope, Harvard College Observatory. (*a*) The prism in its case in position before the objective. (*b*) The prism swung out of the way when the telescope is employed for other purposes.

The *slit spectrograph* is a complete spectroscope, usually containing one or more prisms, which is attached at the eye end of the telescope, with the slit at the focus of the telescope objective (Fig. 8.38). By means of reflecting prisms over parts of the slit, it is possible to introduce the light of a laboratory source on either side of the beam of starlight, and thus to photograph comparison lines adjacent to the star's spectrum. The slit spectrograph is wasteful of the starlight, and in addition the spectrum of only one star can be photographed at a time.

For the classification of stellar spectra the objective prism spectrograph (Fig. 9.2) has important advantages. This is the type used by Fraunhofer, and in recent years by the Harvard observers especially. It consists of a large prism, usually of small angle, placed in front of the objective of a photographic telescope; it is thus a spectroscope without a slit or collimator. In this arrangement it is possible to photograph the spectra of many stars on the same plate, but without comparison spectra. In order to give the spectra width enough to bring out the lines clearly, it is the custom to place the prism so that the spectra extend north and south on the plate; the breadth in the east and west directions can be obtained by setting the driving clock to run a little fast or slow, causing the star to drift slightly in the field, while the plate is being exposed.

9.3. The Henry Draper Catalogue.

Pickering, in 1885, inaugurated the photographic study of stellar spectra with the objective prism, a great work which has been carried on ever since at Harvard and its

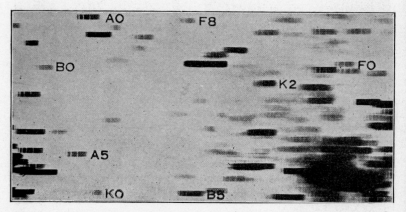

FIG. 9.3. Objective-Prism Spectra of Stars. (From a portion of a photograph at the Harvard College Observatory)

stations in the southern hemisphere. Many thousands of plates have been secured of all regions of the heavens, and the spectra of more than a quarter of a million stars have been studied, under the immediate direction of Miss Cannon. *The Henry Draper Catalogue*, in nine volumes completed in 1924, gives the approximate positions, magnitudes, and spectral classes of 225,300 stars; this catalogue is a memorial to the astronomer who was the first in America to study stellar spectra. Extensions are being published, particularly to the fainter stars in the Milky Way.

9.4. The Draper Classification. One of the outstanding results of the program just described was the discovery that the great majority of stellar spectra fall into a single continuous sequence. This regular gradation of the spectra, in order of increasing redness of the stars, is the basis of the *Draper Classification,* for which Miss Cannon is chiefly responsible. Various stages in the sequence are denoted by the six *principal classes* B, A, F, G, K, M, which are subdivided on the decimal system. Thus a star of class G5 is about halfway between G0 and K0; B2 is nearer to B0 than to A0. Fully 99 per cent of the stars are included in this sequence.

Four other principal classes complete the Draper Classification of ordinary stellar spectra. Class O precedes B at the blue end of the sequence, while classes R and N form one side branch of red stars, and class S another one. In addition, the bright-line spectra of galactic nebulae (11.29) are placed in class P, and those of temporary stars (9.47) in class Q. These twelve letters have survived from an earlier Harvard classification, in which the lettering was in order from A to Q.

The Draper Classification is based on the study of relatively low dispersion spectra, in the violet and blue regions, between 3900 and 5000 angstroms. It is, in general, satisfactory for high dispersion slit spectra also. To meet the requirements of special investigations, the International Astronomical Union recommends certain slight modifications, for example, the prefixing of the letter " g " or " d " to denote that the star is a giant or a dwarf (9.25), and the adding of " e " when the spectrum of the star contains bright lines; thus γ Cassiopeiae is class B0e. The classification of spectra at Mount Wilson is based on different criteria, so that the class to which a star is assigned is likely to differ from that of the Draper Catalogue; but the scale is that of the Draper Classification.

9.5. The Sequence of Stellar Spectra. Each class is characterized by the relative prominence of the dark lines, or bands, of certain chemical elements, or compounds. The hydrogen lines of the Balmer series (page 301) are especially useful in the classification, because they occur throughout the sequence.

Class B. *Helium* lines attain their greatest intensity in class B2, and then fade out, until at B9 they have almost disappeared. Hydro-

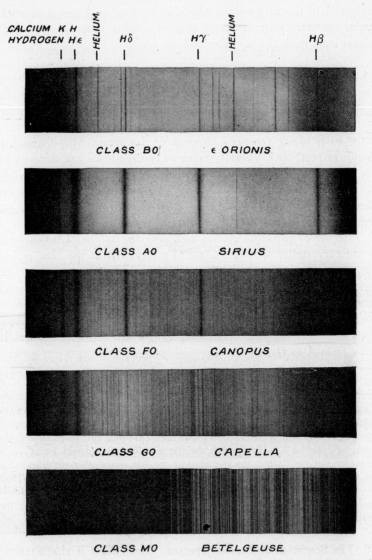

FIG. 9.5. Representative Stellar Spectra. Typical spectra of the principal classes, with the exception of class K which is intermediate between G and M. (From photographs at Harvard College Observatory)

gen lines are increasingly prominent through the subdivisions. Examples are β, γ, and ϵ Orionis.

Class A. *Hydrogen lines* are of maximum intensity at about class Ao. Lines of the metals are developing. Examples are Sirius, Vega, and Castor. Stars of classes B and A are blue.

Class F. Hydrogen lines are diminishing, while lines of the metals increase in intensity, notably the Fraunhofer *H and K lines of calcium.* Canopus and Procyon are examples.

Class G. *Lines of the metals* in great numbers are prominent. These stars are yellow. The sun and Capella are examples.

Class K. Lines of the metals now surpass the hydrogen lines in strength. The H and K lines of calcium reach their greatest intensity in this class. Near the end of the class, bands begin to appear. These stars are orange. Examples are Arcturus and Aldebaran.

Class M. *Bands* of the titanium oxide spectrum are present, in addition to the lines. The violet end of the spectrum is much weakened. The stars in this class are red. Betelgeuse and Antares are examples.

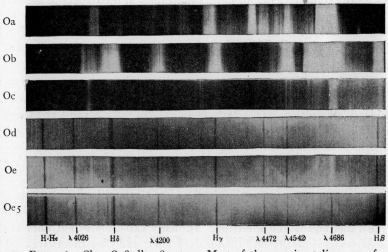

FIG. 9.6. Class O Stellar Spectra. Most of the prominent lines are of hydrogen and helium. Classes Oa, Ob, and Oc are the Wolf-Rayet stars. Spectrum Od is that of λ Cephei; Oe5 is the spectrum of λ Orionis. (From photographs by W. C. Rufus, Observatory of the University of Michigan)

9.6. Class O Stars. The stars of class O, whose provisional subdivisions are Oa, Ob, — — Oe, are placed at the head of the spectral sequence, preceding class B. They are blue stars, having high temperatures and large masses. Miss Payne lists 205 in the Milky Way system; of these 39 are the nuclei of planetary nebulae (11.33). They appear in exterior systems also.

Only one fourth of these stars have purely dark-line spectra; and for these H. H. Plaskett has suggested the decimal subdivision Oo to O9, in order, chiefly, of increasing strength of the helium lines. The remainder have bright lines as well in their spectra, of helium and other elements, and in some cases bright lines exclusively, though always with the continuous spectrum as the background. The *Wolf-Rayet stars* are distinguished from the other Class O stars by the great width of the bright lines in their spectra, notably the helium line at $\lambda 4686$, and the carbon line at $\lambda 4650$, which are often called "bands," although they have not the structure of the true bands in spectra. The brightest Wolf-Rayet star is the second magnitude star γ Velorum.

9.7. Bright Lines in Stellar Spectra.

Less than half of one per cent of all the stars have one or more bright lines in their spectra, according to Merrill; and the great majority of these cases are either the hottest stars, of classes O and B, or the coolest stars, of classes M, S, and N. Bright lines are prominent in the spectra of temporary stars.

The stars of class B whose spectra show bright lines as well as dark ones (designated as classes Boe, B1e, etc.) have received considerable attention, particularly in recent years by Merrill at Mount Wilson, and by Curtiss at Michigan. Examples are Alcyone, the brightest of the Pleiades, and γ Cassiopeiae. Curtiss (1925) gives the number of known examples as 230, of which more than half are of classes Boe to B3e.

The most conspicuous bright lines are those of hydrogen. Often only Hα is bright, and in general the bright lines fade out toward the violet end of the spectrum. In many cases the bright lines are superposed centrally on broader dark lines, and they themselves are divided by narrow dark lines. These bright lines vary in intensity, and some of them are known to have entirely disappeared.

9.8. Branching at the Ends of the Sequence.

For stellar spectra from A to K a single sequence suffices for practically all the stars. Near the two ends the matter is not so simple. As the top of the sequence is approached, bright lines in the spectra are increasingly frequent. Throughout class B the classification proceeds on the basis of the dark lines, the presence of bright lines being denoted by adding the letter " e " to the class designation. But in the class O stars, where bright lines and " bands " predominate, a definite forking of the sequence seems to be indicated.

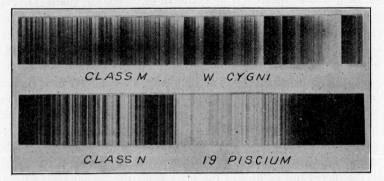

FIG. 9.8.   Spectra of Red Stars.   Portions in the blue region. These spectra are characterized by dark bands as well as lines. (From photographs by R. H. Curtiss and W. C. Rufus, University of Michigan)

At the lower end, among the reddest and coolest stars, the sequence separates into three branches. The spectra of the majority of the known red stars form the continuous gradation represented by the classes K and M; in these spectra bands of titanium oxide and aluminium oxide begin to show at about K5, and steadily strengthen through the subdivisions of class M. The M stars, formerly grouped provisionally, like the O stars, are now arranged on the decimal plan in order of increasing intensity of the titanium oxide bands.

The second branch, formed by the classes K, R, and N, separates from the first at about K2; these spectra are characterized by the presence of carbon bands, and the absence of titanium bands. Pickering, in 1908, introduced class R, which was later, notably by the investigations of Rufus, recognized as the connecting link in this side branch.

The third branch contains class S, in which Merrill (1927) lists 31 stars. These spectra are characterized by bands of zirconium oxide, and sometimes titanium oxide bands as well. The reddest stars of all three branches are frequently variable in light; excluding these, the brightest star of class N is 19 Piscium, whose visual magnitude is 5.3, while the brightest of classes R and S are invisible to the naked eye.

9.9. Significance of the Spectral Sequence. As the Harvard astronomers have pointed out, the arrangement of stellar spectra in the Draper Classification is independent of theoretical considerations relative to the physical conditions of the stars. The classification is based solely on the observed gradations in the patterns of lines. The account of the physical significance of the sequence, in Chapter X, may be briefly anticipated here.

It is remarkable that the vast number of stars whose spectra have been examined can be arranged in a single continuous sequence, with the exception of the statistically negligible classes which branch off from the main line. This linear arrangement means that *variety in the spectral patterns is caused chiefly by the variation of a single physical condition, namely, temperature.* Indeed, this is indicated by the increasing redness of the stars along the sequence. Density of the star, as we shall see, is an important contributing factor.

The rise and fall in the intensities of series of lines of the different chemical elements, as we proceed along the sequence, must not be taken as an indication of the relative abundance of these elements in the different classes; for the strength of the lines in the spectrum of any element varies with the temperature to which it is subjected.

MAGNITUDES OF THE STARS

9.10. Scale of Magnitudes. The grading of the naked-eye stars by Hipparchus into six magnitudes (1.25) was intended primarily to assist in identifying them. There is no evidence that his choice of six groups, rather than some other number, was governed by any definite idea of numerical relations between the groups. For many centuries afterward, the magnitudes of the stars were accepted as Hipparchus and Ptolemy had assigned them. It was not until the comparatively recent times of the Herschels that stellar magnitudes began to enter as important factors into astronomical investigations, for example, in statistical studies of the organization of the stellar system.

About 1830, John Herschel reached the conclusion that a geometrical progression in the apparent brightness of the stars is associated with the arithmetical progression of their magnitudes. The problem was then to ascertain the constant ratio of brightness corresponding to a difference of one magnitude, which would best represent the magnitudes already assigned to the naked-eye stars. Pogson at Radcliffe, in 1856, proposed the adoption of the ratio whose logarithm is 0.4, a convenient value differing only a little from the average ratio derived from his own observations and those of other astronomers. He adjusted the zero of this fixed scale so as to secure as good agreement as possible with the early catalogues at the sixth magnitude. The scale has now been generally accepted.

Pogson's rule is a special case of a general psycho-physical relation established, in 1834, by the physiologist Weber, and given a more precise phrasing by Fechner, in 1859. By Fechner's law, $S = c \log R$, where S is the intensity of a sensation, R is the stimulus producing it, and c is a constant factor of proportionality. Pogson had evaluated the constant in the corresponding relation: $m - n = c \log (l_n/l_m)$, where l_m and l_n are the apparent brightnesses of two stars whose magnitudes are m and n respectively. The constant is 2.5, or 1/0.4, or $1/\log (2.512+)$. If the difference, $m - n$, is one magnitude, $l_n/l_m = 2.512+$.

The logarithm of a number, to the base 10, is the power to which 10 must be raised in order to obtain the number. Thus the logarithm of 100 is 2; the logarithm of 2.512 is 0.4.

9.11. The Light Ratio is the ratio of brightness between two stars which differ by exactly one magnitude; it is the number whose logarithm is 0.4, which is approximately 2.512. For any difference of magnitudes, $m - n$, the ratio of brightness is 2.512 raised to the $(m - n)$th power.

Magnitude difference	Ratio of brightness
1.0 magnitude	2.512
2.0 magnitudes	6.30
3.0 magnitudes	15.84
4.0 magnitudes	39.8
5.0 magnitudes	100.0

On this scale a star of the first magnitude ($1^m.0$) is exactly 100 times as bright as a star of magnitude 6.0, a relation first established approximately by the observations of John Herschel.

In general, the difference, $m - n$, between the magnitudes of two stars, or other sources of light, can be derived from the ratio of their apparent brightness, l_n/l_m, or vice versa, by the equation:

$$\log (l_n/l_m) = 0.4 (m - n).$$

It is to be noted that the number of the magnitude diminishes as the brightness increases, and that the choice of the zero point makes the magnitudes of the very brightest stars negative. The magnitude of Sirius is -1.58. The magnitude of the planet Venus, at greatest brilliancy, is -4.4; of the full moon, -12.5; and of the sun, -26.7. Stars of the twenty-first magnitude can be photographed with the 100-inch telescope at Mount Wilson.

The following examples illustrate some of the uses of the relation between apparent brightness and magnitude:

(1) How much brighter is Sirius (magnitude -1.6) than a star whose magnitude is 21.0?

$$\log (l_n/l_m) = 0.4 \times 22.6 = 9.04$$
$$l_n/l_m = \text{about 1100 million times.}$$

(2) Nova Aquilae, in the course of two or three days, in June, 1918, increased in brightness about 45,000 times; how many magnitudes did it rise?

$$\log (l_n/l_m) - \log 45,000 - 4.69 - 0.4 \ (m - n),$$
$$m - n = 4.69/0.4 = \text{about 11.7 magnitudes.}$$

(3) The bright star Castor, which appears single to the naked eye, is resolved by the telescope into two stars, whose magnitudes are 1.99 and 2.85; what is the magnitude of the two combined?

$$\log (l_n/l_m) = 0.4 \times 0.86 = 0.344,$$
$$l_n/l_m = 2.21; \ (l_m + l_n)/l_m = 3.21,$$
$$\log [(l_m + l_n)/l_m] = 0.507 = 0.4 \ [m - (m + n)],$$
$$m - (m + n) = 0.507/0.4 = 1.27,$$
$$m + n = 2.85 - 1.27 = 1.58, \text{ the combined magnitude.}$$

9.12. Visual Magnitudes. The value of the apparent magnitude of a star depends on the apparatus which receives the light. If it is the eye alone, or the eye at the telescope, it is the *visual magnitude* that is determined.

Observers from the time of Ptolemy have recognized that the eye is sensitive to smaller differences of brightness than those between even magnitudes, and have made use of fractional magnitudes. The smallest difference between two stars that a trained eye can detect is about one tenth of a magnitude, or 10 per cent of the brightness of either one. William Herschel, in 1796, introduced the comparison of two stars in units of just-perceptible differences. This procedure was further developed by Argelander at Bonn in the study of variable stars; it has been widely used ever since in such studies, when the highest precision is not required.

The *Argelander method* consists in estimating the number of just-perceptible *steps* between the variable star and one or more stars supposed to be invariable in light. If the variable star is denoted by v and the comparison stars by a and b, the record $a2v3b$ means that the variable star is two steps fainter than a, and three steps brighter than b. If the magnitudes of the comparison stars are known, that of the variable star can be established from the record. Eye estimates are estimates of magnitude; for in terms of Fechner's law (9.10) the magnitude is the measure of the sensation. One step for any observer is about the same difference of magnitude, whether the stars that are being compared are bright or faint.

More accurate determinations of visible magnitudes are made with *visual photometers*. These are instruments used in connection with the telescope to measure the relative brightness of two stars, from which the difference in magnitude can be calculated.

9.13. Visual Photometry of the Stars. Until the introduction, in recent years, of photographic and other means of measuring the relative brightness of stars, the most accurate measures were made with visual photometers. E. C. Pickering at Harvard was one of the pioneers in this field. The most successful visual photometers are so devised that they can diminish by known amounts the brightness of one, or both, of the stars that are being compared, until the observer decides that the two images are equally bright; this is done by the interposition of a graduated absorbing medium, or " wedge," or of some medium by which the light is polarized.

In one type of visual photometer the two stars are compared successively with an " artificial star " whose image is formed, by an appropriate optical arrangement, beside that of the star itself. In another type, two neighboring stars may be compared directly. In the meridian photometer of Pickering the brightness of the stars can be compared, near the times of their transits, with that of Polaris, or a fainter star near the celestial pole. Corrections are made, as far as possible, for dissimilar conditions of the two stars, such as difference in color, or in distance from the zenith. The average " visual extinction," or diminution of starlight by the atmosphere, increases as the star's zenith distance becomes greater; at the zenith distance of 60°, at sea level, a star is a quarter of a magnitude fainter than it would be, if it were in the zenith.

The *Revised Harvard Photometry* is the most extensive catalogue of stellar magnitudes determined with visual photometers; it contains the magnitudes of over 45 thousand of the brighter stars in all parts of the sky. The *Potsdam Photometric Durchmusterung* gives the visual magnitudes of all stars in the northern celestial hemisphere down to magnitude 7.5; the number of stars in this catalogue exceeds 14 thousand.

9.14. The Brightest Stars. The twenty stars in Table 9.I are brighter than visual magnitude 1.5, and are often known as "stars of the first magnitude," although they range through nearly three magnitudes. The first and second columns give the designation of the star according to Bayer's system, and its proper name, if the star has one. The apparent visual magnitude, taken from *Revised Harvard Photometry*, appears in the third column. In the seven cases where the star can be resolved with the telescope into two stars, the magnitude is that of the two combined; but the spectral class, in the fourth column, is that of the brighter component. All the classes

TABLE 9.I. THE BRIGHTEST STARS

Name		Apparent Visual Magnitude	Spectrum	Parallax	Absolute Visual Magnitude
α Canis Majoris	Sirius	− 1.58 ^{d}	A0	0″.371	+ 1.3
* α Carinae	Canopus	− 0.86	F0	0 .005:	− 7.4:
* α Centauri		+ 0.06 ^{d}	G0	0 .758	+ 4.4
α Lyrae	Vega	0.14	A0	0 .124	+ 0.6
α Aurigae	Capella	0.21	G0	0 .069	− 0.6
α Boötis	Arcturus	0.24	K0	0 .080	− 0.2
β Orionis	Rigel	0.34 ^{d}	B8	0 .006:	− 5.8:
α Canis Minoris	Procyon	0.48 ^{d}	F5	0 .312	+ 3.0
* α Eridani	Achernar	0.60	B5	0 .049	− 0.9
* β Centauri		0.86	B1	0 .011	− 3.9
α Aquilae	Altair	0.89	A5	0 .204	+ 2.4
α Orionis	Betelgeuse	0.92 ^{v}	M0	0 .017	− 2.9
* α Crucis		1.05 ^{d}	B1	0 .014	− 3.2
α Tauri	Aldebaran	1.06 ^{d}	K5	0 .057	− 0.1
β Geminorum	Pollux	1.21	K0	0 .101	+ 1.2
α Virginis	Spica	1.21	B2	0 .014	− 3.1
α Scorpii	Antares	1.22 ^{d}	M0	0 .009	− 4.0
α Piscis Austrini	Fomalhaut	1.29	A3	0 .137	+ 2.0
α Cygni	Deneb	1.33	A2	0 .005:	− 5.2:
α Leonis	Regulus	1.34	B8	0 .058	+ 0.2

* Not visible in latitude 40° N.

v Light varies irregularly through a range of half a magnitude.

d Double star with the telescope. The combined magnitude is given.

from B to M are here represented; evidently, the bluest of the brightest stars are β Centauri and α Crucis, while the reddest ones are Betelgeuse and Antares.

The fifth column, which gives the parallax of the star, shows that the brightest stars are not always the nearest ones. While α Centauri, Sirius, and Procyon are among the nearest stars (8.5), Canopus, Rigel, and Deneb are so remote that the parallax is uncertain, as the colon indicates. The absolute magnitude (9.22), in the last column, would be the apparent visual magnitude of the star, if its parallax were 0″.1. At this standard distance the sun's magnitude would be +4.8.

All but five of the brightest stars are visible, at some time in the year, throughout the United States. These five become visible south of the following latitudes: Canopus, 37° N.; Achernar, 32°; α and β Centauri, 30°; α Crucis, 28°.

9.15. The Number of Visible Stars. The total number of stars in the entire celestial sphere bright enough to be visible to the average eye without the telescope does not greatly exceed 6000 under the best conditions. At any time, about one half of them are above the horizon, but near the horizon only the brighter ones can be seen. Probably not many more than two thousand stars are visible ordinarily to the naked eye at any one time on a clear night. Moonlight reduces this number.

With the telescope the number is greatly increased. Table 9.II gives the total numbers of stars brighter than a given visual magnitude, according to Seares and van Rhijn (1925). The counts were

TABLE 9.II. NUMBER OF STARS BRIGHTER THAN
A GIVEN VISUAL MAGNITUDE

Magnitude Limit	Total Number	Magnitude Limit	Total Number	Magnitude Limit	Total Number
0.0	2	7.0	14,300	14.0	13,800,000
1.0	10	8.0	41,000	15.0	32,000,000
2.0	40	9.0	117,000	16.0	71,000,000
3.0	140	10.0	324,000	17.0	150,000,000
4.0	530	11.0	870,000	18.0	296,000,000
5.0	1,620	12.0	2,270,000	19.0	560,000,000
6.0	4,850	13.0	5,700,000	20.0	1,000,000,000

made on photographs of selected areas of the sky, and corrected to visual magnitudes for the entire heavens. Stars in globular clusters and exterior stellar systems are not included in the counts. The numbers for the nineteenth and twentieth magnitudes are obtained by extrapolation.

These investigators find from the data of the Table that the combined light of all the stars is equal to that of 1092 stars of visual magnitude 1.0. The naked-eye stars contribute 20 per cent of the total light. The many billions of stars fainter than the twentieth magnitude send us only two or three per cent of the total. According to van Rhijn, the total light from the stars accounts for only one sixth of the light of the sky on a clear, moonless night; the remainder is zodiacal and auroral light.

9.16. Numbers of Stars Visible with Different Telescopes. The limiting magnitude, m, to which stars can be seen with a telescope, whose aperture is a inches, is given by the formula: $m = 9 + 5 \log a$, which is easily verified, if it is assumed that the limiting magnitude for a 1-inch telescope is the ninth magnitude. According to this formula the faintest stars that can be seen with telescopes of different sizes are as follows:

Magnitude	9	12	14	15	16	17	18	19	20.5
Aperture, in inches	1	4	10	16	25	40	63	100	200

This theoretical limit is not quite attained by the larger telescopes, owing to absorption of light by the optical parts. By comparison with Table 9.II it appears that a 1-inch telescope is able to show about 100,000 stars; a 40-inch telescope, more than 100 million stars; the 100-inch telescope, half a billion stars; while the new 200-inch telescope will pass the billion mark. These are visual magnitudes. The photographic limit of the 100-inch Mount Wilson telescope is about the twenty-first magnitude.

9.17. Photographic Magnitudes. Visual methods of determining the magnitudes of the stars are now largely replaced by photographic methods, which are more rapid, and can be made to give greater precision. Two ways of deriving the relative brightness of stars from the photographs are the following:

(1) By measuring the diameters of the images of the stars on plates taken exactly in focus. Bright stars produce larger images

than faint ones. The diameters may be measured with a micrometer, or simply estimated by comparison with a standard graduated scale of images on a separate plate. It is necessary, of course, to establish by an appropriate method the relation between increase in diameter and increase in brightness of the star.

(2) By measuring the degree of darkening of the circular images of the stars on plates exposed a little out of focus. The brighter the star, the denser is its extra-focal image (Fig. 8.44). The density of each image can be measured in turn by sending a beam of light through the image; the amount of dimming of the light is a measure of the density, from which the relative brightness of the star can be determined. There are other methods.

9.18. Visual and Photographic Magnitudes Compared; Color-Index. Since the ordinary photographic plate is less sensitive than the eye to red light, and more sensitive to blue and violet light, red

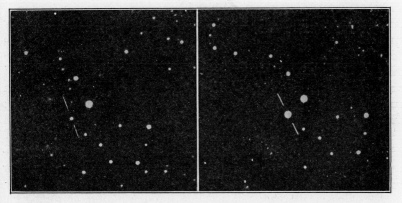

Fig. 9.18. Photographic and Photo-Visual Brightness of U Cygni. In comparison with the neighboring white stars, this red star is less conspicuous photographically (left) than photo-visually (right). (From photographs by F. C. Jordan, Yerkes Observatory)

stars are fainter photographically than they are visually, as compared with blue stars.

The *color-index* of a star (Table 10.I) is a measure of its color; it is the photographic magnitude *minus* the visual magnitude. The photographic scale is adjusted so that the color-index is zero, on the average, for class Ao stars between magnitudes 5.5 and 6.5. For the bluest stars the color-index is negative, amounting to as much as $-0^m.3$, or a little more; it is positive for the red stars, increasing along the spectral sequence ordinarily to a maximum of nearly $+2^m.0$, although for some of the red stars it is considerably more. It is not the same for all stars of the same spectral class, but depends also on the density and luminosity of the star, and the amount of absorbing material intervening (11.12).

For a particular star the color-index varies with the telescope, eye, and kind of plate that are employed. They are largely differences in scale, so that the index systems of different observers can be harmonized by multiplying each one by a constant factor.

It is possible to obtain magnitudes photographically that are in close agreement with the visual scale, by the use of stained plates and a suitable color filter. These *photo-visual magnitudes* have certain advantages, in the matter of control, over visual magnitudes, and have been used extensively in determinations of color-index.

Fig. 9.20. Photo-Electric Cell. A quartz potassium cell, made by Jakob Kunz. Starlight enters the cell through the clear window and falls on the sensitive inner surface of potassium hydride which becomes positively charged at a rate depending on the star's brightness.

9.19. Standard Magnitude Sequences. In many investigations in which the magnitudes of the stars are involved, including some of the major problems of astronomy, it is imperative that the same scale be employed for stars of all degrees of brightness. On the other hand, it has been a matter of great difficulty to establish a consistent magnitude system over such a wide range; for the brightest star is more than a thousand million times brighter than the faintest one that can now be conveniently photographed.

As a means of control for all observers, *sequences* of magnitudes have been determined as carefully as possible. They are lists of stars, either photographic or visual, or both, whose magnitudes form

a graduated consistent series, supposed to be on the correct scale.
The Harvard standard north polar sequence, inaugurated by Pickering, and the Mount Wilson polar sequence of Seares cover the widest
ranges of magnitude. These
stars are within two degrees of
the north celestial pole, and are
therefore available as standards
throughout the year to observers
in the northern hemisphere.

9.20. The Photo-Electric Pho-
tometer. The first successful use
of the photo-electric cell in stellar photometry was made by
Guthnick at Berlin, about 1913.
Soon afterward, Stebbins and
Kunz at Illinois introduced it in
America. The most satisfactory
cell for this purpose is of quartz;
the interior is coated with the
hydride of an alkaline metal,
usually potassium.

When a beam of starlight,
concentrated by the telescope, is
admitted through a clear window
in the cell to the sensitive surface, this surface becomes electrically charged at a rate which
depends directly on the brightness of the star. With a 15-inch
telescope Stebbins finds that a
first magnitude star of class Ao

FIG. 9.20A. Photo-Electric Photometer Attached to the 15-inch Refractor of the Washburn Observatory,
University of Wisconsin. Starlight is
concentrated by the telescope upon the
photo-electric cell within the box.
The rate at which the cell is charged
thereby is measured by an electrometer
which is observed with the lower eyepiece.

charges the photo-electric cell at the rate of three volts a second; and
that for a seventh magnitude star the rate of charging is not too slow
to be conveniently measured with the electrometer which is connected with the cell.

The value of the photo-electric stellar photometer is its high precision. The magnitude of a star can be determined from a single
set of readings with a probable error of ± 0.008 magnitude; so that
variations in the light of the stars can be studied which are too small

to be detected otherwise. With larger telescopes and greater refinements this photometer can measure the light of much fainter stars, and of many globular clusters and exterior systems.

9.21. Radiometric and Bolometric Magnitudes. Two other scales of stellar magnitudes relating to the total radiation of energy from a star have become important in recent years, as devices for measuring the heat produced by a star have been perfected. For these minute measurements Pettit and Nicholson at Mount Wilson employ a vacuum thermocouple, made of wires of bismuth and bismuth-tin alloy, whose weight, including the connecting wires, is one thousandth part of that of a drop of water. The heating of this tiny receiver by the radiation of the star brought to a focus upon it by the 100-inch telescope is measured by a galvanometer. The heating effect of a star as faint as the thirteenth magnitude can be measured, which is about equal to that of a candle at the distance of 2,000 miles.

Since radiations of all wave-lengths produce heat when they are absorbed, the *radiometric magnitude,* that is determined in this way, is a measure of the entire radiation of the star that penetrates through the atmosphere. The scale is adjusted to agree with the visual scale at spectral class Ao. *Heat-index* is the difference: visual *minus* radiometric magnitude; for the red stars the heat-index is positive and large, sometimes exceeding ten magnitudes.

Bolometric magnitude relates to the total radiation of the star; it is obtained from the radiometric magnitude by adding a correction, based on theoretical considerations, for the selective absorption of the atmosphere. The bolometric scale of magnitudes is made to agree with the visual scale at class Go, for giant stars. As Table 9.III shows, Sirius, the brightest star in the sky visually, stands third in the list radiometrically, being surpassed by the red stars Betelgeuse and Antares. On the bolometric scale, which would be appropriate if the thermocouple could be employed above the atmosphere, Sirius retains the lead, but the other stars are not in their order of visual magnitude (Table 9.I).

LUMINOSITIES OF THE STARS

9.22. Absolute Magnitude. The apparent magnitude of a star relates to its brightness as we observe it, depending on its real bright-

TABLE 9.III. THE TEN LEADING STARS IN ORDER OF APPARENT
RADIOMETRIC MAGNITUDE AND OF APPARENT BOLOMETRIC
MAGNITUDE (ABOVE THE ATMOSPHERE)

Star	Spectrum	Radiometric Magnitude	Star	Spectrum	Bolometric Magnitude
Betelgeuse	Mo	− 1.7	Sirius	Ao	− 1.4
Antares	Mo	− 1.3	Betelgeuse	Mo	− 1.3
Sirius	Ao	− 1.3	Antares	Mo	− 1.0
Canopus	Fo	− 1.1	β Centauri	B1	− 0.8
γ Crucis	M5	− 1.0	Canopus	Fo	− 0.7
Arcturus	Ko	− 1.0	γ Crucis	M5	− 0.6
Aldebaran	K5	− 0.6	Arcturus	Ko	− 0.5
α Centauri	Go	− 0.5	Achernar	B5	− 0.3
Capella	Go	− 0.4	Rigel	B8	− 0.3
o Ceti (max.)	M6	− 0.2	Spica	B2	− 0.2

ness, or *luminosity,* and on its distance. One star may appear brighter
than another only because it is nearer; thus the sun appears brighter
than Capella. In order to rank the stars fairly with respect to
luminosity, it is necessary to place them all the same distance away,
or what amounts to the same thing, to calculate how bright they
would appear, if they were placed at the same distance. By agreement the standard distance is ten parsecs (8.4).

*The absolute magnitude of a star is the magnitude it would have,
if its distance were 10 parsecs (parallax 0″.1).*

When the parallax, p, is known, and the apparent magnitude, m,
has been determined by observation, the absolute magnitude, M, can
be calculated from the relation:

$$M = m + 5 + 5 \log p.$$

The absolute magnitude is of the same sort as the apparent magnitude employed in the calculation; it may be visual, photographic,
radiometric, etc.

When the absolute magnitudes, M_1 and M_2, of any two stars are
known, the ratio of their luminosities is given by the formula:

$$\log (L_2/L_1) = 0.4(M_1 - M_2).$$

9.23. Luminosities of the Stars. It is customary to express the
luminosity of a star in terms of the sun's luminosity, that is to say,

the number of times the star would outshine the sun, if both were at the same distance. This ratio can be obtained for any star from the second formula of the preceding Section, if the absolute magnitudes of the sun and star are known.

The sun's apparent visual magnitude, m, is -26.72; its parallax, p, on the same basis as those of the stars, must be taken as $206,265''$, of which the logarithm is 5.314. By the first formula of the preceding Section, the sun's absolute visual magnitude is $-26.72 + 5 + 26.57$, or $+4.85$. *At the standard distance of 10 parsecs the sun would appear only a little brighter than a star of the fifth magnitude.* The expression for the star's visual luminosity, in terms of that of the sun, becomes:

$$\log(\text{luminosity}) = 0.4(4.85 - \text{absolute magnitude}).$$

Since the majority of the brightest stars are more remote than 10 parsecs, they must be actually brighter than the sun. Indeed, this is the case for all the stars in Table 9.I, as shown by their absolute magnitudes. Canopus, Rigel, and Deneb are of the order of ten thousand times more luminous than the sun. At the same time, we have noticed that many stars which are much nearer than the standard distance are visible only with the telescope, and are therefore less luminous than the sun. The most luminous star known is the variable star S Doradus, in the Large Magellanic Cloud. Its median absolute magnitude is -8.9, according to Shapley. The faintest star is Wolf 359 (Table 8.I); its absolute magnitude, according to van Maanen, is $+16.5$, so that its luminosity is only 0.00002 that of the sun. The conclusion is that *the stars differ enormously in luminosity.*

In the following examples the formulas of this and the preceding sections are employed:

(1) Compare the luminosity of Sirius with that of the sun. From Table 9.I we find for Sirius: $m = -1.58$; $p = 0''.371$.

$$M = -1.58 + 5.00 + 5 \log 0.371 = 1.27,$$
$$\log L = 0.4(4.85 - 1.27) = +1.43.$$

The luminosity of Sirius is 27 times the sun's luminosity.

(2) Compare the luminosities of Proxima Centauri and the sun. From Table 8.I we find for Proxima: $m = +10.5$; $p = 0''.765$.

$$M = +10.5 + 5.0 + 5 \log 0.765 = +14.9,$$
$$\log L = 0.4(4.85 - 14.9) = -4.02.$$

The luminosity of Proxima is $1/10,000$ that of the sun.

9.24. The Main Sequence. When the absolute magnitudes of the stars are plotted against the spectral classes, as in Fig. 9.24, it is found that the majority of the points are arranged in a narrow band running diagonally across the diagram. More than half of the points

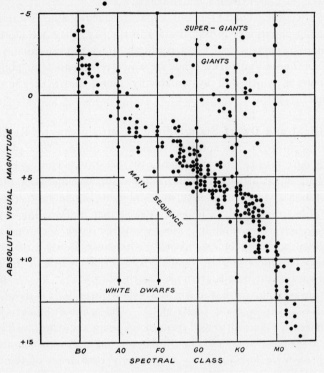

FIG. 9.24. Spectrum-Luminosity Diagram. Absolute visual magnitude is plotted against spectral class for a number of representative stars. The majority of the stars belong to the main sequence. The point at class Go and absolute magnitude +4.8 represents the sun.

in the band are within one magnitude of the curve which they define. The mean curve drops steadily along the spectral sequence, from absolute magnitude −2.5, for stars of class Bo, to +10 for class Mo. This is known as the *main sequence.*

The sun (class Go, absolute magnitude +4.85) is close to the mean curve, occupying a fairly central position along the main sequence. It is about a hundred times fainter than the average class A star, and the same amount brighter than the average class M star of the main sequence. Inasmuch as the sun, if it were placed at the relatively small distance of 10 parsecs, would be an inconspicuous star to the naked eye, the red stars of the sequence ought generally to be telescopic objects. Indeed, this is true of many of the nearest red stars, such as Proxima and Barnard's star.

On the other hand, the red stars Betelgeuse and Antares are among the apparently brightest stars in the sky; they are more distant than 10 parsecs, and are accordingly much more luminous than the sun. These and many other stars are represented by points in the diagram which fall systematically above those of the main sequence.

9.25. Giant and Dwarf Stars. Since its introduction by Russell at Princeton, in 1913, the spectrum-luminosity diagram has played a leading part in directing the studies of the stars. Hertzsprung, in 1905, had called attention to the sharp distinction between the red stars of high and low luminosity, and had named them *giant stars* and *dwarf stars* respectively. Russell showed that the division extends to the yellow stars, and less conspicuously to the blue ones, and formulated a theory of its physical significance (10.32). As more data have become available, the main features of the first diagram are confirmed, but the details are more clearly shown.

In the original sense, the sun is a yellow dwarf (class dGo), and Capella is a yellow giant (class gGo). The original "dwarfs" are now generally referred to as "stars of the main sequence," while the giants, or super-giants, and the dwarfs are those stars which are decidedly more or less luminous respectively than stars of the same spectral class in the main sequence.

Super-giant stars are extraordinarily luminous giants; examples are Rigel, Deneb, Canopus, and Antares. They are sometimes distinguished by prefixing the letter "c" to the usual designation; thus Canopus is of spectral class cFo. Spectroscopically, the super-giants are characterized by the exceptional sharpness of the lines in their spectra. The few points in the diagram that appear far below the main sequence represent the *white dwarfs* (10.13), small and very dense stars, of which an example is the faint companion of Sirius.

9.26. Relative Frequencies of Stars of Different Luminosities. The relative numbers of stars of different absolute magnitudes in a given volume of space, as derived by the statistical investigations of Kapteyn and Seares, are shown in Table 9.IV. The formula by which these values are defined is known as the *luminosity function*. The relative number is apparently still increasing for the faintest stars. These data for the sun's neighborhood do not apply necessarily to other parts of the galactic system.

TABLE 9.IV.   RELATIVE NUMBERS OF STARS
OF DIFFERENT LUMINOSITIES

Absolute Magnitude	Luminosity	Relative Number
− 5.0	10,000	1
− 2.5	1,000	90
0.0	100	3,300
+ 2.5	10	42,000
+ 5.0	1	200,000
+ 7.5	0.1	350,000
+ 10.0	0.01	500,000
+ 12.5	0.001	600,000

As the Table shows, for every five super-giants of absolute magnitude −5.0, there are a million stars of magnitude + 5.0, like the sun. *In a given region of space,* stars of low luminosity far outnumber those of high luminosity; but *as seen with the naked eye,* the giant stars are the more numerous. The reason is that the volume of surrounding space occupied by the less luminous stars of the main sequence, that are visible to the naked eye, is much smaller; and it shrinks as we progress down the main sequence, until even the nearest stars at the red end are visible only with the telescope.

The greatest distance, D, in parsecs, at which a star of a given visual absolute magnitude, M, can be seen with a telescope of given aperture, a, in inches, is derived from the formula: $M = m + 5 + 5 \log p$, after the substitution: $m = 9 + 5 \log a$ (9.16). The resulting expression is: $5 \log D = 5 \log a + 14 − M$. For the 100-inch telescope this becomes: $5 \log D = 24 − M$. Thus a super-giant star of magnitude −5 can not be seen, if its distance exceeds 630,000 parsecs. A main-sequence star of magnitude +5, such as the sun, can not be seen at a greater distance than 6300 parsecs (about 20 thousand light-years). A dwarf star of absolute magnitude +12.5 must be within 200 parsecs in order to be visible with the 100-inch telescope.

9.27. Spectroscopic Parallaxes. While in general the spectra of giant and main-sequence stars of the same spectral class are the same, the intensities of some of the less prominent lines depend on the luminosity of the star; some of them become stronger, while others are weakened with increasing luminosity (10.21). From the study of these lines in the spectra of stars of known absolute magnitude, Adams and Kohlschütter, in 1914, were able to express the relationships graphically. The curves were then employed to give the absolute magnitudes of other stars in whose spectra the intensities of these lines could be estimated. When the absolute magnitude, M, becomes known, and the apparent magnitude, m, has been measured, the parallax, p, of the star can be derived from the relation: $M = m + 5 + 5 \log p$.

In this way the parallaxes of thousands of stars have been determined at Mount Wilson, Victoria, and elsewhere. At first, the method could be employed only for the yellow and red stars, for these sensitive lines are not measurable in the spectra of the blue stars. Later, Adams and Joy developed other criteria of absolute magnitude for stars of classes A and B. Comparisons with the trigonometric parallaxes that are available show that the method is reasonably reliable.

It appears that the absolute magnitude of a star can be determined from its spectrum with a probable error of ± 0.4 magnitude, and that the resulting parallax has a probable error of 20 per cent, whether the parallax is large or small. On the other hand, the probable error of the trigonometric parallax is numerically the same, regardless of the size of the parallax, being somewhat less than 0".01. Thus for a star whose parallax is 0".05, the two methods seem to be equally reliable. For stars nearer than this, the trigonometric method is the better; but for stars more remote, which means the great majority, spectroscopic parallaxes are generally the more dependable. Spectra of considerable dispersion are required for this purpose.

VARIABLE STARS

9.28. In general, *variable stars* are stars that vary in *brightness;* they may vary also in spectral class, and frequently do. We have already considered the type of variable star in which the light fluctuates periodically because of eclipses (8.44), and now turn the attention to other types, in which the light varies, either regularly or irregularly, owing to variations going on in the stars themselves. These variations, in the main, are fluctuations, and not progressive changes, so that they do not, by subtractions and additions, alter permanently the configurations of the stars.

Before the invention of the telescope the records of a few remarkable temporary stars, and the recognition of the variability of the red star Mira Ceti, in 1596, comprised the information concerning variable stars of all types. Up to 1844, only eighteen variable stars had been discovered, aside from the novae, for the most part incidentally in the course of other investigations. The publication, in that year, of the first catalogue of variable stars, by Argelander, marks the beginning of systematic studies of variable stars, which have progressed ever since with increasing momentum. The importance of these studies will become evident as we proceed.

9.29. Designation of Variable Stars.

Argelander introduced the plan of designating variable stars, which, with extensions made necessary by the great increase in their numbers, has been generally used. Unless the star already has a letter in the Bayer system (1.24), it is assigned a capital letter, or two, in the order in which its variability was recognized, which is followed by the genitive of the constellation name. For each constellation the letters are used in the order: R, S, . . . Z; RR, RS, . . . RZ; SS, . . . SZ; and so on, until ZZ is reached; subsequent variables are lettered AA, AB, . . . AZ; BB, . . . BZ; etc. By the time QZ is reached (the letter J is not employed), 334 variable stars are so designated in the constellation. Examples are R Leonis, SZ Herculis, and AC Cygni. In 1932, the lettering of variables in Sagittarius had reached QZ; subsequent designations are V335, V336, etc.

The responsibility for the designations of variable stars is undertaken by the Astronomische Gesellschaft. The complete list of stars recognized as variables, including their positions and the elements of the light variations, whenever they are known, is published annually by Prager at the Berlin-Babelsberg Observatory. The list for 1933 numbers 5826 variables exclusive of those in globular clusters, remote star-clouds, and external systems. The total number of variable stars known at that time was greater by several thousand, and the number is rapidly increasing.

It is the custom not to include the star in the permanent list until its variability has been sufficiently confirmed. A provisional designation is at first given by a number, in the order that the announcement of the discovery was received, followed by the year; thus 22.1929 was the twenty-second variable star discovered in 1929.

9.30. The Light Curve. When a variable star has been discovered, it remains to determine the character of the variation, by comparing its brightness repeatedly with that of a neighboring star, or stars, supposedly constant in light. From the measured differences between the variable and the comparison stars, and the constant magnitudes of the latter, the magnitude of the variable star can be derived from each comparison.

If the star is varying slowly, and an observation is made every night or so, the character of the variation becomes evident, after a while. The usual procedure is to plot the observed magnitudes against the dates of the observations. The curve that best fits the points on the diagram, the *light curve,* shows how the magnitude varies with the time. If, however, the variation is rapid, the successive observations may be in different cycles, and a series of observations throughout the night may be required in order to decide the matter.

If it turns out that the variation is regular, or nearly so, the intervals between the times of greatest or least brightness will eventually permit the *elements of the light variation* to be derived, namely, the *epoch,* or time of a chosen maximum, or minimum, and the *period* of the light variation.

As an example, the elements of the Cepheid variable star η Aquilae are: Maximum brightness $= 2414827.15 + 7^{d}.1766.E$, where the first number is the epoch, which is expressed in Julian days (2.40), and the second number is the period in days. In order to predict the times of future maxima we have simply to multiply the period by $E = 1, 2, \ldots$, and to add the results successively to the epoch.

The *mean light curve* is obtained by plotting all the observed magnitudes with respect to *phase,* or interval of time since the maximum preceding the observation. For this purpose, especially when the total variation is not great, the more accurate photometric methods of observation are desirable.

In the many cases where the light variations are large and only approximately regular, the Argelander method of estimating magnitudes gives a sufficient degree of precision. The American Association of Variable Star Observers, under the direction of Leon Campbell, at Harvard, is securing large numbers of valuable observations with telescopes of moderate size.

9.31. Types of Variable Stars. More than forty years ago, E. C. Pickering proposed the classification of variable stars in five groups, which has served ever since as the basis of the discussions of these stars. In the order in which they are described here, and with some modifications in the names to conform to present usage, the original types are: (1) Eclipsing variables; (2) Cepheid variables; (3) Long-period variables; (4) Irregular variables; (5) Novae, or temporary stars.

Eclipsing variables, or eclipsing binary stars (Chapter VIII), are not *intrinsically* variable in brightness; their variations are caused, for the most part, by the mutual eclipses of two revolving stars. Temporary stars (9.44) are really variable in luminosity, but they exhibit characteristics which set them apart from the other variable stars. The three remaining types comprise the stars ordinarily regarded as variable stars, namely:

> Cepheid variables,
> Long-period variables,
> Irregular variables.

The order in which these types appear is the order of their punctuality. Cepheid variables are generally very regular, both in period and form of light curve. Long-period variables are only approximately regular in these respects. Irregular variables fluctuate in a less readily predictable manner, although certain groups are distinguished by remarkable uniformities in their general behavior. By subdivision of these types a more detailed classification can be given; Ludendorff recognizes ten principal types of variable stars.

9.32. Cepheid Variables. All periodic physical (not eclipsing) variable stars having periods between a few hours and about 50 days are known as *Cepheid variables;* the name comes from that of one of the earliest recognized examples, δ Cephei. Because their light variations show a marked

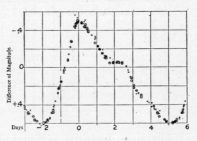

Fig. 9.32. Light Curve of η Aquilae. A typical Cepheid variable star having a period of about seven days. (Light curve by C. C. Wylie from his photo-electric observations at the University of Illinois)

preference for two different periods, and for other reasons that will be noted, these stars are often divided into *cluster type Cepheids,* or *cluster variables,* having periods of the order of 12 hours, and *typical Cepheids,* whose periods are most frequently about a week. Nearly 500 Cepheids are listed in Prager's catalogue (1932), of which somewhat more than half are of the cluster type.

Typical Cepheids are yellow stars (spectral classes F and G). They are super-giants (9.25), and are therefore rare; probably not more than one star in a million in space is a Cepheid. Their great luminosity, however, raises them to apparent prominence out of proportion to their actual numbers, not only among the stars around us, but also in the very remote star-clusters and clouds, and in the spiral nebulae. About a dozen typical Cepheids are visible to the naked eye; the brightest are δ Cephei, η Aquilae, ζ Geminorum, and β Doradus; with the exception of Polaris, whose very small range in magnitude (0.08 visually) raises some doubt as to its full membership.

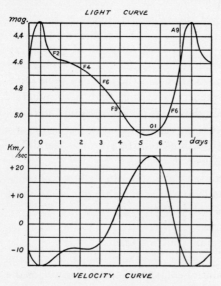

FIG. 9.33. Light and Velocity Curves of W Sagittarii. Maximum brightness coincides with greatest velocity of approach; minimum light with greatest velocity of recession. From maximum to minimum light the spectrum changes by more than a whole class. (From a diagram by Curtiss in *Lick Observatory Bulletins*. Spectral classes are added as given by Shapley)

9.33. Characteristics of Cepheid Variables.

Both long and short-period Cepheids have a number of characteristics in common:

Their light variations are continuous and remarkably regular, with minor exceptions. The increase in brightness is generally more rapid than the decline. Hertzsprung finds a definite correlation between the period and the degree of asymmetry in the light curve.

The range of the visual light variation is generally not far from one magnitude. The variation in photographic light is about 50 per cent greater, which indicates that these stars become cooler and redder as the light diminishes. From maximum to minimum light the spectral class advances, on the average, slightly more than a whole class.

The lines in the spectra of these stars oscillate, through a small range, in the period of the light variation. The velocity curve is very nearly similar to the light curve, except that it is inverted. Thus the greatest velocity of approach occurs always near the time of greatest brightness, and the greatest velocity of recession near the time of minimum brightness. Owing to the simultaneous variations in light and radial velocity, it was formerly supposed that Cepheid variables are spectroscopic binaries, and that the light variations are caused in some manner by the star's revolution. It is now generally believed that these variables are single stars.

9.34. The Pulsation Theory. Shapley, in 1914, set forth the evidence that had accumulated against the binary theory of Cepheid variation, and definitely proposed the pulsation theory in its place. According to Eddington, whose mathematical work supports the new theory in some respects, the most convincing disproof of the binary theory is that the small "orbit," as calculated from the observed radial velocities, places the "secondary star" generally *inside* the principal star. The pulsation theory, or a somewhat more generalized one, appears now to be applicable to all periodic physical variable stars. It is mentioned at this time in connection with Cepheid variables, and will be given further consideration (9.43) after the different types of variable stars have been described.

On the pulsation theory the gaseous star alternately contracts under the action of gravity, and expands owing to the excess heat produced by the contraction; overcooled by expansion the star contracts again, and so on. On this theory the observed radial velocities are those of the surface of the star, which is turned toward us, as it rushes outward and is drawn in again. The semi-major axis of the "orbit" now becomes the amount of contraction, or expansion, of the radius with respect to its average size. These values are given for a few Cepheids (Table 9.V) as percentages of the theoretical radii of the stars. The data are adapted from a table by Eddington.

TABLE 9.V.   CEPHEID VARIABLE STARS

Star	Period (days)	App. Vis. Magnitude Max.	Min.	Spectrum Max.	Min.	Absolute Magnitude (Median)	Radius of Star $\odot = 1$	Fractional Change in Radius
RR Lyrae	0.57	7.1 to 7.8		B9 to F2		− 0.4	6	0.04
SZ Tauri	3.15	6.5	6.9	A9	G0	− 1.6	20	0.03
δ Cephei	5.37	3.6	4.3	F0	G2	− 2.2	30	0.06
η Aquilae	7.18	3.7	4.3	A8	G5	− 2.6	35	0.05
Y Ophiuchi	17.12	6.2	7.0	F5	G3	− 4.0	70	0.04
l Carinae	35.52	3.6	4.8	F8	G9	− 5.1	115	0.10

The Cepheid variables in the Table are chosen with successively longer periods so as to represent the characteristics of all the variables of this type as well as possible with a few samples. It will be noticed that the average range in magnitude of the six stars is 0.7 magnitude, and the average change of spectrum is 1.2 spectral classes.

It is especially to be noticed that as the period of the light variation increases, the spectral class advances (period-spectrum relation), and the luminosity becomes greater, as shown by the absolute magnitudes (period-luminosity relation).

9.35. Period-Luminosity Relation for Typical Cepheids.

In the course of a study of the numerous Cepheid variables in the Small Magellanic Cloud, Miss Leavitt at Harvard, in 1912, noticed a re-

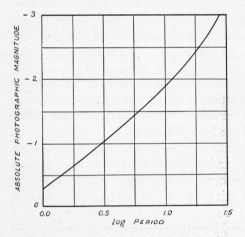

markable relation between the apparent magnitudes of these stars and the lengths of the periods of their light variations — the brighter the star, the longer the period. Since the Cloud is very remote, the differences in distance of its stars can be neglected. The relation is really between the absolute magnitudes and the periods.

FIG. 9.35. Period-Luminosity Curve for Typical Cepheid Variables. From this curve, by Shapley, the absolute median photographic magnitude of a typical Cepheid variable can be read, when the period of its light variation is known.

Shapley, in 1918, reached the conclusion that this relation holds for all typical Cepheids, and published a curve showing how the absolute magnitude varies with the period. In order to shift the scale, in the diagram for the Cloud, from apparent to absolute magnitude, it was necessary to determine the distance of at least one typical Cepheid somewhere, and for this purpose it was natural to turn to the Cepheids in the Milky Way which is nearer than the Cloud. But even the nearest of the galactic Cepheids is still too far away to give an appreciable parallax. Employing less direct methods, Shapley obtained the desired distance, and the value 17.55 which must be subtracted from the apparent magnitudes of the Cepheids in the

Cloud in order to obtain their absolute magnitudes. This "zero point" is believed to be of the right order of magnitude, but is subject to slight alteration with further data. In 1929, Shapley shifted the whole curve downward by 0.23 magnitude. Hubble has shown that the form of the curve is the same for the typical Cepheids in the spiral nebulae.

The *period-luminosity curve* (Fig. 9.35) shows the relation between the period and absolute magnitude of any typical Cepheid *anywhere*. As soon as the period of the light variation has been observed, the absolute magnitude can be read from the curve. It is then possible to calculate the star's distance (9.22).

9.36. Cluster Type Cepheids. The presence of variable stars in the globular star-clusters (11.17) was first observed by Bailey, in 1895. The majority are of the same type, having periods of about half a day; these are known as cluster variables, although they are found

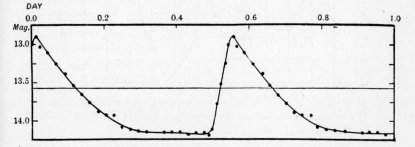

FIG. 9.36. Light Curve of a Cluster Type Variable. The extremely rapid rise to maximum light is characteristic of many cluster type Cepheids. The median magnitude is represented by the horizontal line. (From *Harvard College Observatory Circular* 315)

outside the clusters also. Not one of them is bright enough to be visible to the naked eye; the brightest ones, RR Lyrae and R Muscae, are of the seventh magnitude. They are mainly class A stars.

In addition to their bluer color and lower luminosity, cluster variables differ from typical Cepheids in other respects. The light curves frequently exhibit extreme asymmetry, the ascent in some cases being so abrupt that the light is doubled in an hour. Cluster variables outside the clusters have high peculiar velocities, and are widely scattered over the sky, while the typical Cepheids have low velocities and are found near the Milky Way.

Cluster type Cepheids do not show the period-luminosity relation of the typical Cepheids, but they do show a uniformity that is equally remarkable and valuable. *The median absolute magnitude has nearly the same value for all cluster variables.* Shapley adopts zero as the best value for all. The *median* magnitude of a variable star is the average of the maximum and minimum magnitudes. Accordingly, it is necessary only to observe the apparent magnitude of a cluster variable in order to be able to calculate its distance.

9.37. Long-Period Variables. This type of variability is restricted to the red stars, particularly those of class M, although classes R, N, and S are also represented. The periods range from two months to more than two years, having the greatest frequency in the neighbor-

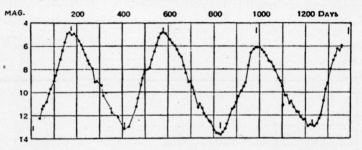

FIG. 9.37. Light Curve of the Long-Period Variable χ Cygni. (From observations, during the years 1922 to 1925, by the American Association of Variable Star Observers)

hood of 300 days. The range of the light variation is often several magnitudes, and in extreme cases, such as χ Cygni, exceeds eight magnitudes. In periodicity, range of brightness, and form of the light curve, long-period variables exhibit an approach to regularity, resembling in this respect the curves of sun-spot numbers.

In the *Harvard Catalogue of Long-Period Variable Stars* 1760 stars are listed, the great majority of which are believed to be of this type. Many of these variables were discovered at Harvard from their peculiar spectra on the objective prism plates. It is a rule, with few exceptions, that class M stars whose spectra show bright lines are long-period variables.

9.38. Mira ("The Wonderful"). About twenty long-period variables are visible at times to the naked eye. Of these the brightest and best known is **o** Ceti, or Mira, whose light variations have been observed for more than three centuries. At maximum it is of magnitude 3.5, on the average, while at the minimum it can be seen only with

FIG. 9.38. Spectrum of Mira. Titanium oxide bands are prominent at the right. Hydrogen lines are bright. (From a photograph by W. C. Rufus, University of Michigan)

the telescope, averaging about the ninth magnitude. The mean period is 330 days; the interval from maximum to maximum brightness has varied as much as a month.

Joy, at Mount Wilson, has recently made a careful study of its spectrum at various stages of the light variation. The lines in the spectrum oscillate slightly in the period of the light variation; the greatest velocity of recession occurs at maximum brightness, and the greatest velocity of approach at minimum brightness, which is

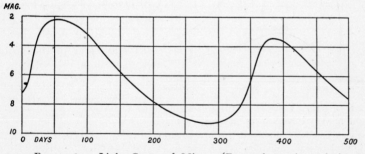

FIG. 9.38A. Light Curve of Mira. (From observations, during the years 1906 to 1908, by members of the British Astronomical Association)

the reverse of the rule for Cepheid variables (9.33). At maximum light the spectrum is characterized by strong titanium oxide bands and by narrow bright lines of hydrogen (and sometimes other elements). At minimum the bands are stronger, and the bright lines have vanished. It must not be supposed that the bright lines are responsible for the great increase of the star's brightness; Miss Payne and Hogg have found that they add only about one tenth of a magnitude to the light at maximum.

The diameter of Mira is of the order of 260 million miles, as deduced from Pease's measurements with the interferometer (10.7). If the mass is taken to be five times the sun's mass, the average density of this star is two ten-thousandths of the density of air at sea level. From the radial velocities, Joy has shown that the diameter varies at least 32 million miles from the average. He estimates that the temperature of the visible surface of the star varies from 2300° to 1800° K between maximum and minimum light.

9.39. Long-Period and Cepheid Variables Compared.

The proposal of the pulsation theory (9.34) of Cepheid variability prepared the way for its extension to long-period variables. In the meantime, a number of the authorities in these matters have expressed the opinion that a single dynamical process may be responsible for the phenomena of the long-period variables as well. Although this process can scarcely be expected to produce identical results in the red stars and in the hotter yellow stars, it becomes necessary, if we are to accept this view, to reconcile the observed differences in the two types of variable stars under consideration. Long-period variables differ from Cepheid variables notably in respect to (1) range of the light variation, (2) length of period and class of spectrum, (3) degree of regularity, and (4) relation between the phases of the velocity and light variations.

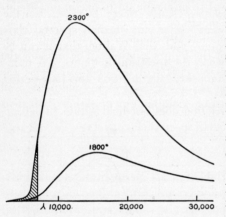

FIG. 9.39. Variation of Mira in Light and in Total Radiation. Energy curves at maximum and minimum. At maximum light the total radiation, represented by the area under the curve, has increased only two or three times. The visible radiation, represented by the shaded area, has increased many times. (From a diagram by Joy, in *Contributions from the Mount Wilson Observatory*)

Long-period variables exhibit variations in brightness considerably greater than those of Cepheid variables. But Pettit and Nicholson find with the thermocouple that in its total radiation the variation of Mira is about one magnitude, as it is for the average Cepheid variable. The variation of this red star that is visible to the eye is not representative of the whole variation in its output of energy. Thus the first difference becomes unimportant, so far as the physical theory is concerned.

9.40. Period-Spectrum Relation. All spectral classes are represented among the periodic variable stars. Cepheids of very short period are of class B. Cluster type Cepheids are mostly class A stars. Typical Cepheids show a decided preference for classes F and G, but some of them are as far advanced as K. Long-period variables belong to classes M, N, R, and S. Not only does the class of spectrum advance from one type to another, but typical Cepheids and long-period variables exhibit this relation clearly *within* the type. For the former type the relation between period and median spectral class is so definite, according to Shapley and Miss Walton, that it can be used to estimate the period, when the spectrum is known. A number of investigators have established the relation for long-period variables.

But the period-spectrum relation does not hold within the group of cluster variables. Their median spectral class averages A6, regardless of the period.

9.41. Peculiar Groups of Variable Stars. Between the regular variables and those whose fluctuations conform to no known rule, there are several groups whose light curves show certain uniformities. Three groups are well known; each one is designated by the name of a star that is typical of the group.

(1) *RV Tauri group.* The light curves sometimes resemble those of eclipsing binaries, having alternately deep and shallow minima; at other times they are more nearly like the curves of Cepheid variables. With respect to the length of period, which is also fairly regular, and the spectrum (classes G and K), they are intermediate between Cepheids and long-period variables. Gerasimovic finds about a dozen stars belonging to this group.

(2) *R Coronae Borealis group.* Remaining normally at their brightest for several months, and sometimes years, they then diminish in brightness in a few weeks, sometimes as much as eight or nine magnitudes. The return to maximum is irregular, and often occupies many months. The typical star, which was the first discovered, is

barely visible to the naked eye at maximum; its spectrum at maximum is class Go, resembling that of a typical Cepheid; at the minimum light bright lines appear in its spectrum. Five other examples are known, of spectral classes G and R.

(3) *U Geminorum group.* Normally faint for a month or more, they suddenly increase in brightness four or five magnitudes, and soon drop back again. The maxima of the light curve are alternately

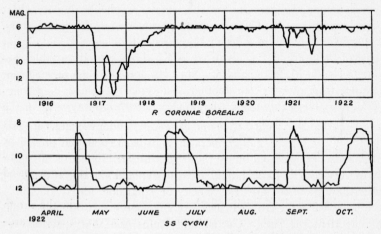

FIG. 9.41. Light Curves of Peculiar Variable Stars.

wide and narrow, as a rule. The brightest of this group, SS Cygni, is about the eighth magnitude at maximum; its spectrum at maximum is characterized by broad, dark hydrogen lines; at minimum it is of the Wolf-Rayet type (9.6). In the variations in brightness and spectrum this group bears some resemblance to temporary stars.

9.42. Irregular Variables.

Many red stars of classes M and N vary in light in a manner that seems to be unpredictable, except that the variations are within narrow limits, seldom exceeding half a magnitude, and often much less. Stebbins and Huffer at the Washburn Observatory (1928) have added from 40 to 60 new examples to the list, from observations of class M stars with the photo-electric photometer; they find that the percentage of variables among the stars examined increases with increasing redness of the stars.

Betelgeuse, the brightest of the irregular variables, sometimes rivals its neighbor, Rigel; at other times it is only a third as bright. Its spectral lines oscillate in a period of 5.8 years, according to Jones, at the Cape Observatory. Stebbins finds a similar long period for the light variation. In both cases there are variations in shorter intervals which seem not to be periodic.

9.43. Nature of Stellar Variability. It is generally agreed that much is yet to be learned before we have a real understanding of the physical causes of stellar variability. Evidence is accumulating that the periodic variations are caused by variations in the effective temperatures of the stars, and that behind these changes is a *single dynamical process* going on within the stars. It is not known to what extent this statement can be applied to irregular variable stars. Regarding the nature of the process, two theories have received considerable attention:

(1) *The theory of symmetrical pulsations* (9.34). This model, of a star rhythmically contracting and expanding under the alternate predominance of gravity and temperature, has been employed provisionally, and is not insisted on by those who use it. Indeed, it does not show very clearly, for example, why the Cepheid variable is brightest near the time of the greatest velocity of expansion, unless, of course, the upheaval serves to clear away an envelope which otherwise dims and reddens the light. Curtiss and Rufus find that spectral lines originating at different levels in the atmospheres of Cepheid variables give different velocity curves, suggesting pulsations of different amplitude and phase at the different levels.

(2) *The theory of rotational instability.* Jeans has proposed the theory that a variable star is in a stage of instability preceding its division into a spectroscopic binary. The star is rotating so rapidly that it is drawn out into an ellipsoid, one of whose equatorial axes is about twice as long as the axis of rotation. Alternate expansion and contraction of the long axis, combined with the rotation, can produce at least some of the types of stellar variability, in his opinion.

NOVAE, OR TEMPORARY STARS

9.44. Temporary Stars are stars that rise from comparative obscurity with remarkable rapidity, and then gradually subside, perhaps permanently, to something like their former faintness. They are "new stars" only in the sense of their temporary grandeur. The *galactic novae* are those that belong to our own stellar system, and that appear, almost always, in regions of the Milky Way. Novae in exterior systems, such as the spiral nebulae, will be discussed separately, in Chapter XII.

More than fifty galactic novae had been recorded up to 1928, of which two thirds were discovered in the present century. About twenty became visible to the naked eye, while six were of the first magnitude, or brighter. The very conspicuous ones are likely to be noticed by many people at about the same time; there is no special interest in trying to decide what person happened to be the first observer. The fainter novae are usually discovered, like the variable stars, by the comparison of photographs. Bailey estimates that twenty novae brighter than the ninth magnitude appear every year; but the majority of the fainter ones escape detection.

They are designated by the word "Nova," followed by a number in the order of their appearance in the constellation, and the genitive of the constellation name; but the number is often omitted, when the nova is otherwise identified. An example is Nova Aquilae, of 1918. A few novae have received letters in the variable star designation; T Aurigae and RR Pictoris are examples.

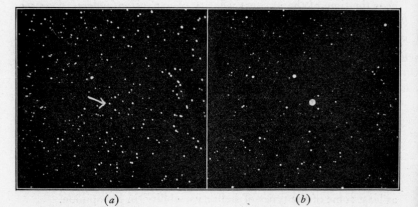

(a)   (b)

FIG. 9.45. Nova Aquilae, No. 3, Before and After the Outburst. (a) In 1905, as an apparently invariable star of the tenth magnitude. (b) On July 12, 1918, more than a month after the outburst. (From photographs by E. E. Barnard, Yerkes Observatory)

9.45. Remarkable Novae. The brightest temporary star on record appeared in November, 1572, in Cassiopeia; it was observed by Tycho. This star attained a brightness equal to that of Venus at greatest brilliancy, and was visible in full daylight; thereafter it gradually faded, disappearing from view (there were then no telescopes) in the following May. Next in order of brightness was "Kepler's star" in Ophiuchus, in 1604, which rivaled Jupiter in brightness, and remained visible to the naked eye for eighteen months. It is interesting that the remaining four of the six brightest novae on record appeared in the first quarter of the present century.

Nova Persei (1901) rose to magnitude 0.1, a little brighter than Capella; Nova Aquilae (1918) was of magnitude −1.1, approaching the splendor of Sirius; Nova Cygni, in 1920, was not much inferior to Deneb; and Nova Pictoris, visible in the southern hemisphere in 1925, was of magnitude 1.2, about as bright as Spica. These four stars rose suddenly from the eleventh and fainter magnitudes.

Since the distances of most galactic novae are not, for the present, subject to very reliable determination, the absolute magnitudes of individuals are likely to be uncertain. On the average, the absolute magnitude at maximum is −6.2, according to Lundmark, which means that they are 25,000 times more luminous than the sun. In the few hours of their greatest splendor, novae are the most luminous of the stars.

9.46. Light Variations of Novae. Characteristic of the light curve of a temporary star is the abrupt rise to maximum, and the almost immediate decline thereafter, at first rapidly and then more slowly,

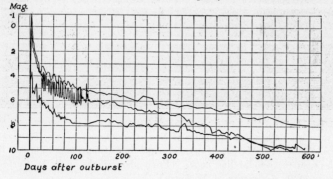

FIG. 9.46. Light Curves of Nova Aquilae, 1918; Nova Persei, 1901; and Nova Geminorum, 1912. They are designated in order of decreasing height. (From *Harvard College Observatory Annals*)

with occasional partial recoveries. After the discovery of a nova, it is often possible to trace its previous history from photographs which have been taken of that region of the sky.

Nova Persei increased in brightness in twenty-seven hours from below the eleventh magnitude to magnitude 2.7, and in thirty-eight hours more to its maximum brightness. Nova Aquilae, on June 5, 1918, was of magnitude 10.5, and had shown no evidence of conspicuous variability during the previous thirty years in which the records are available. On June 8, it shone as a star of the first magnitude, and was still rising. These are examples of the rapid rise of a nova to maximum brightness, which generally occupies not more than two or three days. A dozen years or more may elapse before the star has resumed its original faintness.

There are departures from the usual form of light curve. P Cygni is an example; it appeared as a nova in 1600, but its decline in light, and the usual progression of changes in its spectrum seem to have been arrested. This star is now of the fifth magnitude and is apparently constant in light.

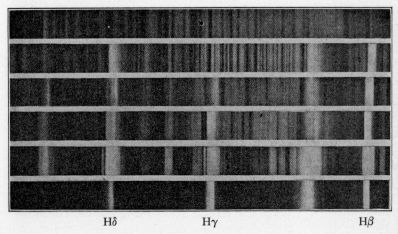

Hδ   Hγ   Hβ

FIG. 9.47. Changing Spectrum of Nova Geminorum, 1912. The first spectrogram was secured March 13, 1912, near the time of maximum light; the last on April 15, at the nebular line stage. (From photographs by R. H. Curtiss, Observatory of the University of Michigan)

9.47. Changing Spectra of Novae. The spectra of several temporary stars, presumably typical of all, have exhibited about the same series of remarkable changes. Since the rise to maximum light is unexpected and rapid, the known history of the spectrum during the ascent is not extensive. At and after the maximum several distinct stages are reached:

(1) *Class A stage.* Near the time of maximum light, the spectrum resembles that of the super-giant star, α Cygni; but the dark lines of hydrogen and other elements are strongly and increasingly displaced toward the violet, corresponding finally to an enormous radial velocity of approach (1700 km./sec. in the case of Nova Aquilae). These dark lines border, on the violet sides, very wide bright lines ("bands") whose centers are not appreciably displaced, and which grow brighter, while the dark lines fade.

α Cygni (Class A2)

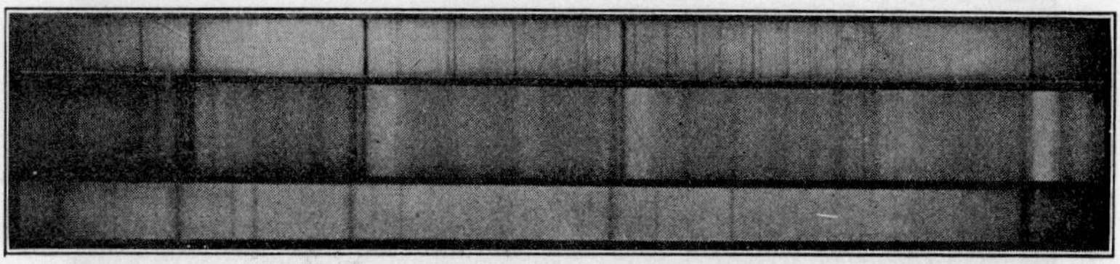

γ Orionis (Class B2)

Fig. 9.47A. Class A and Class B Stages in the Spectrum of Nova Geminorum, 1912. For comparison with the nova spectrum, photographed March 30, 1912, the spectrum of α Cygni is shown above, and that of γ Orionis below. The comparison spectra are shifted to the left to bring their lines into coincidence with the strongly displaced lines in the spectrum of the nova. (From a photograph by W. H. Wright, Lick Observatory)

(2) *Class B stage.* Two or three days after maximum light, an entirely new pattern of lines appears with the first one, and gradually replaces it. These lines, in dark and bright pairs as before, are of hydrogen, helium, and other elements characteristic of spectral class B. The new dark lines are displaced, at first, even farther toward the violet; in Nova Aquilae their shifts corresponded to a velocity of 2300 km./sec. of approach, which after the first month diminished to 1700 km./sec.

(3) *Nebular line stage.* After several weeks when the nova has become considerably fainter, the lines of the second stage fade away, and the continuous background of the spectrum as well. Then the bright lines appear which characterize the bright-line spectrum of the gaseous nebulae (11.29).

(4) *Class O stage.* Finally, after several years, the typical nebular lines fade, and the star settles down, for a longer time, as a Wolf-Rayet star of spectral class O. In the meantime, as the distribution of the bright lines has changed, the color of the star has altered from white to red, and then to green, and finally to white again.

9.48. Expanding Envelopes of Novae. Barnard, at the Yerkes Observatory in 1916, discovered a symmetrical envelope expanding around Nova Persei, giving it the appearance of a planetary nebula (11.32). This was nearly sixteen years after the outburst of the nova, which in the meantime had become very faint. Again in October, 1918, only about four months after Nova Aquilae blazed into prominence, he saw a similar envelope around this star. As ob-

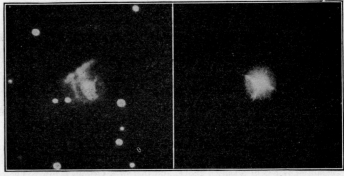

Nova Persei
November 15, 1917

Nova Aquilae
April 25, 1927

FIG. 9.48. Expanding Envelopes Around Nova Persei and Nova Aquilae. (From photographs at the Mount Wilson Observatory)

served by Barnard, and by Aitken at the Lick Observatory, the envelope of Nova Aquilae increased in radius at the rate of 1″ a year. On Hubble's photographs with the 100-inch telescope the radius was 8″.2 at the end of 1926, and was still increasing. The steady velocity of the expansion, as determined from the strongly displaced dark lines in the spectrum, and when these had faded, from half the widths of the bright bands, has already been given as 1700 km./sec.

Since the tangential velocity of expansion, T, is presumably the same as the radial velocity, and the angular velocity, μ, is known, the distance, in parsecs, of this nova can be found by the relation (8.13): $D = 0.211 \ T \ \mu$. The distance of Nova Aquilae is therefore 360 parsecs, or about 1200 light-years. The diameter in April, 1927, was 6000 astronomical units, and was increasing at the rate of one astronomical unit a day. The absolute magnitude of the nova was $+2.7$ before the outburst, equal to that of a normal class F star of the main sequence (9.24); at the maximum, the absolute magnitude was -8.9, when the nova was 300,000 times more luminous than the sun. These envelopes are not to be confused with another sort of nebulosity which appeared on Wolf's photographs at Heidelberg in August, 1901, in the vicinity of Nova Persei, and seemed to be expanding with surprising speed. Later observations made it evident that a neighboring dark nebula was being lighted up by the outburst from the nova, and that the illumination was spreading from day to day to more remote parts of the nebula.

9.49. The Nature of Novae. Concerning the physical cause of the outburst of a temporary star, very little is definitely known. It is now generally believed that the cause is within the star — perhaps a sudden readjustment, which results in an excessive output of energy for a short time. The frequency of these outbursts, in our own stellar system and in the spiral nebulae, is great enough to suggest that the majority of stars, perhaps all of them including the sun, may be novae at some time in their histories.

The expanding envelopes, thus far noticed in only two or three novae including Nova Pictoris, and the series of changes in the spectra that have been mentioned, are doubtless characteristic of novae in general. Some of the star's gaseous material is propelled outward at terrific rates in the form of two shells. The dark lines in the spectrum are displaced strongly toward the violet, because the absorbing material between us and the star is rushing toward us at full speed. The bright bands are the emission spectra of the shells. Since their light is taken from all parts of the shells, some parts approaching and others receding, the bright bands occupy wide spaces in the spectrum between the positions corresponding respectively to maximum velocity of approach and of recession. Dilution of the intervening absorbing material by the expansion of the shells, and the diminishing light of the star account satisfactorily for the fading of the dark lines and continuous spectrum. Since the light of the shells themselves is concentrated in a few bright bands, these become relatively much more conspicuous.

The later changes of the spectrum to the nebular line and Wolf-Rayet stages are not so well understood, nor is it clearly understood why larger images of the envelopes are produced by the light of the nebular lines proper, than by that of the hydrogen lines, as Wright was the first to observe. Both sets of lines show the same radial velocities.

Owing to the infrequency of Wolf-Rayet stars, it is difficult to believe that this stage is the final one in the series of spectral changes. In fact, the nova of 1866, T Coronae Borealis, is now a class M star. On the other hand, this nova was unusual in being far from the Milky Way, and in other respects.

REFERENCES

Caroline E. Furness, *An Introduction to the Study of Variable Stars* (Houghton Mifflin, 1915).

Karl Schiller, *Einführung in das Studium der Veränderlichen Sterne* (Barth, Leipzig, 1923).

Edward S. King, *A Manual of Celestial Photography* (Eastern Science Supply Co., 1931).

The 72-inch Reflecting Telescope, Dominion Astrophysical Observatory, Victoria.

CHAPTER X

THE CONSTITUTION OF THE STARS

EFFECTIVE TEMPERATURES AND DIMENSIONS — STELLAR ATMOSPHERES
— THE INTERIORS OF THE STARS — THE SOURCE OF STELLAR ENERGY

Like the sun, the stars are globular masses of intensely hot gas. Although they are of enormous size, their vast distances prevent us from seeing them as disks, even with the aid of powerful telescopes. The radiations which come to us from the stars emerge from their photospheres and filter through their atmospheres. Observations can deal directly only with the superficial phenomena, except as the mutual attractions of members of binary systems reveal the masses and densities of the material inside. The purpose of this Chapter is, first, to present the information which the starlight conveys concerning the exteriors of the stars, and second, to consider what conditions in the interiors can produce the exterior phenomena.

EFFECTIVE TEMPERATURES AND DIMENSIONS

10.1. Methods of Determining Effective Temperatures. The *effective temperature* of a star is the temperature calculated by the radiation laws (7.38) from the observed quantity and quality of the star's radiation. These laws apply to a perfect radiator. It is probable that the stars are so nearly perfect radiators that the results of the calculation represent fairly their photospheric temperatures.

When the rate at which the star's total radiation is received on the earth has been measured, and the distance and diameter of the star are known, the rate of the radiation can be calculated, for example, the number of calories emitted in one minute by a square centimeter of the star's surface; then by Stefan's law the effective temperature becomes known. The procedure is similar to that employed in determining the sun's temperature from the solar constant.

Another way is to find the closest match between the observed energy curve of the star and curves calculated for different temperatures by Planck's formula, as in the determination of the sun's temperature (7.40).

In the past twenty years, the energy curves of the stars have been studied by many investigators. At first, the relative brightness in various parts of the star's spectrum was observed visually. Later, the spectrum was photographed, and densities were measured along the spectrogram. Sampson, at Edinburgh, has determined the temperatures of many stars in this way, relative to that of Capella, which he assumes as 5500°. Greaves and Davidson, at Greenwich (1932), publish absolute stellar temperatures obtained by comparing the starlight with the filtered light of an acetylene flame several hundred feet away.

10.2. Temperatures Calculated from Color and Heat-Indices. It is possible to derive from Planck's formula the following relation between the absolute magnitude, M, of a star, its diameter, D, in terms of the sun's diameter, and its effective temperature, T:

$$M = -5 \log D + 1.555 / \lambda_0 T + \text{a constant.}$$

For the present purposes, λ_0 is the *effective wave-length* — a sort of average wave-length which has about the same effect as all the observed wave-lengths combined. For the calculation of the photographic magnitude, M_p, the effective wave-length is taken to be $\lambda 4250$; for the visual magnitude, M_v, Brill's determination, $\lambda 5290$, has been adopted by many. Substituting these values of the effective wave-length, we have expressions for the photographic and visual magnitudes; their difference is the color-index, I (9.18), of the star:

$$I = M_p - M_v = 7200/T + \text{a constant.}$$

For the sun (spectral class G0, of the main sequence) the color-index is about 0.57, and the effective temperature is 5750° K, the value already given (7.40). The constant is then equal to $0.57 + 7200/5750$, or -0.68, so that the above relation becomes:

$$T = \frac{7200}{I + 0.68}.$$

Table 10.I gives the color-indices for the chief spectral classes, as determined by King at Harvard and Seares at Mount Wilson, and the corresponding temperatures calculated by the formula. It is believed that this system represents the photospheric temperatures of the stars fairly well, say within ten per cent.

A similar relation can be derived for calculating the effective temperature of a star from its heat-index (9.21). Since 1922, Pettit and Nicholson have determined from measurements with the thermocouple the heat-indices of 124 stars. By this means, and by observing also the percentage of absorption of the radiations by a water-cell, they have deduced a system of stellar temperatures which run a little below the color temperatures.

TABLE 10.I.   COLOR-INDICES AND CALCULATED
EFFECTIVE TEMPERATURES OF THE STARS

Spectrum	Color Index	Temperature	Spectrum	Main Sequence		Giants	
				Color Index	Temperature	Color Index	Temperature
O	....	35,000° K to 25,000	Go	0.57	5,750° K	0.67	5,300° K
Bo	− 0.33	21,000	G5	0.65	5,400	0.92	4,500
B5	− 0.18	14,000	Ko	0.78	4,900	1.12	4,000
Ao	0.00	10,600	K5	0.98	4,300	1.57	3,200
A5	0.20	8,200	Mo	1.45	3,400	1.73	3,000
Fo	0.33	7,100	M2	....	2,870	....	2,810
F5	0.47	6,300	M8	....	.....	....	1,780

10.3. Effective Temperatures of the Stars.   In general, stars differ in color because their surface temperatures are different. With increasing temperature, according to Wien's law, the most intense radiation moves toward the violet end of the spectrum. Because of absorption effects in the atmospheres of the stars and of the earth, and for other reasons, the rule is not without exceptions. Class O stars are somewhat yellower than stars of class B; their temperatures must be determined from other considerations (10.20). For stars cooler than class Mo the temperatures in Table 10.I have been calculated from the heat-indices.

The surface temperatures of the stars run from 35,000° K, or over, down to somewhat less than 2000° which is about the melting point of platinum. Even the coolest of these stars is still very hot, by ordinary standards; and the temperatures of all of them increase enormously with increasing depth, to millions of degrees at their centers.

It is to be noticed in the Table that the yellow and red stars of the main sequence have effective temperatures considerably higher than giant stars of the same spectral class. Evidently the characteristics of stellar spectra are not controlled entirely by temperature. The density of the stellar atmosphere is a contributing factor (10.21).

10.4. Calculation of Stellar Diameters.   When the angular diameter and distance of a celestial body are known, the linear diameter, in miles or kilometers, is easily derived. Thus we know the diameters of the sun, moon, and principal planets. But even the largest and nearest of the stars are so remote that their angular diameters are comparable with that of a golf ball at the distance of a hundred miles. No telescope in existence can show the true disk of any star, except the sun. Nevertheless, the sizes of many stars are now available as the result of calculation from other data.

The total luminosity of a star is known from the absolute magnitude. The brightness of unit area, say of a square mile of the star's surface, can be derived from the surface temperature which becomes known when the spectral class has been established by observation. Dividing the total luminosity by that of a square mile, we obtain the number of square miles in the spherical surface, and thus the diameter of the star. By this procedure the diameters of representative stars in Table 10.II were calculated.

TABLE 10.II. CALCULATED TEMPERATURES AND DIAMETERS OF REPRESENTATIVE STARS

Star	Spectrum	Temperature	Diameter (Sun = 1)	Mass (Sun = 1)	Density (Water = 1)
Giants					
Antares	Mo	3,100° K	480	30	0.0000003
Aldebaran	K5	3,300	60	4	0.00002
Arcturus	Ko	4,100	30	8	0.0003
Capella A	Go	5,500	12	4.2	0.002
Main Sequence					
β Centauri	B1	21,000	11	25	0.02
Vega	Ao	11,200	2.4	3	0.1
Sirius A	Ao	11,200	1.8	2.4	0.4
Altair	A5	8,600	1.4	2	0.6
Procyon	F5	6,500	1.9	1.1	0.2
α Centauri A	Go	6,000	1.0	1.1	1.1
The Sun	Go	6,000	1.0	1.0	1.4
70 Ophiuchi A	Ko	5,100	1.0	0.9	0.9
61 Cygni A	K7	3,800	0.7	0.5	1.3
Krueger 60 A	M3	3,300	0.3	0.3	9
White Dwarfs					
Sirius B	F	7,500	0.034	0.96	27,000
o₂ Eridani B	Ao	11,000	0.019	0.44	64,000

The formula for these calculations is easily derived from the relation already given (10.2). When the effective wave-length for visual observations ($\lambda_0 = 5290$) is employed, the quantities related by the formula are the diameter, D, in terms of the sun's diameter, the absolute visual magnitude, M_v, and the effective temperature, T. This relation assumes the form:

$$\log D = 5900/T - 0.2M_v - 0.22.$$

Thus the star's diameter can be calculated with a considerable degree of accuracy when its effective temperature and absolute visual magnitude are known.

It has been mentioned previously (8.49) that the diameters of stars which form eclipsing systems can be evaluated when the conditions are favorable.

10.5. The Stellar Interferometer.   Direct measurement of the angular diameters of some of the larger stars is accomplished by the use of a special type of interferometer.   In its simplest form the *stellar*

FIG. 10.5.   Fringes Observed with the Interferometer.   The two sets of fringes are from two artificial stars of the same brightness. At the left end of the series the fringes are superposed; at the right, they are out of step, so that they disappear near the center of the pattern.   (From a photograph by J. A. Anderson, Mount Wilson Observatory)

interferometer is a telescope having its objective covered, with the exception of two small apertures equidistant from the center and on opposite sides of the same diameter.   The separation of the apertures can be varied.   If only one aperture were used, the effect would be simply that of reducing the size of the telescope; the image of the star would be made fainter and the diffraction disk (1.41) would be enlarged.   With both apertures, this spurious disk is crossed by a number of parallel interference fringes alternately bright and dark.   There are really two similar patterns superposed, formed by light from the two halves of the star's true disk.

As the distance between the apertures is increased, the two patterns get out of step, until a separation is reached, if the size of the objective permits, at which the bright lines of one pattern fall on the dark lines of the other, and vice-versa, so that the fringes disappear. At this critical separation, D_o, the theory shows that the angular diameter of the star equals 1.22 λ/D_o, where λ is the effective wavelength of the starlight.   If the star is less luminous at the limb, as much so as the sun's disk, the multiplier must be increased to 1.43. When the angular diameter, d'', has been measured, and the parallax,

p'', is known, the linear diameter of the star, D, in terms of the sun's diameter, can be found from the relation: $D = 107 \, d''/p''$.

As early as 1868, Fizeau proposed the idea of using a telescope in this way. About 1891, Michelson employed the stellar interferometer to measure the diameters of Jupiter's satellites, and in 1920, he was active in developing unexpected possibilities of this instrument for the measurement of stellar diameters.

10.6. The Beam Interferometer.   The principle of the stellar interferometer does not, in fact, require that the two apertures be placed over the objective, or in the converging beam proceeding from it.   If

Fig. 10.6.   Beam Interferometer.   Twenty-foot interferometer beam on the end of the 100-inch telescope, Mount Wilson Observatory.

this were necessary, it would be almost impossible to measure the diameter of any star with present telescopes.   Almost without exception, the separation of the apertures required to make the fringes disappear exceeds 100 inches.

For the purpose of measuring the angular diameters of the stars the effective diameter of the 100-inch reflecting telescope has been increased to twenty feet by the introduction of the *beam interferometer*. This consists of a structural steel beam twenty feet long which is placed across the top of the telescope tube, and upon which two pairs of 6-inch mirrors are mounted, the mirrors of each pair being equidistant from the center. One pair of mirrors, having a separation less than the diameter of the objective, remains fixed during the measurements. The separation of the second pair can be increased up to 20 feet; this pair, whose distance apart gives the value D_o in the formula, receive the starlight and reflect it inward to the two fixed mirrors, which send the two beams to the objective.

Even with the separation of twenty feet the fringes vanish for only a few stars. Another interferometer having 15-inch mirrors on a 50-foot beam was installed in 1930 at the Mount Wilson Observatory.

The stellar interferometer has been employed also for resolving binary stars which are a little too close to be separated with the telescope alone. For this purpose, Anderson devised a special type of interferometer, in which the line of apertures can be rotated. When this line is made parallel to the line joining the two stars, and when the separation of the apertures is increased until the fringes become the least conspicuous (they do not vanish, unless the two stars are of equal brightness), the angular separation of the stars equals $0.5 \, \lambda/D_o$. The position angle can be determined also. By this means the visual orbits of Capella and Mizar, both formerly known only as spectroscopic binaries, were studied by Merrill and Pease respectively.

10.7. Stellar Diameters Measured with the Interferometer. Betelgeuse was the first star to be measured with the 20-foot interferometer. The calculations had indicated that this giant red star would be a promising subject. On December 13, 1920, the interferometer was ready for the test of its usefulness, and the great telescope was set on the star. It was found that the fringes were invisible when the mirrors were separated by 121 inches (307 cm.). The diameter of Betelgeuse is therefore 260 million miles, or slightly less than the diameter of the orbit of Mars. The successful completion of this undertaking, which must be counted among the major triumphs of modern astronomy, aroused great public interest. It was a triumph for the calculators as well as for the observers, for the measured and predicted diameters are in substantial agreement.

In order to obtain the diameter of Betelgeuse from the critical separation of the mirrors, $D_o = 307$ cm., at which the fringes vanish, we return to the formula for the angular diameter: d (in radians) $= 1.22 \, \lambda/D_o$, where λ, the effective wave-length, is taken to be 5750 angstroms. Thus d (in radians) $= 1.22 \times 0.0000575/307 = 0.000000228$ radians, or $0''.047$. If the parallax of the star is $0''.017$, the linear diameter, in terms of the sun's diameter, is

107 $d''/p'' = 107 \times 0''.047/0''.017 = 295$, or in round numbers 300 times
the sun's diameter (864,000 miles). The diameter of Betelgeuse is 260
million miles.

Pease has measured the angular diameters of seven stars (Table
10.III), for which the fringes disappear before the maximum separation of 20 feet is reached, or so nearly disappear that the required
critical separation can be estimated. Betelgeuse, Antares, and Mira
Ceti require separations around 10 feet, while Arcturus and Aldebaran need 24 feet. Considerable uncertainty in the parallaxes of
α Herculis and Mira is passed on to their linear diameters which are
therefore placed in parentheses in the Table. Continued observations
of Betelgeuse by Pease indicate that its diameter varies considerably.
The largest and smallest diameters are given.

TABLE 10.III. DIAMETERS OF RED GIANT STARS
MEASURED WITH THE INTERFEROMETER

Star	Spectrum	Angular Diameter	Parallax	Diameter	
				Sun = 1	Millions of miles
Antares	Mo	0''.040	0''.0095	450	390
α Herculis	M8	0 .030	(0 .008)	(400)	(350)
Betelgeuse	Mo	{ 0 .047 \\ 0 .034	0 .017	{ 300 \\ 210	{ 260 \\ 180
Mira Ceti	M7	0 .056	(0 .02)	(300)	(260)
β Pegasi	M5	0 .021	0 .016	40	35
Aldebaran	K5	0 .020	0 .057	38	33
Arcturus	Ko	0 .020	0 .080	27	23

10.8. Diameters of the Stars. The giant stars have the greatest
diameters, as Table 10.II shows. First called "giants" because of
their high luminosities, these stars have proved to be giants indeed.
The red giants are the largest and, according to present calculations,
Antares heads the list with a diameter of about 400 million miles,
nearly fifty per cent greater than the diameter of the orbit of Mars.
It will be understood that this figure gives the order of the linear
diameter. The specified value can be no more accurate, at least, than
the adopted value of the parallax, which in this case has a probable
error of 20 per cent.

The stars of the main sequence are generally comparable in size with the sun; the blue stars are somewhat larger, and the red ones smaller. The great decrease in luminosity down this sequence must be ascribed mostly to diminishing surface temperature. The smallest known stars are the white dwarfs, such as the faint companion of Sirius; these stars are not much larger than the earth.

10.9. Masses of the Stars. The gravitational effect of a single star on its neighbors is too small to give any information about its mass. It is only when the star is a member of a binary system that the mass can be evaluated on this basis, and then only under favorable circumstances (8.35, 8.40, 8.48). In the case of visual binaries, their orbits must be determined and their distances known. Precise determinations of the masses of spectroscopic binaries require that both spectra appear and, in addition, that the two stars mutually eclipse, or else be separated with the telescope. These requirements are not so often fulfilled. Fortunately, the masses of stars, whether double or single, can be derived with considerable confidence from a simple relation which they bear to their absolute magnitudes (10.10).

In Table 10.II, which is adapted from data tabulated in *Astronomy*, by Russell, Dugan, and Stewart, the letters A or B following the name of the star denote the brighter or fainter component of a binary system. For stars not designated in this way, except for the sun, the masses are taken from the mass-luminosity curve.

The great majority of the stars have masses between one fifth and five times the sun's mass. The smallest known masses are those of Krueger 60B and of the faintest member of the triple system o_2 Eridani, both about one fifth of the sun's mass. Exceptionally large masses are found for some of the giant stars, and especially for the highly luminous class O stars; among these, the constituents of a spectroscopic system studied by J. S. Plaskett at Victoria have masses at least 75 and 63 times the sun's mass.

10.10. The Mass-Luminosity Relation. When the absolute bolometric magnitudes (9.21) of stars are plotted against the logarithms of their masses, it is seen (Fig. 10.10) that the points lie very nearly along a smooth curve. Both giant stars, such as δ Cephei, and stars of the main sequence, such as the sun and Krueger 60, conform to the rule; but the white dwarf stars (10.13) are much fainter than their masses would indicate. Eddington called attention to the mass-luminosity relation, in 1924, not only as shown by the observed data, but also as required by the particular model of a star on which his theory of stellar constitution was based. The close agreement in form between the observed and theoretical curves was believed at first to argue for the validity of Eddington's model (10.29).

More recently, Russell, Vogt, and others have explained that the theoretical curve changes form slowly as the model of a star is altered; thus the ability of a specific model to predict the observed relation gives little assurance that this model can tell us much about actual stars. For the present, the mass-luminosity curve is valuable chiefly as a means of determining the masses of stars to which it applies.

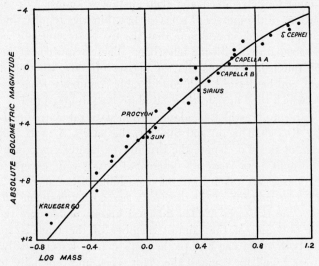

Fig. 10.10.   Mass-Luminosity Relation.   The dots show how the observed magnitudes of stars are related to the logarithms of their masses. The curve is derived theoretically by Eddington.

10.11. Densities of the Stars. The mean density of a star is found by dividing the mass by the volume which is derived from the linear diameter. The density is not the same throughout the star; it increases toward the center where the density is probably twenty, or more, times the average value.

There is great diversity in the densities of the stars, as Table 10.II shows. The lowest values are found for the red giants. Antares, for example, has a mean density three ten-millionths of the density of water, or *1/3000 of the density of ordinary air.* If Einstein's theory of gravitation is correct, a star as large as Antares could not have a density as great as the sun's and at the same time be visible; for gravity at its surface would be so powerful that the light could not escape.

From these amazingly low values there is a steady upward gradation along the giant sequence, from red to blue, until the densities merge into those of the main-sequence stars. Along the latter sequence, from blue to red, the density increases slowly. In the white dwarfs it has risen abruptly to *tens and perhaps even hundreds of thousands times the density of water.*

10.12. The Companion of Sirius. By the relation which connects the mass and brightness of an ordinary star, the faint companion of Sirius (8.33) should be about as luminous as the sun. Its mass is nearly equal to the sun's mass, and it is bluer than the sun (about spectral class F). But this star has only 1/360 the luminosity of the sun; its absolute visual magnitude is 11.3. The companion of Sirius is no ordinary star. It has the mass of a star, but a size more appropriate for a planet. The diameter, calculated from the effective temperature and absolute magnitude (10.4), is 30,000 miles — only three or four times the earth's diameter. The mean density is therefore enormous; it is of the order of 30,000 times the density of water.

Such high compression of matter would have been considered impossible a few years ago; and even now it might be regarded with some suspicion, if it were not confirmed by an independent observational test. Adams at Mount Wilson, in 1925, observed a large shift of the lines in the spectrum of this star toward the red end of the spectrum, in practical agreement with the displacement predicted by the general theory of relativity (4.35) for a star of this order of density.

This result is considered both a successful test of the general theory of relativity and a confirmation of the belief that ionized material in the stars is capable of enormous compression.

The amount of the displacement of the lines in the spectrum of a star toward the red, predicted by the theory of relativity, is directly proportional to the mass of the star and inversely proportional to its radius. In the case of the sun the predicted shift is equivalent to the Doppler effect for a radial velocity of 0.6 km./sec., which is about the value of the relativity shift for all stars of the main sequence. This displacement in the solar spectrum has probably been observed (7.9). The predicted displacement in the spectrum of the companion of Sirius, owing to the small radius, is more than thirty times the shift in the solar spectrum, being equivalent to the Doppler effect for a radial velocity of 20 km./sec.

After allowance for true Doppler effects due to the orbital motion of the companion, and to the motion of the binary system as a whole (derived from observations of the spectrum of Sirius), Adams found a shift toward the red in the spectrum of the companion equivalent to the Doppler shift for a velocity of 19 km./sec. More recently, Moore has observed practically the same shift on spectrograms of the companion taken at Mount Hamilton.

10.13. White Dwarfs. The companion of Sirius is an example of the class of *white dwarf stars* which do not conform to the mass-luminosity relation and which stand apart from the other stars on the spectrum-luminosity diagram (Fig. 9.24), far below the white stars of the main sequence. Two other known examples are the brighter of the two companions of o_2 Eridani and a twelfth magnitude star, sometimes designated as Van Maanen's star. The faint companion of Procyon and several other stars are suspected of belonging to this class.

The fact that a very few white dwarfs are now known does not mean necessarily that they are really scarce. Owing to their feeble light it is difficult to identify any except the nearest ones. The three known examples above mentioned are within four parsecs of the sun.

These peculiar stars present problems of the greatest interest. It is believed that the majority of the atoms in their interiors are stripped of their electrons down to the nuclei. Radiation is feeble, because there is not much atomic machinery in sufficient repair to radiate. Gravitation has the upper hand, jamming together the fragments of atoms in such high concentration that the gas laws do not hold.

Stellar Atmospheres

The conditions of the gases in stellar atmospheres are revealed by the patterns of dark lines and bands which these gases absorb from the continuous spectrum of the photosphere, and, less obviously at present, by the bright lines which their own radiations sometimes superpose upon it. As we have seen (9.5), there is a progressive change in these characteristics of stellar spectra, from the complex patterns of the red stars to the simpler ones of the blue stars. As we shall now see, temperature and density (or pressure) are the chief factors which control these changes in stellar spectra.

In order to interpret the spectral sequence in terms of varying conditions in stellar atmospheres it is necessary to consider the ability of the atoms of the different chemical elements to absorb and emit light selectively under different conditions of temperature and pressure.

10.14. Normal and Excited Atoms. According to the conventional Bohr theory an atom consists of a positively charged nucleus surrounded by a number of electrons, each possessing unit negative charge of electricity. The electrons are revolving in orbits whose semi-major axes are proportional to the numbers 1, 4, 9, and so on, the squares of the integers. For every quantum of energy that is added to the atom, an electron is shifted from one orbit to the orbit next above. For every quantum emitted by the atom an electron is transferred to the next orbit below. By this convention the dark and bright lines in the spectrum can generally be accounted for satisfactorily, especially when further orbits are provided, having radii proportional to the squares of the half-integers. If one prefers, he may dismiss the orbits entirely and refer merely to various energy levels or states of the atom.

The *normal atom* is in its lowest energy state. It can not emit light. When this atom absorbs energy, an electron is transferred to a higher level, from which it almost immediately falls again with the emission of the energy. *Ultimate lines* in the spectrum, either dark or bright, are produced by transitions from or to the lowest energy level of the atom. The *excited atom* is in a higher energy state. *Subordinate lines* in the spectrum are produced by transitions upward from or back again to this state. The atoms of each chemical element have characteristic series of ultimate and subordinate lines in their spectra.

10.15. Neutral and Ionized Atoms. The *neutral atom* of any chemical element contains its full quota of electrons — as many of these negative charges as there are positive charges on the nucleus. In this condition the atom is electrically neutral. The number of electrons, or of positive unit charges on the nucleus, is the *atomic number* of the element, which ranges from one, for hydrogen, up to 92 for uranium (Table 10.VIII).

The *ionized atom* has lost one or more of its electrons; it has absorbed energy enough to transfer these electrons successively beyond the outermost orbit. They have accordingly become *free electrons* — free to dart about independently until they are captured by ionized atoms, which have positive charges, and therefore trap by their attractions the stray electrons, if they come too close. A *singly ionized atom* has lost a single electron, and has acquired thereby a single unit positive charge. A *doubly ionized atom* has lost two electrons and is doubly charged. A convenient way of indicating the extent of the ionization of an atom is by adding a plus sign to the abbreviation for the element for each electron the atom has lost. Thus singly ionized sodium is written Na+, doubly ionized silicon Si++, and so on.

The pattern of lines in the spectrum of the ionized atom is not the same as the pattern produced by the neutral atom of the same element. The removal of an electron leaves the superstructure of the atom similar in arrangement to that of the element next lower in atomic number, and causes its spectrum to become nearly the same. Doubly ionized lithium (atomic number 3), singly ionized helium (2), and neutral hydrogen (1) give spectra very nearly alike.

The spectra of four stages of silicon, Si, Si+, Si++, and Si+++, have been studied in the laboratory by A. Fowler, and identified in the stars. Millikan has removed seven electrons from the atom of chlorine. At the enormous temperatures in the interiors of the stars it is believed that the atoms of all the elements are almost completely stripped of their electrons.

10.16. Ionization of Atoms.   In order to remove an electron against the attractive force of the remainder of the atom, more energy is required than is added to the atom when it absorbs visual radiation. The necessary energy may be provided by radiation of higher frequency, such as x-rays, or by violent collisions of the atom with electrons, or with other atoms. All these factors are active in the interiors of the stars, but in their atmospheres the last named factor is the most important. In this process of *thermal ionization* the atom is disrupted by energy supplied from its highly heated surroundings.

The physicist Saha, of Calcutta, was the first to show, in 1920, that thermal ionization of the atom can be treated in the same way as the dissociation of a chemical compound by heat. The extent of this dissociation increases with the temperature to which the compound is raised. It depends also on how firmly the compound is held together, and on the number of the separate constituents in the neighborhood, which are combining to offset the dissociation. Similarly, in a highly heated gas the fraction of the atoms which have lost an electron increases with the temperature of the gas, and, for a given temperature, is greater when the density of the gas is low, and when the electron is loosely bound to the atom.

The last consideration is usually stated numerically as the *ionization potential,* a number of "volts," which is proportional to the energy required to remove an electron from a neutral or an already ionized atom. These numbers are given, for a few elements, in the second column of Table 10.IV.

10.17. Effect of Temperature on Spectra. The theory of thermal ionization has been amplified and given more precise form, especially by R. H. Fowler and Milne. Their formulae permit the calculation, for a gas at an assigned temperature and pressure, of the fraction of the atoms in any state of ionization, and of these the fraction at any level of excitation. It is possible, therefore, to predict how the pattern of lines in the spectrum of the gas will change as the temperature is altered.

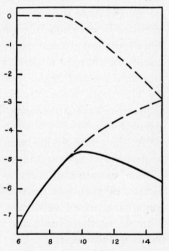

The strength of a line in the spectrum of a gas depends on the abundance of the gas — the number of atoms present — and on the fraction of these atoms which are in the correct state to produce the line in question. If, for example, it is a subordinate line of the singly ionized atom, the atom must have lost an electron, and have acquired sufficient additional energy to raise a second electron to the required level. When this fraction is calculated for various temperatures,

FIG. 10.17. Relative Strength of Mg+ Absorption Line λ4481 at Different Temperatures. (From *Stellar Atmospheres,* by Cecilia H. Payne)

and plotted against them, the curve through the plotted points shows how the strength of the line in the spectrum of the gas varies as the temperature of the gas is increased — at what temperatures the line makes its appearance, becomes strongest, and disappears (Fig. 10.17).

In the Figure, the ordinates are logarithms of computed fractional concentrations. The abscissas are temperatures, in thousands of degrees absolute Centigrade. Curve (1) represents the fraction of the Mg atoms present which are singly ionized. Curve (2) represents the fraction of these that are suitably excited to produce the absorption line $\lambda 4481$. The full curve, formed by combining the ordinates of (1) and (2), shows the fraction of all the Mg atoms which are able to absorb $\lambda 4481$; it therefore gives the relative strength of this line at the various temperatures.

10.18. Interpretation of the Spectral Sequence; the Cooler Stars.
It has been pointed out (9.4) that stellar spectra fall into a single sequence, except that there are branches at the two ends, for the coolest and hottest stars. Along the sequence, from the red to the blue stars, the photospheric temperatures increase; and the patterns of lines in the spectra show a gradual change, becoming in general less complex. In the atmosphere of a star, where the lines are produced, the temperature is not much less than that of the photosphere. The pressure is very small, probably of the order of 10^{-4} atmosphere. Since low pressure and high temperature are conducive to ionization, important changes must occur in the states of the atoms of stellar atmospheres, and in the spectra, along the sequence from the red to the blue stars. The observed sequence of stellar spectra is a consequence of the progressive increase in the temperatures of stellar atmospheres.

At the relatively low temperatures of the red stars the spectra of neutral atoms are prominent, particularly of those elements, such as sodium, calcium, titanium, and iron, which are easily excited, as indicated by their low ionization potentials (Table 10.IV). Chemical compounds which can resist dissociation at these temperatures, for example, titanium oxide and zirconium oxide, add their characteristic bands to the spectra.

At the higher temperatures of the yellow stars nearly all compounds have been broken up. The titanium oxide bands disappear as early as class K2. The spectra of the more easily ionized neutral atoms are fading, while those of atoms having higher ionization potentials are becoming prominent. With the removal of an electron the atom gives an entirely different pattern of lines. But the conspicuous lines of many ionized metals lie outside the region of the spectrum which can be photographed ordinarily; and this is true of double and triple ionization also. Thus with increasing temperature and degree of ionization in stellar atmospheres the spectra become less complex.

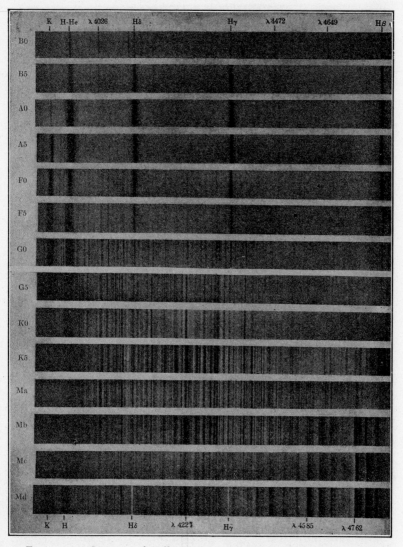

FIG. 10.18. Sequence of Stellar Spectra. Classes B to M. Class O spectra are shown in Fig. 9.6. The stars whose spectra are taken as representative of the various classes are: Bo, ε Orionis; B5, q Tauri; Ao, Sirius; A5, β Trianguli; Fo, δ Geminorum; F5, Procyon; Go, Capella; G5, κ Geminorum; Ko, Arcturus; K5, Aldebaran; Ma, Betelgeuse; Mb, ρ Persei; Mc, W Cygni; Md, o Ceti. (From photographs by R. H. Curtiss and W. C. Rufus, University of Michigan)

10.19. Spectra of the Hottest Stars. The neutral atoms of the elements having the highest ionization potentials (Table 10.IV) are the slowest to reach their maximum activity. The hydrogen lines of the Balmer series are most conspicuous in class Ao, although they are visible throughout the sequence. In still hotter stars the hydrogen lines decline, as more and more of their atoms become ionized. Having only one electron to lose, the hydrogen atom then ceases to absorb light. Neutral helium is the latest to appear, in class B9; it becomes strongest at B3, and fades away in the spectra of the class O stars, where its ionized lines appear.

In the very hottest stars we find, in addition to neutral hydrogen and singly ionized helium, lines of doubly ionized nitrogen, carbon, and silicon, and of trebly ionized silicon also — a simple pattern because most of the prominent lines are in unavailable regions of the spectrum. In his studies of the spectra of these very hot stars, H. H. Plaskett assigns class Oo as the theoretical upper limit of the spectral sequence, in which no lines at all appear. The nearest observed approach is his class O5.

The changing patterns of lines along the sequence are therefore, in large measure, caused by changing temperature. At any point in the sequence, the prominence of any specified series of lines is conditioned also by the ionization and excitation potentials of the atom which produces these lines, by the wave-lengths of the lines, which determine whether or not they fall in the observable part of the spectrum, and by the abundance of this chemical element in stellar atmospheres.

10.20. Temperatures from the Spectral Lines. By the ionization theory it is possible to calculate for different temperatures the fraction of the atoms of an element in stellar atmospheres which are ready to absorb a particular dark line, and thus to predict how the strength of the line varies with the temperature. Miss Payne has determined the theoretical intensity-temperature curves for a number of prominent lines in stellar spectra, assuming as a first approximation that the pressure in the regions where the lines are formed is 10^{-4} atmosphere. Next, by observing these lines in the spectra of stars of the various classes she has drawn other curves to show how the intensities vary along the spectral sequence — at what classes each line appears, reaches maximum intensity, and disappears. Some of the observed results are given in Table 10.IV.

TABLE 10.IV. ELEMENTS WHOSE LINES ARE PROMINENT
IN STELLAR SPECTRA

Atom	Ionization Potential	Spectral Class in Which the Lines		
		Appear	Have Maximum Intensity	Disappear
He+	54.2	O	O	...
N++	47.2	Bo	O	...
Si+++	45.0	Bo	O	...
O+	35.0	B3	B2	Bo
He	24.5	B9	B3	O
C+	24.3	B9	B3	O
H	13.6	...	A3	...
Ca+	11.8	...	K	...
Fe	7.8	...	K	A
Ti	6.8	...	...	A2
Ca	6.1	...	...	B9
Na	5.1	...	...	Ao

The agreement between the forms of the theoretical and observed curves justifies the next step in the procedure, which is to slide one set of curves horizontally until the peaks of the curves (maximum intensities of the lines) coincide with those of the other set. The relation of the two horizonal scales, of temperature and spectral class, now establishes the temperature scale of the spectral sequence.

This temperature scale refers to the reversing layers of the stars, where the temperatures are somewhat lower than they are in the photospheres, as determined, for example, from the color indices.

Class O stars are yellower than class B stars. But their spectra indicate much higher temperatures. Beals, at Victoria, makes the valuable suggestion that these stars are surrounded by extensive envelopes of light atoms blown away continuously by radiation pressure — not in shells as with the novae (9.49). The envelopes absorb much of the radiation from the hot stars, and reradiate it at lower frequencies.

10.21. Spectra of Giant and Main-Sequence Stars.
The effective temperatures of giant stars are lower than those of main-sequence stars of the same spectral class (10.3). The reason is given by the ionization theory. According to this theory, the degree of ionization in stellar atmospheres increases with the temperature, and at any

specified temperature is greater when the pressure of the gases is low. Giant stars have less dense, although more extensive atmospheres than main-sequence stars. Accordingly, their atmospheres attain a particular degree of ionization, and the corresponding class of spectrum, at a lower temperature.

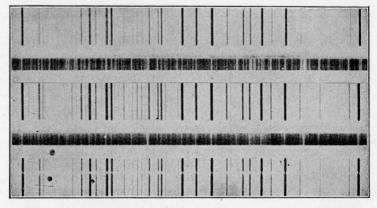

FIG. 10.21. Spectra of a Giant and a Main Sequence Star of the Same Class. The spectrum of Polaris, a class F9 giant star, is above; the spectrum of ξ Ursae Majoris, a class F9 star of the main sequence is below. Some lines are relatively stronger in the upper spectrum, while some are less conspicuous. The long vertical lines belong to the comparison spectrum. These are negatives. (From photographs at the Dominion Astrophysical Observatory, Victoria)

While the spectra of giant and main-sequence stars of the same class are the same in general appearance, certain lines are stronger for the giants, and some lines are weaker also. The effects of diminished temperature and pressure do not entirely compensate. Elements whose atoms are easily ionized give relatively weaker lines in the spectra of giant stars; those having high ionization potentials give relatively stronger lines. The lines of the majority of the elements do not show this effect noticeably.

Giant stars are distinguished from main-sequence stars by the strengthening and weakening of certain lines in their spectra relative to the intensities of the other lines. They are distinguished by other spectral characteristics also. Since the atmospheres of giant stars are more extensive and less dense, the lines in their spectra are generally stronger and somewhat narrower. All these effects are more pronounced in the super-giants.

10.22. Relative Abundance of the Elements. There is now considerable evidence that the chemical composition of stellar atmospheres does not vary greatly from star to star. If it were not so, it would scarcely be possible to arrange stellar spectra into so simple a sequence. Yet there must be some differences. Otherwise the points in the spectrum-luminosity diagram (Fig. 9.24), especially those for giant stars, might be expected to lie along curves more definitely than they do.

From the conditions under which the lines in the spectra of different elements make their appearance in the sequence at lower temperatures, and disappear at higher temperatures, Miss Payne has determined the relative abundance of prominent elements in the atmospheres of the stars. Other things being equal, lines of the more abundant element will appear sooner and last longer. By a different method, which depends also on observations of stellar spectra and on the theory of thermal ionization, Russell (1929) has studied the relative abundance of the elements in the sun's atmosphere. The two sets of results are in good agreement.

Table 10.V shows the twelve elements which are the most abundant in stellar atmospheres, according to Miss Payne, and their relative abundance. For the sun, the number of atoms of a particular element above one square centimeter of the photosphere is obtained by adding 19 ciphers to the number in the Table. Thus the number of hydrogen atoms above one square centimeter of the sun's surface is 5×10^{25}. In the deep chromospheres of the super-giant stars, Russell and Adams have found that the number of atoms is a hundredfold greater than in the sun's atmosphere, at least for the metallic gases.

TABLE 10.V.   THE MOST ABUNDANT ELEMENTS
IN STELLAR ATMOSPHERES

Element	Relative Number of Atoms	Element	Relative Number of Atoms
Hydrogen	5,000,000	Aluminium	5
Helium	10,000	Iron	3
Oxygen	60	Manganese	2
Magnesium	18	Calcium	2
Silicon	18	Carbon	2
Sodium	6	Zinc	1

The overwhelming preponderance of hydrogen is especially interesting; it is not surprising, therefore, that hydrogen lines are to be found throughout the spectral sequence. Two other non-metallic elements, helium and oxygen, easily hold the second and third places. Oxygen, although a poor third, is still more abundant than all the metallic gases combined. The metals which are most abundant in stellar atmospheres are generally the most abundant in the earth also, within ten miles of the surface.

THE INTERIOR OF A STAR

Aside from considerations of mass and mean density, the account of the constitution of a star has been confined thus far to the exterior. There remains the important problem of what is going on inside the star. It is not necessary to suppose that the problem is impossible to solve, simply because we can not look inside. The energy which leaks out from the interior and causes the star to shine must convey a message of conditions in the regions from which it comes.

It may be argued that a number of radically different internal constructions may be able to produce almost identical external phenomena. This statement, in its general form, applies to the majority of scientific theories. To meet this difficulty there is the expectation that the incorrect theory will ultimately betray itself by predicting a phenomenon that does not occur.

10.23. Equilibrium of a Star. The exploration of the interior of a star proceeds on the reasonable assumption that the great ball of gas has adjusted itself in a state of *mechanical equilibrium,* such that the heat at any point within the star supplies just enough outward pressure to support the weight of the gas above it. To insure the stability of the star, a second condition of *thermal equilibrium* requires that the temperature at any point remain the same, despite the continual flow of energy from one part of the star to another. On these two conditions the existence of the star depends. That they hold, at least approximately, is evident from the fact that the stars are neither collapsing noticeably nor exploding.

Within a stable star, therefore, two opposing forces are balanced. The incessant motion of the molecules which constitutes the heat of the gas, as we ordinarily understand the term, and the outward flow of radiation, both increasing with the temperature, tend to scatter the gas and thus to expand the star indefinitely. On the other hand, gravity at any point, increasing with the mass below it, urges the molecules downward toward the center. If the star contracts, it becomes hotter, until contraction is checked by increasing outward pressure; if the star expands, it is cooled thereby until the expansion is checked by gravity.

This theory of equilibrium was employed, as early as 1870, by the physicist Lane to calculate the internal temperature of the sun. More recently, the usefulness of the theory has been greatly extended. The main features of the procedure, apart from its mathematical setting, and some of the conclusions claim attention.

10.24. Laws of a Perfect Gas. The relation between the pressure, p_G, density, ρ, and absolute temperature, T, of a gas is given by *Boyle's law:*

$$p_G = R\rho T/\mu,$$

where R is a constant, and μ is the mean weight of the particles in terms of the weight of the hydrogen atom. A *perfect gas* is one to which this law applies. In the laboratory, a gas that is compressed to a density exceeding one tenth the density of water ceases noticeably to obey this law. But in the stars, with some probable exceptions that will be noted, it is generally believed that the law holds, even at densities far exceeding that of water.

According to Boyle's law the gas pressure varies directly as the density and temperature of the gas. It is owing to the incessant motion of the molecules that a gas exerts pressure on the walls of a container; the intensity of the bombardment increases with the number of molecules, and with their speed which by the kinetic theory of gases (3.13) is directly proportional to the temperature, and inversely proportional to the weight of the molecules. Everywhere in its interior the intensely hot star is kept inflated like a tire, but with far less immediate danger of blow-out or collapse. By Boyle's law and the equilibrium conditions imposed, the product of the density and temperature at every point is maintained in direct proportion to the gravitational pressure. If the latter and the distribution of density within the star are known, the temperature can be calculated. It is this relation that allows the exploration of the star's interior to proceed.

One of the notable results of the pioneer investigation of a gaseous star is *Lane's law,* which states that the temperature of a perfect gas is inversely proportional to its radius. The law is sometimes given in the form of a paradox, namely, that if a star cools (and therefore contracts), it becomes hotter.

10.25. Condition of Material in a Star. Since the weight of the overlying layers increases as we descend into the star's interior, the product of the density and temperature must increase in order to support the weight. It is found, in fact, that the temperature rises from a few thousand degrees at the photospheric level to millions of degrees at the center. Under these extreme conditions, processes may be, and probably are, going on which can not now be investigated in the laboratory. This greatly increases the interest in the exploration of the star's interior, and introduces difficulties as well.

Studies of the constitution of the stars proceed by means of mathematical models which are made as simple as possible for convenience of the analysis. These models are not expected to represent faithfully the complex stellar interiors in all respects. It is hoped that a satisfactory fit can be effected in general, and that the successful model can announce itself unmistakably by requiring the exterior properties of the stars that are observed.

As an example of the procedure we examine Eddington's model. Jeans, Milne, and others have worked with models having different properties. Expositions and criticisms of the various theories have been published, especially in *Monthly Notices of the Royal Astronomical Society*.

Eddington's model is simplified in one respect by the assumption that the molecular weight of the material in all parts of the star's interior is nearly the same, averaging about twice the weight of the hydrogen atom. This comes about regardless of chemical composition, because the atoms are almost completely shattered at these high temperatures into a confusion of free electrons and nuclei.

Consider, for example, an atom of iron (atomic weight 55.8), which normally consists of a nucleus and 26 electrons. If the iron atom is completely ionized, the average weight of each part is 55.8/27, or 2.1. For the chemical elements from lithium to uranium the mean weight of the separate parts varies from 1.8 to 2.6. Completely ionized hydrogen and helium give the low values 0.5 and 1.3 respectively, but their influence on the general mean is offset by the lack of complete ionization of the heavier elements.

10.26. A Star as a Perfect Gas. A perfect gas is one for which Boyle's law holds, so that the volume is inversely proportional to the pressure; if the pressure is doubled, the gas is compressed to half the original volume at the same temperature. If the molecules were rigid particles and well separated, this relation might continue, as the compression increased, until the particles began to jam; then the law would fail. For a reason not thoroughly understood the normal atom behaves, in this respect, like a rigid body. Jamming ensues when gas in the laboratory is compressed to a density comparable with that of the material in the liquid or solid state.

In Lane's time, and in fact until very recently, it seemed incredible that a star as dense as the sun could behave as a perfect gas. In 1924, Eddington showed that the mass-luminosity relation (10.10) deduced from the gas laws applies as well to the densest stars of the main sequence as to the tenuous red giants. It seemed to follow that all stars, except the white dwarfs, behave as a perfect gas. The reason is found in the nearly complete destruction of atomic structures in the stellar interiors. With the loss of most of its electrons, the stellar atom occupies, on the average, only one millionth of the space filled by the terrestrial atom. Compression can proceed until the gas has at least the density of platinum without serious jamming of its particles.

By virtue of the intense heat of stellar interiors another phenomenon, which has a subordinate rôle in the laboratory, rises to considerable importance. It is the pressure which the outflowing radiation exerts on the material.

10.27. Importance of Radiation Pressure.
It is well known that radiation exerts a pressure on anything that obstructs its progress. We have already noticed two effects which are usually ascribed to the pressure of the sun's radiation, namely, the pointing of comets' tails away from the sun and the supporting of the chromospheric gases against the sun's attraction. In most cases, however, the effect is relatively negligible; for example, the pressure of 75,000 tons which sunlight exerts on the earth is very small in comparison with the gravitational force urging it toward the sun.

Radiation pressure is proportional to the rate of the radiation, which by Stefan's law increases as the fourth power of the temperature. On the other hand, the gas pressure, by Boyle's law, increases only as the first power of the temperature. Eddington, in 1916, was the first to point out that at the high temperatures in the depths of the stars the pressure of the outflowing radiation may have an important share in supporting the weight of the overlying gases.

For the assumed molecular weight of the material, radiation pressure increases as the mass is greater. It increases very rapidly when we come to masses such as the stars have, and becomes the chief disruptive force for masses ten times the sun's mass.

10.28. Radiation in the Interior. At the photosphere of a star, energy is being radiated away at an enormous rate. Since the average star shines steadily year after year, it is evident that energy is being supplied to the photosphere as fast as it leaks away; presumably it is passed upward from the interior. Moreover, the condition of thermal equilibrium requires that every point within the star must be supplied with energy at the same rate that it loses energy.

In Lane's time it was supposed that the transfer of heat was accomplished by convection — the sinking of cooled gases and the rising of hotter ones; but this process is much too slow. As early as 1894, Sampson grasped the principle of *radiative equilibrium,* namely, the transfer of energy through the star by radiation, absorption, and reradiation at such a rate that each part is maintained at the appropriate temperature. Schwarzschild, in 1906, proposed the theory anew.

In addition to the thermal agitation of the gas particles within the star, we must imagine a continual flow of radiation. Since the temperature is exceedingly high, this radiation must be, for the most part, of very short wave-length, comparable with soft x-rays. It is therefore quickly absorbed. In the star Capella, according to Eddington, at the depth where the gas is as dense as the air around us (about the average density of this star), a layer only a foot or so in thickness can absorb all the radiation from below. Thus most of the radiation is trapped for a long time within the star. It is passed on from one atom to another, in various directions, but, in the long run, upward to the star's surface where it escapes into space. Meanwhile, as the result of scattering by free electrons, according to the effect observed by A. H. Compton, and in the course of repeated absorption and reradiation, the x-rays are transformed, to a large extent, into visible radiation.

10.29. The Model of a Star. The exploration of a star's interior can not go far without a statement of the manner in which the density of the gas varies with distance from the center of the star. Ultimately it may be possible to determine the distribution of density independently. At present it must be assumed. It is assumed also that the stars, in general, are built on the same model. By this we mean that at corresponding points within two stars the densities are the same fraction of the central density. There will be a like correspondence in the temperatures and pressures. The knot of the problem is to determine the most satisfactory model.

Eddington's model is based on the supposition that the pressure at any point within a star is proportional to the four-thirds power of the density at that point. This relation, together with Boyle's law and the condition of mechanical equilibrium, permits the calculation of the density, temperature, and pressure anywhere within the star in terms of their values at the center. The distribution of density and temperature, according to this model, is shown in Table 10.VI.

TABLE 10.VI. DISTRIBUTION OF DENSITY AND TEMPERA-
TURE WITHIN A STAR IN PERCENTAGES OF VALUES AT
THE CENTER (EDDINGTON'S MODEL)

Distance from center (radius)	Density	Temperature
0.0	100	100
0.2	42	75
0.4	7	41
0.6	1	19
0.8	0.1	7
1.0	0.0	0

When the mass and radius of a star are known, the mean density is known also, and the density at the center, by this model, is 54 times greater. Formulae are available for calculating the central temperatures and pressures. Conditions in other parts of the star can then be derived from the Table. These results are subject to revision as the investigations proceed.

10.30. Conditions at the Center of a Star. Temperature, density, and pressure increase with increasing depth in a star. At the center the extreme conditions obtain. Eddington has given formulae for determining these central conditions, when the mass and spectral class of the star are known, and the results of such calculations for a number of stars (Table 10.VII). The order of these quantities is the thing to be noticed. The values of the central temperatures and densities in the Table are approximations subject to considerable revision as refinements are added in the treatment. The molecular weight is here supposed to be constant throughout the star. More probably it increases somewhat with distance from the center. When this is taken into account, the central temperatures of Capella and the sun, for example, are reduced 25 per cent, and the central densities more than 50 per cent.

As the Table shows, the central temperatures of the giant stars are less than those of the main-sequence stars. As Russell was the first to point out, the central temperatures derived for the stars of the main sequence are so nearly the same that the true values may be actually the same.

TABLE 10.VII. TEMPERATURES AND DENSITIES AT THE CENTERS OF THE STARS

Star		Spec-trum	Mass (Sun = 1)	Surface Temperature	Central Temperature (Millions of degrees K)	Central Density (Water = 1)
Giant stars	{ * Capella	Go	4.2	5,200° K	9	0.12
	δ Cephei	F9	9.0	5,200	6	0.02
Main sequence stars	* V Puppis	B1	19.2	19,000	42	3.4
	Sun	Go	1.0	6,000	40	76
	* Krueger 60	Mo	0.3	3,100	32	493

* Brighter component of binary system.

These are numerical conclusions from the Eddington model which we have taken as an example. Other theories give other values of the central temperatures and densities, though all agree in assigning enormous temperatures to the centers of the stars.

THE SOURCE OF STELLAR ENERGY

10.31. Classical Theory of Stellar Development. Previous to 1913, the spectral sequence, from class O to class M, or N, was believed to be the single track along which every star progressed, from its origin out of the diffuse nebulae to its final stage as a dark star. In its youth, according to this view, the star was intensely hot and therefore blue. The frequent association of blue stars with nebulae, for example, the Pleiades (Fig. 10.31) and the stars involved in the Orion nebula, and the corresponding simplicity of their spectra seemed to stamp them as young stars. Owing to the radiation of its heat, the star cooled and therefore contracted. Supposedly already too much compressed to obey Lane's law (10.24), it did not gain heat by contraction fast enough to offset the loss by radiation. Accordingly, the star continued to cool and to contract; it became yellow like the sun, in its middle age, red in its old age, and ultimately cold and dark.

As the star advanced from the blue stage of Sirius, where the spectrum shows hydrogen lines predominantly, to the yellow stage of the sun, where the spectrum is characterized by the multitude of metallic lines, it was commonly supposed that the chemical composition of the star was being altered. Thus the stars were the "cosmic crucibles" within which the heavier elements were built up from the lighter ones. In this respect the theory was in accord with the prevailing view that the normal course of evolution is from the simple to the complex organism. It is now known,

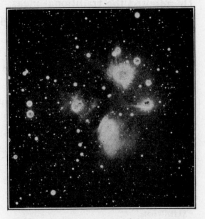

FIG. 10.31. The Pleiades. (From a photograph by E. E. Barnard at the Mount Wilson Observatory)

however, that the atoms of hydrogen are more active at the higher surface temperature of Sirius in absorbing and emitting light, while the normal atoms of metals are more active at the lower temperature of the sun.

The classical theory adopted Laplace's idea that the stars condense from nebulae. It was consistent with his nebular hypothesis, and with Helmholtz's contraction theory of the sun's radiation. Its downfall was foreshadowed by Lockyer's proposal, as early as 1887, of a two-branch track of stellar development, with the red stars at the two ends and the blue stars in the middle; and more definitely in 1905, when Hertzsprung discovered that the red stars form two distinct groups with respect to luminosity.

10.32. The Two-Branch Theory. In 1913, Russell prepared a diagram showing the relationship between spectral class and absolute

magnitude (Fig. 9.24). For the stars then available for this purpos
the points fell along two lines, diverging from the region in which the
blue stars were represented; the upper branch contained the giant
stars, the lower branch the main-sequence stars. Taking this V-dia-
gram to be the main track of stellar development, Russell proposed
a new theory which was at once favorably received, and which had
a strong influence on astronomical thought for the following ten years.
He adopted the traditional ideas, that a star arises from the nebula,
and that the order of its development is the order of increasing
density.

According to this theory, the youngest star is the very large and
exceedingly diffuse red giant. As the star shrinks, it grows hotter
(Lane's law), and passes upward along the spectral sequence to the
blue stage. Increasing surface brightness is balanced by diminishing
area of the surface, so that the luminosity of the giant star does not
change greatly. Whenever the star becomes compressed to the point
where the laws of a perfect gas cease to hold (at the blue stage or
before, depending on the mass), it begins to cool; and since shrinking
continues, surface brightness and area are now both diminishing.
The star passes down the main sequence, from blue to red, and to
extinction.

At the time the theory was proposed, considerable evidence had
accumulated to show that giant stars are far less dense than the
sun — rare enough, in fact, to justify the application of the gas laws
to them. It is less certain that the temperature of the photosphere
would follow the rising temperature of the interior to which Lane's
law refers. In general, the theory was remarkably successful in
correlating the observational data, until a serious weakness was
brought to light, in 1924, by the unexpected success of the mass-
luminosity relation with reference to the stars of the main sequence
(10.10).

10.33. Diminishing Masses of the Stars. It is usually assumed that
the stars are undergoing a process of gradual change, and that different stages in the process must be represented in the different kinds
of stars that we observe. If this is true, the problem of stellar evolution is to arrange the various stages in the correct sequence with respect to age. In order to do so, it is necessary to determine what
condition or conditions in the stars are progressively altered as the
stars grow older.

In the classical theory the order of development was taken to be the order of diminishing temperature, and incidentally of increasing density. In the two-branch theory of 1913 it was simply increasing density. The attention is now turned to diminishing mass as the change possibly accompanying the ageing of the stars. It has already been noticed (Table 10.II) that the masses of the stars become progressively smaller down the main sequence.

According to the theory of relativity (4.33), energy possesses mass. The energy that the star contains adds to the mass of the star. Since the energy is continually radiated away, the mass must diminish unless, of course, the star continually acquires an equal amount of energy from outside.

According to the theory, a quantity of energy E ergs has the mass of E/c^2 grams, where c is the velocity of light. The rate at which a star loses mass by virtue of its radiation is therefore easily calculated from the rate of the radiation. The sun, for example, is radiating energy at the rate of 1.9 ergs per gram per second. Accordingly, it is losing mass at the rate of 4,200,000 tons a second. Capella is radiating energy at the rate of 58 ergs per gram per second, and it is 4.18 times more massive than the sun; it is therefore losing mass $58/1.9 \times 4.18$ times more rapidly than the sun, or at the rate of 530 million tons a second.

10.34. The Problem of Stellar Evolution. If all the stars were included in the main sequence, and if it were agreed to regard this sequence as the track of stellar development, the account could be a simple one. It might relate to a star endowed at birth with a vast store of stuff which is convertible into energy, and to the depletion of that store by the star's radiation, resulting in diminishing mass, diminishing and reddening radiation, and increasing density, until the star ceases to shine. But the giant stars and the white dwarfs must be taken into account also.

It has been the custom to assemble the observational data on the basis of evolution. There is considerable doubt, however, as to whether celestial phenomena of the present can tell us much about the remote past or future of the stars, or nebulae, or of the solar system, at least until methods of greater generality can be employed.

The problem of stellar evolution has been reduced to the problem of interpreting the spectrum-luminosity diagram. The sequences into which the stars fall on this diagram have been regarded as the main tracks of stellar evolution, or as the edges of precipices toward which the stars crowd before jumping to another sequence. From another point of view the sequences represent simply a frame of stable configurations; the mass of a star and other conditions determine where on the frame the star must rest.

Writing in 1926, Eddington remarks: "Today we have no theory of stellar evolution pending the settlement of the laws of subatomic energy . . . : these must determine its [the star's] track, if it is evolving, or its halting place, if it is stationary."

10.35. Maintenance of Stellar Radiation. Enormous quantities of energy are continually pouring out of the stars. From a single square yard of the sun's surface, for example, the outflowing energy is equivalent to 70,000 horsepower; and for the same area at the surfaces of some of the blue stars this figure must be multiplied by a hundred or so. By the law of the conservation of energy, the radiation must be at the expense of vast stores of energy possessed by the stars. In searching for the source of the energy it must be kept in mind that the stars are not only spending energy lavishly at present, but they have been doing so for a very long time. It is believed that the sun has been shining for at least ten thousand million years.

We may dismiss at once any idea that the stars continue to shine simply because they are very hot. Energy must be supplied from some source in order to keep them so highly heated. Certainly, also, the heat is not being supplied by chemical combination going on in the stars. For the spectra show that even in the relatively cool atmospheres, except in those of the red stars, the elements are usually uncombined, while in the interiors even the separate atoms can not hold together. The stars are too hot to burn.

The suggestion, made long ago, that the fall of meteors into the stars supplies enough energy to maintain their radiation has not proved to be acceptable. It is well known that when a meteor's swift flight is arrested, a considerable quantity of heat is developed. But from the estimated number of meteors which encounter the earth daily (6.18), the number falling into the sun daily has been calculated and found to be altogether inadequate to supply the sun with heat for the day's radiation. Further objection has as its basis the calculation that if the number were sufficient, the inflowing meteors would double the sun's mass in about 30 million years.

Eddington insists that superficial heating of a star from without, by the impact of meteors, or by some subtle radiation, or by any other agent regardless of its amount, does not solve the problem.

From his viewpoint the energy must be liberated deep in the star's interior. Otherwise the star will collapse.

10.36. Contraction as a Source of Radiation. It now seems impossible to suppose that contraction of the sun makes an important contribution to the maintenance of its radiation (7.43). The sun has been shining for too long a time to have been dependent on the heat developed by its contraction. The same reasoning applies to stars in general. A red giant star 11.5 times as massive as the sun would change to a blue star in 72,000 years, if contraction were the only source of its heat. Eddington has shown that Cepheid variable stars appear to offer convincing evidence against such rapid change. If δ Cephei is contracting fast enough to entirely maintain the radiation, the period of its light variation should decrease 17 seconds annually. But this star, whose variable light has been under observation for nearly 150 years, shows no such change in period.

In dismissing contraction as a considerable factor in the problem before us, it ought to be mentioned that *there is no certain observational evidence that any star is progressively contracting.* Nevertheless, all theories of stellar evolution assume that a star contracts as it grows older, although none depends necessarily on contraction alone. In the classical theory and the original two-branch theory, contraction directed the life-track of the star; but other sources of energy were not prevented from prolonging the star's life.

The success of the mass-luminosity relation deposed contraction as a leading factor in the star's career, leaving it perhaps only as a perpetual threat which the star must meet by keeping up its supply of internal energy. Having failed to find the source of this supply elsewhere, the astronomer now looks hopefully within the atoms.

10.37. Subatomic Sources of Energy. Whatever the process by which energy is liberated in a star, the equilibrium conditions require that it be supplied at precisely the same rate that it is radiated from the surface. Otherwise the continued existence of the star is in question. The rate of the liberation of energy is, therefore, a matter of observation. For each gram of the sun, for example, 1.9 ergs of energy are radiated or liberated every second; and the sun's mass is 1.985×10^{33} grams. Assuming that the sun shines for at least 10^{10} years, it is possible to estimate the minimum total requirement of the sun.

√ Three ways have been thought of, whereby the atoms of a star may be able to supply the energy required to keep the star shining:

(1) *Radioactivity.* It is well known that the radioactive elements, such as radium, liberate large quantities of energy in the course of their transformation into lighter elements. A single gram of radium emits 1,600,000 ergs of energy in a second. Thus the sun's radiation could be accounted for, if 1/840,000 of its mass is composed of radium. But the average life of a radium atom is less than 3000 years. If the sun were composed entirely of radioactive material, from uranium down, and in appropriate proportions, it has been calculated that the rate of liberation of energy by this material would be only half the rate of the sun's radiation. Moreover, it is probable that these heavy elements do not constitute a very large percentage of the stellar material.

(2) *Formation of Helium from Hydrogen.* The atomic weight of the hydrogen atom is 1.008, on the usual scale (oxygen = 16). The weight of the helium atom is 4.000. If the hydrogen in the stars is being built up into helium, each combination of four hydrogen atoms involves the disappearance of 0.8 per cent of their mass, which might be taken to represent released energy. Calculation shows that an original proportion of seven per cent of hydrogen in the sun, if it is ultimately entirely combined into helium, would keep the sun shining for 10^{10} years.

(3) *Atom-Building from Helium.* Atkinson has developed the theory that stellar radiation results from more extensive atom-building processes in the interiors of stars. He supposes that helium nuclei trap in turn stray protons and electrons, and thus gradually form more complex atoms. The difference in mass between the raw material and the products becomes available for radiation as energy.

Suggestions of this sort represent the prevailing view that the source of stellar energy is to be sought within the atoms. The rate at which the energy is being released for radiation is subject to observation; it must, in general, equal the rate of the star's radiation, in order to preserve the stability of the star.

10.38. Relation between Energy and Mass. By the theory of relativity, a change in the amount of the energy which a body contains changes its mass also, according to the relation: energy, in ergs, equals mass, in grams, times the square of velocity of light, in centimeters a second.

TABLE 10.VIII. THE CHEMICAL ELEMENTS

Element	Symbol	Atomic Number	Atomic Weight	Element	Symbol	Atomic Number	Atomic Weight
Hydrogen	H	1	1.008	Silver	Ag	47	107.88
Helium	He	2	4.000	Cadmium	Cd	48	112.41
Lithium	Li	3	6.94	Indium	In	49	114.8
Beryllium	Be	4	9.02	Tin	Sn	50	118.70
Boron	B	5	10.82	Antimony	Sb	51	121.77
Carbon	C	6	12.00	Tellurium	Te	52	127.5
Nitrogen	N	7	14.01	Iodine	I	53	126.93
Oxygen	O	8	16.000	Xenon	Xe	54	130.2
Fluorine	F	9	19.00	Caesium	Cs	55	132.81
Neon	Ne	10	20.2	Barium	Ba	56	137.37
Sodium	Na	11	23.00	Lanthanum	La	57	138.91
Magnesium	Mg	12	24.32	Cerium	Ce	58	140.25
Aluminium	Al	13	26.96	Praseodymium	Pr	59	140.92
Silicon	Si	14	28.06	Neodymium	Nd	60	144.27
Phosphorus	P	15	31.02	Illinium	Il	61	
Sulphur	S	16	32.06	Samarium	Sm	62	150.43
Chlorine	Cl	17	35.46	Europium	Eu	63	152.0
Argon	A	18	39.91	Gadolinium	Gd	64	157.26
Potassium	K	19	39.10	Terbium	Tb	65	159.2
Calcium	Ca	20	40.07	Dysprosium	Dy	66	162.52
Scandium	Sc	21	45.10	Holmium	Ho	67	163.4
Titanium	Ti	22	47.9	Erbium	Er	68	167.7
Vanadium	V	23	50.96	Thulium	Tm	69	169.4
Chromium	Cr	24	52.01	Ytterbium	Yb	70	173.6
Manganese	Mn	25	54.93	Lutecium	Lu	71	175.0
Iron	Fe	26	55.84	Hafnium	Hf	72	178.6
Cobalt	Co	27	58.97	Tantalum	Ta	73	181.5
Nickel	Ni	28	58.69	Tungsten	W	74	184.0
Copper	Cu	29	63.57	Rhenium	Re	75	
Zinc	Zn	30	65.38	Osmium	Os	76	190.8
Gallium	Ga	31	69.72	Iridium	Ir	77	193.1
Germanium	Ge	32	72.38	Platinum	Pt	78	195.23
Arsenic	As	33	74.96	Gold	Au	79	197.2
Selenium	Se	34	79.2	Mercury	Hg	80	200.61
Bromine	Br	35	79.92	Thallium	Tl	81	204.4
Krypton	Kr	36	82.9	Lead	Pb	82	207.20
Rubidium	Rb	37	85.44	Bismuth	Bi	83	209.00
Strontium	Sr	38	87.62	Polonium	Po	84	(210)
Yttrium	Y	39	89.0			85	
Zirconium	Zr	40	91.	Radon	Rn	86	222.
Columbium	Cb	41	93.1			87	
Molybdenum	Mo	42	96.0	Radium	Ra	88	225.95
Masurium	Ma	43		Actinium	Ac	89	
Ruthenium	Ru	44	101.7	Thorium	Th	90	232.15
Rhodium	Rh	45	102.91	Protoactinium	Pa	91	(234)
Palladium	Pd	46	106.7	Uranium	U	92	238.17

For the sake of argument, let us suppose that the store of energy which keeps the stars shining is contained in their interiors, and presumably within their atoms. This energy can not then be entirely hidden, because it adds to the mass of the star; and its equivalent in mass can not exceed the total mass of the star, unless, of course, the star requires additional energy from outside. As an example consider the sun; its mass is about 2×10^{33} grams, and the velocity of light is about 3×10^{10} cm. By the above relation, the maximum possible energy stored in the sun is 1.8×10^{54} ergs. If the sun's total radiation is always equal to its present value (1.2×10^{41} ergs a year), the longest possible life of the sun would be 1.5×10^{13} years.

We do not know how much of a star's mass represents releasable energy, or anything about the process by which it is released. It must be understood also that there is no certain observational evidence that the masses of the stars are diminishing as times goes on. It is observed that the stars of the main sequence decrease in mass with increasing redness. The problem of the source of stellar energy is for the future to solve.

10.39. The Constitution of the Stars. Having now examined various characteristics of the stars, we may ask and briefly answer in summary the question implied by the heading of this Chapter. What is a star?

A star is a ball of intensely hot gas encompassed by a photosphere from which the radiation emerges, and an atmosphere through which it filters. Energy is supplied to the photosphere from below as fast as it is radiated away. The source of the energy is obscure, and accordingly, many properties of stellar interiors remain obscure also. Nor do we have a satisfactory account of the ultimate disposal of the energy so lavishly radiated, except the minute fraction which is intercepted by celestial bodies.

The stars are the power houses of the universe. They are its chief building blocks as well. In quantity of material they approach uniformity. In size they vary enormously, ranging from dwarf stars scarcely larger than the earth to the red super-giants whose diameters run into hundreds of millions of miles. In mean density, therefore, the stars show great variety; some are thousands of times as dense as water, while others are thousands of times more rarefied than the air around us. The main-sequence stars, which are believed to greatly outnumber the giants and dwarfs, have masses, diameters, and densities not much different from those of the sun.   In these and other respects the sun appears to represent a fair average of the general run of stars.

By their different colors, from blue to red, and in other ways, the stars announce a considerable range in photospheric temperature. Below their photospheres the temperature rises to millions of degrees, it is believed, at their centers.   Many stars are variable in light. Some burst forth explosively to temporary grandeur.   Such are the stars.

REFERENCES

Cecilia H. Payne, *Stellar Atmospheres* (Harvard Observatory, 1925).

A. S. Eddington, *The Internal Constitution of the Stars* (Cambridge University Press, 1926).

A. S. Eddington, *Stars and Atoms* (Yale University Press, 1927).

J. H. Jeans, *Astronomy and Cosmogony* (Cambridge University Press, 1928).

Cecilia H. Payne, *The Stars of High Luminosity* (Harvard Observatory, 1930).

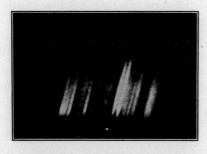

Spectrum of a Meteor, December 15, 1931. The first meteor spectrum ever photographed. The meteor was as bright as Jupiter. The original plate shows 41 bright lines, of which the H and K lines of calcium are the brightest. (From a photograph by P. M. Millman, Harvard Observatory)

The Milky Way in Cygnus. The bright star to the right of the North America nebula is α Cygni. The other stars of the Northern Cross appear in the photograph, except β Cygni at the foot of the Cross, which is out of picture at the lower right. (From a photograph by F. E. Ross, Yerkes Observatory)

CHAPTER XI

THE GALACTIC SYSTEM

DISTRIBUTION OF THE STARS — STAR-CLUSTERS AND CLOUDS — GALACTIC
NEBULAE — THE STRUCTURE OF THE GALACTIC SYSTEM

Just as the earth and the other planets are units in the planetary system, so the sun and probably not less than one hundred thousand million other stars are units in the vast *stellar system.* Since this system contains the star-clouds of the Milky Way, it is known also as the *galactic system,* perhaps more appropriately, because nebulae as well as stars are important factors in its organization.

The galactic system is an aggregation of single stars, groups of stars, star-clusters, star-clouds, bright nebulae, and the dark nebulosities which obscure the view in certain directions. Separated from the galactic system by distances which must be reckoned in millions of light-years are other systems, the *extra-galactic systems,* which are described in Chapter XII.

DISTRIBUTION OF THE STARS

11.1. If it were possible to determine the direction and distance of every object in the galactic system, the investigation of the organization of this system would be a straightforward problem, although a very lengthy one. But not more than three per cent of the stars in our system are visible with the most powerful telescope; and until recently, the distances of the stars were almost entirely unknown. The study of the structure of the galactic system is now proceeding from at least three different directions:

(1) *By statistical methods based on counts of stars* in limited representative areas of the sky. This is the oldest method, and the one that we shall consider first.

(2) *By the distribution of stars whose distances are known.* This direct method began to be available as soon as it became possible to determine the distances of many stars; it was employed

effectively by Shapley, in 1918, in connection with the distribution of the globular clusters. This procedure and its important contributions to our knowledge of the galactic system will receive attention later in the Chapter.

(3) *By the study of exterior stellar systems.* Since Hubble's demonstration, in 1925, that the spiral nebulae lie beyond the Milky Way, considerable evidence has accumulated to suggest that some of them resemble our system. It is possible, therefore, that certain characteristics of the galactic system which are imperfectly revealed to the observer within it may be more clearly shown in the distant view of the exterior systems.

11.2. Herschel's Star Guages. For a long time, the luminous girdle of the Milky Way and the conspicuous crowding of the stars toward it have been taken to mean that our stellar system has a greater extension in this plane. The first systematic attempt to determine the precise form of the system of stars was made by William Herschel, and described by him in 1784.

Herschel's method was to make counts or " gauges " of the numbers of stars visible in the field of his 19-inch reflecting telescope, when it was directed toward various parts of the heavens. In all, he made more than three thousand counts. He assumed that the extension of the system in any direction is proportional to the cube root of the number of stars counted. This would be true, if the stars were uniformly spaced and of the same absolute brightness, and if his telescope had been powerful enough to show all the stars in the directions toward which it was pointed. As he clearly understood, these conditions were far from being fulfilled.

Herschel reached the conclusion that the system of stars has the shape of a grindstone — a cloven grindstone, if the bifurcation of the Milky Way is taken into account — whose diameter is to its thickness as 850 is to 155. The scale of distance, which was unknown to him, makes the diameter about 6000 light-years. The small size of the system as determined by Herschel is partially explained by the small size of his telescope which could reach only to the stars of the fifteenth magnitude.

This pioneer investigation was extended to the southern hemisphere by John Herschel. From the times of the Herschels to the present, the problem of the structure of the stellar system has been considered one of the major problems of astronomy. Many astronomers have contributed toward its solution. The present account of the statistical approach is concerned particularly with some of the more recent results.

11.3. Counting the Stars. The statistical study of the organization of the stellar system is based now, as it was in Herschel's time, on counts of stars in representative areas of the sky. The stars are now counted on photographs of these areas. In their extensive studies at Greenwich, Chapman and Melotte made use of the Franklin-Adams photographic chart of the sky. Seares at Mount Wilson employed photographs of the Kapteyn areas (11.8) made with the 100-inch telescope. Bok, at Harvard, has rediscussed the counts in some of these areas.

Counting stars, as Seares remarks, is not unlike counting pebbles on the seashore. The astronomer's difficulty is not in the counting, but in knowing where the counting must start and stop. The value of the counts depends on being able to determine correctly the magnitudes of the stars that are counted. A star of the first magnitude is 100 million times brighter than a star of the twenty-first magnitude, which represents the working photographic limit of the 100-inch telescope. To hold to the magnitude scale over this great range is a matter of considerable difficulty. The most fundamental part of the work was to establish the magnitudes of a sequence of comparison stars over the whole range (9.19).

The recently published results concerning the structure of the stellar system required the determination of the photographic magnitudes of 70,000 stars, which represents the work of a number of members of the observatory staff over a period of several years. The 206 areas in which the faintest stars were counted cover less than a thousandth of the whole sky. A complete count would have taken practically forever.

11.4. Galactic Longitude and Latitude. In problems relating to the galactic system it is often convenient to locate a celestial body with reference to the Milky Way. For this purpose we define a new set of circles and of coordinates on the celestial sphere.

The north and south *galactic poles* are the two opposite points which are farthest from the central line of the Milky Way. They are located respectively in right ascension $12^h 40^m$, declination $+28°$, in Coma Berenices, and in R. A. $0^h 40^m$, Decl. $-28°$, in Sculptor.

The *galactic equator* is the great circle halfway between the galactic poles; it runs about a degree north of the central line of the Milky Way, which shows that the sun is situated somewhat to the north of the central plane of the star-clouds. The galactic equator is inclined about 62° to the celestial equator, crossing it from south to north in the constellation Aquila, and southward at the opposite point which is east of Orion.

Galactic longitude is reckoned in degrees from the first named crossing point (R. A. 18^h 40^m) toward the north along the galactic equator. *Galactic latitude* is measured perpendicularly from the galactic equator.

Limiting Magnitude 15   Limiting Magnitude 20

FIG. 11.5. Increasing Number of Stars with Decreasing Brightness. A small field in the vicinity of η Aurigae, showing stars to the 15th and 20th magnitudes. The bright star, of the third magnitude, is necessarily much over-exposed. (From photographs at the Mount Wilson Observatory)

11.5. Thinning Out of More Remote Stars.

If the stars were uniformly spaced and of the same absolute brightness, the total number of stars down to a limiting magnitude would increase four times for each fainter magnitude to which the limit is extended. Consider, for example, the total number of stars brighter than the seventh magnitude as compared with the total number brighter than the sixth magnitude.

Since the apparent brightness of equally luminous stars varies inversely as the squares of their distances from us, a seventh magnitude star, which is apparently 1/2.5 as bright as a sixth magnitude star, would be the square root of 2.5, or 1.6 times farther away. Thus the stars brighter than the seventh magnitude would occupy a volume of space around us $(1.6)^3$, or about four, times greater than the space occupied by the stars brighter than the sixth magnitude; and with the assumption of equal distribution in space they would be four times more numerous. It is certainly true that the stars are not equally luminous, but in the long run their lack of uniformity in absolute brightness does not seriously alter the factor 4 as the ratio for uniformly distributed stars.

As Table 11.I shows, the observed ratio of increase, when the limit of brightness is carried an even magnitude fainter, is always less than 4. The conclusion is that the stars around us are not uniformly distributed. They thin out more and more as the distance from the earth increases.

TABLE 11.I.   NUMBER OF STARS BRIGHTER THAN
A GIVEN PHOTOGRAPHIC MAGNITUDE

Magnitude Limit	Total Number	Ratio of Increase	Magnitude Limit	Total Number	Ratio of Increase
4.0	360		13.0	2,720,000	
		2.9			2.4
5.0	1,030		14.0	6,500,000	
		2.9			2.3
6.0	2,940		15.0	15,000,000	
		2.8			2.2
7.0	8,200		16.0	33,000,000	
		2.8			2.1
8.0	22,800		17.0	70,000,000	
		2.7			2.0
9.0	62,000		18.0	143,000,000	
		2.7			1.9
10.0	166,000		19.0	275,000,000	
		2.6			1.8
11.0	431,000		20.0	505,000,000	
		2.6			1.8
12.0	1,100,000		21.0	890,000,000	
		2.5			

11.6. Concentration of the Stars Toward the Milky Way. The stars are not distributed uniformly over the sky. It is well known that they are more numerous near the Milky Way than far from it. This is true not only of the naked-eye stars, but also, and even more noticeably, of the telescopic stars (Fig. 11.6). Moreover, the concentration is about equally pronounced in both galactic hemispheres.

In order to study the crowding of the stars toward the Milky Way, Seares has assembled the Mount Wilson star-counts with respect to galactic latitude. Table 11.II shows the average number of stars per

TABLE 11.II   DISTRIBUTION OF STARS

Limiting Magnitude	Galactic Latitude								Galactic Concentration
	0°		30°		60°		90°		
	Number of stars per square degree	Ratio of increase per mag.	Number of stars per square degree	Ratio of increase per mag.	Number of stars per square degree	Ratio of increase per mag.	Number of stars per square degree	Ratio of increase per mag.	
5.0	0.045		0.021		0.015		0.013		3.4
		2.8		2.8		2.8		2.8	
7.0	0.36		0.17		0.12		0.10		3.6
		2.8		2.8		2.7		2.6	
9.0	2.81		1.31		0.87		0.72		3.9
		2.7		2.6		2.5		2.4	
11.0	20.8		9.1		5.5		4.3		4.8
		2.6		2.4		2.3		2.2	
13.0	146		54		29		21		6.8
		2.5		2.2		2.1		2.0	
15.0	910		272		123		87		10.4
		2.3		2.0		1.9		1.8	
17.0	4,780		1,090		428		288		16.6
		2.1		1.8		1.7		1.6	
19.0	20,800		3,440		1,190		770		27
		1.9		1.6		1.5		1.5	
21.0	73,600		8,690		2,650		1,670		44

square degree at 30° intervals from the galactic equator to its poles. In the last column of the Table we have the *galactic concentration,* that is to say, how many times the number of stars of a certain kind in a square degree of the sky near the galactic equator exceeds the number in an equal area near the galactic poles. It appears that the concentration is three and a half times for the naked-eye stars, and that it increases to 44 times when the very faintest stars are included. It is now evident that the stars thin out, with increasing remoteness, least rapidly in the direction of the Milky Way, and most rapidly toward its poles.

In the Milky Way   Near the Galactic Pole

FIG. 11.6.   Concentration of Stars Toward the Milky Way.   Two regions of the same size, in the Milky Way and near the galactic pole.   The faintest stars shown in both regions are of the eighteenth magnitude.   (From photographs at the Mount Wilson Observatory)

11.7. Interpretation of Galactic Concentration.

The increase in the galactic concentration for the fainter, and on the average more distant, stars shows that the stars of our system crowd toward the *plane* of the Milky Way.   The majority of them are contained in a region of space roughly in the form of a thin watch, having the sun not far north of its principal central plane.   In a spherical region around the sun, so long as the radius of the sphere does not exceed the short radius of the lenticular region of congestion, the stars are about equally numerous in all directions.

When the sphere of observation is enlarged beyond this radius, galactic concentration appears, becoming more pronounced as the radius of the sphere is further increased.   The very remote members of our galactic system are found within or near the Milky Way.   In general, except for the nearest objects, galactic concentration is a conspicuous badge of membership in the galactic system. On this basis we distinguish between *galactic objects* and the *extra-galactic objects* which, although distant, do not exhibit this concentration (Chapter XII). Among the members of our system the blue stars, super-giant stars, novae, gaseous nebulae, and open star-clusters show a marked preference for the Milky Way.

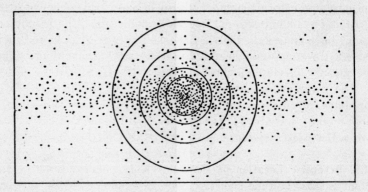

FIG. 11.7. Increasing Galactic Concentration of the More Distant Stars. A schematic cross-section of the galactic system. Within spheres of increasing radius around the earth the percentage of the stars in the direction of the Milky Way increases.

11.8. Contributions of Kapteyn. The statistical study of the construction of the stellar system is peculiarly associated with the name of the Dutch astronomer Kapteyn who devoted his life to this problem. One of his notable achievements was the discovery of the two star streams (8.23). He inaugurated the plan of selected areas, inviting the cooperation of astronomers in determining the numbers, magnitudes, and motions of the stars in selected representative areas of the sky. On these data the recent statistical investigations of the stellar system are based. Kapteyn's last contribution, which appeared in 1922 shortly before his death, completes the first phase of the solution of the great problem. He describes it as the " first attempt at a theory of the arrangement and motion of the sidereal system."

As the first approximation Kapteyn considered the arrangement of the stars with respect to the sun as the center. He assumed that the stars thin out with increasing distance in such a manner that surfaces of equal star-density are ellipsoids of revolution, similarly placed and having as their common axis the line joining the galactic poles.

The equatorial diameters of the ellipsoids are 5.1 times their polar diameters. It was pointed out that in order to be stable, this flattened system must be rotating. There is now considerable independent evidence that the galactic system is rotating (8.25).

At the distances of 1660 parsecs in the direction of the galactic poles and of 8500 parsecs (about 27,000 light-years) in the plane of the galactic equator the number of stars in a specified volume of space is reduced to a hundredth of the value near the sun. On the spheroid having these dimensions there is only one star in every thousand cubic parsecs, if we suppose that the stars in the sun's neighborhood average one star in every ten cubic parsecs.

The "Kapteyn universe" prepared the way for the next step in the statistical program, namely, the reconsideration of these and the more recently assembled data on the basis of the sun's eccentric location in the galactic system.

11.9. Eccentric Location of the Sun. The counts of stars in different galactic latitudes, averaged for all longitudes, show that the stars are concentrated toward the Milky Way. From the symmetrical arrangement of the stars on both sides of the Milky Way it is evident that the sun is not far from the plane which passes through the central line of the Milky Way and the central point of the galactic system. If the sun is not near the central point, there must be a progressive variation in the counts, when they are arranged with respect to longitude. Indeed, such a variation is to be expected. The Milky Way is not uniform in general brightness around its course; it is exceptionally brilliant in Sagittarius, and is rather inconspicuous near Auriga in the opposite part of the heavens.

If the sun is not centrally located in the galactic system, and if the stars are distributed symmetrically in relation to the center of the system, the stars should appear in the greatest numbers in the direction of the center. In order to study this effect Seares has arranged the counts in the Kapteyn areas near the Milky Way with respect to galactic longitude. He finds that the counts down to the eighteenth magnitude in equal areas of the sky increase to a maximum in galactic longitude 325°, in Sagittarius. This, then, is the direction of the center of the galactic system. Accordingly, the sun is not at the center.

When, however, the counts in these areas are limited successively to stars brighter than magnitudes 17, 16, and so on, the direction of the maximum shifts southward along the Milky Way. Finally, when only the naked-eye stars are counted, the maximum is found in galactic longitude 235°, in Carina.

11.10. Double Distribution of the Stars. It appears that we are concerned with two different plans of distribution of the stars which come under observation. The majority of the naked-eye stars and many telescopic stars as well are most numerous in the direction of the constellation Carina. They are symmetrically distributed with respect to a great circle which is inclined 12° to the galactic equator. The position of this circle is marked by a rather narrow belt of bright stars, including the brightest stars of Canis Major, Orion, Taurus, Cassiopeia, Cygnus, Lyra, and Scorpio.

The influence of this smaller system of stars around us is found in the counts as far as the eighteenth magnitude, according to Seares. About here the fainter stars, owing to their great numbers, predominate and exhibit clearly the plan of their distribution in the greater galactic system whose center lies in the direction of Sagittarius.

Long ago, John Herschel called attention to the lack of coincidence of the belt of bright stars and the Milky Way. Gould suggested that the stars in the sun's vicinity form a flattened, tilted cluster. We call it the *local system*.

11.11. Effect of Absorption on the Star-Counts. Until recently, the analysis of star-counts proceeded on the assumption that interstellar space is practically empty, aside from regions occupied by nebulae. No evidence had appeared of any considerable dimming or reddening of the light of distant stars, which could be ascribed to an intervening dusty or foggy medium. Indeed, the investigations of Shapley, van Rhijn, Lundmark, and others have shown that the light of the remote globular star-clusters, and of the still more remote extra-galactic nebulae is not greatly affected, as a general thing, in this way. But these objects avoid low galactic latitudes. In 1930, Trumpler's studies of the open clusters (11.16), which frequent the low latitudes, suggested important absorption effects in the direction of the Milky Way.

Bok, at the Harvard Observatory, in 1931, rediscussed van Rhijn's star-counts in the Kapteyn areas of low galactic latitude, taking into account the effect of an absorbing medium which he assumed uniform. The effect to be expected is an apparent falling off in the numbers of stars with increasing distance from the sun. It might be imagined that the removal of this effect from the star-counts would be likely to erase the local system from the picture. But after the most probable correction for absorption, there remains this region of high star-density around the sun.

11.12. Hypothesis of an Absorbing Layer. On the basis of his results for the open clusters, Trumpler proposes the hypothesis that absorbing material is strongly concentrated toward the galactic plane, like the clusters themselves. Most of it is contained within a layer along this plane not more than two or three hundred parsecs thick. Owing to absorption of their light in this layer, stars near the central line of the Milky Way are reduced in photographic brightness 0.67 magnitude per thousand parsecs of their distance from the earth. Their visual brightness is diminished 0.35 magnitude per thousand parsecs.

Accordingly, the color excess of these stars increases 0.32 magnitude per thousand parsecs; their light is reddened, like that of the setting sun. *Color excess* is the amount by which the color index of a star exceeds its accepted value (Table 10.1) for stars of the same spectral class. On this hypothesis, a star at the distance of 3000 parsecs and in the Milky Way should have a color excess of a whole magnitude; if its spectrum resembles that of the blue star Vega, it should have the color of the reddish Aldebaran. Owing to the thinness of the layer, the absorption would decrease rapidly with increasing distance from the Milky Way to almost negligible amounts in high galactic latitudes.

11.13. Evidence of Interstellar Absorption. The conclusions of other astronomers concerning the absorption are conflicting. Assuming a uniform layer along the galactic plane, Bok finds a photographic absorption of 0.4 magnitude per 1000 parsecs. Van de Kamp and others confirm the increase in color excess with increasing distance. Stebbins' photo-electric measurements at Mount Wilson show pronounced reddening of globular clusters in the lowest latitudes.

On the other hand, Seares concludes from the star-counts that uniform absorption in the galactic plane is inadmissible. Elvey's photo-electric measurements at Yerkes lead to a similar conclusion. Hubble and Humason find little indication of general absorption for extra-galactic nebulae in low latitudes. These results suggest patchy absorption in the Milky Way, such as we see more conspicuously in the dark nebulae.

The relation, which we have already noticed (9.22), between the distance, apparent magnitude, and absolute magnitude of a star supposes that the intervening space is perfectly transparent. For a uniform absorbing medium the relation becomes: $\log d = m - M + 5 - kr$, where k is the change in magnitude produced by absorption of the starlight through 1000 parsecs of the medium, and r is the distance in kiloparsecs that the light travels through the medium. If there is considerable interstellar absorption of light, even if the absorbing medium is not uniform, a determination of the size of the galactic system which uses this relation but neglects the absorption is likely to give too large a value. This possibility must not be overlooked.

But before the problem of the form and extent of the galactic system as a whole is taken up, it will be in order to examine the star-clusters, star-clouds, and nebulae, and their relation to the greater structure.

STAR-CLUSTERS AND CLOUDS

11.14. Types of Star-Clusters. As distinguished from the enormous star-clouds of the Milky Way, star-clusters are relatively small aggregations. They are of two types: open clusters and globular clusters. *Open clusters* are groups, such as the double cluster in Perseus (Fig. 11.14), whose separate stars are usually distinguishable with the telescope, and in some cases even with the naked eye. They contain a few thousand stars, at the most.

FIG. 11.14. Double Cluster in Perseus. (From a photograph by E. E. Barnard, Yerkes Observatory)

Globular clusters are more compact groups having a slightly flattened spheroidal form, such as the cluster Messier 13 in Hercules (Fig. 11.17). They contain more stars, and are more distant than the visible open clusters. Globular clusters are strongly concentrated in the region of Sagittarius.

Star-clusters and nebulae, including the extra-galactic objects, have been catalogued together, owing to the frequent difficulty in former times of distinguishing between them. They are usually designated by their number in one of the catalogues. The great Hercules cluster, for example, is known as N. G. C. 6205, or as Messier 13. The first designation is its number in Dreyer's *New General Catalogue* (1887). This catalogue and its extensions, in 1894 and 1908, known as the *Index Catalogue* (I. C.), contain over thirteen thousand clusters and nebulae. The second designation is its number in the catalogue of 103 bright clusters and nebulae which the comet hunter Messier prepared for the *Connaissance des Temps* of 1784.

11.15. Open Clusters. The conspicuousness of an open cluster depends on its distance and the number of stars it contains. In the Pleiades and Hyades, in Taurus, and in the Coma Berenices cluster

Fig. 11.15.   Praesepe in Cancer.   (From a photograph by E. E. Barnard, Yerkes Observatory)

the brighter stars can be seen without the telescope. The Praesepe cluster in Cancer, the double cluster in Perseus, and a few others are visible to the naked eye, and are resolved into stars with slight optical aid. Telescopes of moderate size show many open clusters, while the large telescopes add others.

Over three hundred open clusters are recognized. These have attracted attention because of the obvious congestion of stars, or by the common motion of their members. Open clusters are also moving clusters (8.14). The number of stars in a cluster ranges from thousands in the Perseus clusters to so small a membership that it becomes difficult to establish the existence of the cluster. They lie in or near the Milky Way, except the ones that are nearest us, such as the Coma Berenices cluster.

Groups such as the double cluster in Perseus appear to be merely nuclear condensations in much larger aggregations, according to Shapley and Miss Sawyer. As an example, the open cluster N. G. C. 6231 contains a hundred stars brighter than the twelfth magnitude within 6' of its center. More scattered stars belonging to this cluster are found over an area having at least four times the apparent diameter of the full moon.

11.16. Distances of Open Clusters. Since the stars of a cluster are nearly at the same distance, the points obtained by plotting spectral class against apparent magnitude have a similar arrangement to those of the spectrum-luminosity diagram (Fig. 9.24) for the stars generally. The difference between the apparent magnitudes of stars of various spectral classes in the cluster and the absolute magnitudes of these classes in the diagram permits the calculation of the distance of the cluster (9.22).

In this way Trumpler, at the Lick Observatory (1930), determined the distances of a hundred open clusters. From the distances and angular diameters he then calculated the linear diameters, with the interesting result that the sizes of the clusters appear to increase with increasing distance. On the assumption that all clusters of the same constitution really have the same linear diameter, it would seem that the distances were measured too large with about the same percentage of error. This could occur if the light from the clusters is dimmed by absorption in the intervening spaces.

Trumpler concludes that absorption takes place in a thin layer extending along the galactic plane. It is therefore particularly effective for the open clusters which lie close to this plane, and is not very great for celestial objects in higher galactic latitudes. The photographic light of a star is reduced two thirds of a magnitude for every thousand parsecs of its journey through the absorbing medium. There is also reddening of the light, which is greater for the more distant stars.

The nearest open clusters are the Hyades, at 37 parsecs, the Coma Berenices cluster, at 81 parsecs, the Pleiades and Praesepe, 150 parsecs. The most remote cluster is nearly 6000 parsecs away.

11.17. Globular Clusters. Ninety-four globular clusters are known in the galactic system. They are usually easily distinguished in the telescope from the open clusters, by their more regular form and great central concentration, and because they contain only faint stars.

The brightest of the globular clusters is ω Centauri (Fig. 11.31); it appears to the naked eye as a hazy star of the fourth magnitude, and therefore has a place in the star maps, and a letter in Bayer's system. Owing to its low declination, −47°, this cluster is not favorably placed for observers in the United States. The cluster 47 Tucanae (Fig. 11.19), the second in order of brightness, is still far-

FIG. 11.17. Globular Cluster Messier 13, in Hercules. (From a photograph at the Dominion Astrophysical Observatory, Victoria)

ther south; it is only 17° from the south celestial pole and is not far from the Small Magellanic Cloud.

Among the globular clusters that can be well observed in northern latitudes, Messier 13 in Hercules is the brightest. It is a fine object in the telescope, and still more remarkable on photographs with powerful telescopes. This cluster is just visible to the naked eye under the best conditions.

11.18. Determination of the Distances of Globular Clusters. A

number of globular clusters contain variable stars, largely cluster type Cepheids (9.36). Shapley has shown that the median absolute magnitude appears to be the same for all variable stars of this type, regardless of the period, and equal to $0^m.00$ (photographic). Thus, whenever the median apparent magnitude of one of these variables has been measured, its distance and that of the cluster containing it can be calculated.

He has found also that the brightest stars in the globular clusters of the same degree of compactness have, on the average, the same absolute magnitude, which is between one and two magnitudes brighter than that of the variable stars. The measurement of the apparent magnitude of the brightest stars in a cluster gives, therefore, the distance of the cluster.

FIG. 11.18.   Globular Cluster Messier 3, in Canes Venatici.   (From a photograph at the Mount Wilson Observatory)

Judging from the data for more than half of the clusters, whose distances have been determined from the apparent magnitudes of the variable stars and brightest stars, there is evidence that they are remarkably uniform in size and total luminosity. On the assumption that this uniformity holds for all, it becomes possible to deduce the distances of the remaining clusters from their apparent size and brightness.

11.19. Distances and Dimensions of Globular Clusters. By the methods which have been mentioned, Shapley and Miss Sawyer at Harvard have determined (1929) the distances of all known globular clusters in the galactic system. For the majority they are redeterminations, in the light of new data, of distances found by the former at Mount Wilson, in 1917.

According to these authorities the nearest globular clusters are ω Centauri and 47 Tucanae, which we have already noted as the brightest; their distance is about 6800 parsecs, or 22,000 light-years.

FIG. 11.19. Globular Cluster 47 Tucanae and Small Magellanic Cloud. This cluster (near the right edge of the photograph) and ω Centauri (Fig. 11.31) are the nearest and brightest of the globular clusters. (From a photograph by S. I. Bailey at the Arequipa station of the Harvard College Observatory)

The Hercules cluster, Messier 13, is at a distance of 10,300 parsecs, or 34,000 light-years. The most distant known cluster in the galactic system is N. G. C. 7006, at 56,800 parsecs, or 185,000 light-years.

The densest part of a globular cluster is about ten parsecs in diameter. In this central region the separate stars are not distinguishable on photographs with long exposures. The greater part of the cluster is included within a sphere having a diameter of 20 parsecs, or 65 light-years; but stars evidently belonging to the group are found as far as a hundred light-years from the center. The two nearest clusters have apparent diameters exceeding 20′, or two thirds the apparent diameter of the moon. A half dozen others exceed 10′ in diameter.

11.20. The Stars in Globular Clusters. The number of stars bright enough to be observed in any of the nearer clusters is believed to be at least fifty thousand. The number in the central part of the cluster must be estimated, because the stars in this congested region can not be counted separately on the photographs. In addition, there must be many thousands of stars in each group, which are not bright enough to be seen with present telescopes. At the distance of the nearest globular cluster, ω Centauri, a star as bright as the sun becomes invisible ordinarily. The visible stars in these clusters are the supergiants, the giants, and the white stars of the main sequence.

Throughout the main part of a cluster the bright stars are spaced, on the average, five or six times closer than the stars in the sun's vicinity. They are separated by distances fifty thousand times as great as the earth's distance from the sun. It is probable that the clusters are slightly flattened because they are rotating. Even if the rotation is as swift as the earth's revolution around the sun, several centuries must elapse before the displacement of the stars becomes large enough to be detected.

The globular clusters are in rapid motion relative to the sun, and to one another. V. M. Slipher at the Lowell Observatory has measured the radial velocities of eighteen of them; he finds some velocities as high as 300 km./sec. With respect to the system of clusters the sun is moving at the rate of about 300 km./sec. (8.24); but when allowance is made for the solar motion, the peculiar velocities of the clusters average more than a hundred kilometers a second.

11.21. The Milky Way. The central line of the Milky Way is nearly a great circle of the celestial sphere, inclined 62° to the celestial equator. Owing to this high inclination its course across the sky is quite different at different hours of the night, and at the same hour through the year.

At nightfall in the early autumn the Milky Way forms a luminous arch which passes overhead, stretching from the northeast to the southwest horizon. In the northeast it rises as a single wide stream, and extends upward through Perseus, Cassiopeia, and Cepheus (page

471), where it makes the closest approach to the north celestial pole. Entering Cygnus (page 430), the stream is interrupted by dark lanes, which occur in other parts of its course also, where portions are hidden by intervening dust-clouds (11.30). A great longitudinal rift (Fig. 11.30), beginning in this fine region of the Northern Cross, divides the Milky Way into two parallel branches almost as far as the Southern Cross.

The long rift is not exactly in midstream. The western branch is the broader, and it is the brighter one, at first. Farther south, in Ophiuchus, it fades and nearly vanishes, becoming conspicuous again in Scorpio. The eastern branch grows brighter as it continues southward, and gathers into the great star-clouds of Scutum and Sagittarius (Fig. 11.39A). Near the Southern Cross (Fig. 11.31) the stream, now united, is nearest the south celestial pole.

In the evening skies of the late winter and early spring the Milky Way passes nearly overhead again, now from northwest to southeast. From Perseus, its course runs between Auriga and Taurus, to the east of Orion and Canis Major, and through Carina. This part of the stream is not so spectacular; its star-clouds and dark lanes are less pronounced.

11.22. Star-Clouds of the Milky Way.

The most impressive part of the Milky Way for observers in northern latitudes extends from Cygnus to the region of Sagittarius and Scorpio. This part is above the horizon in the evening during the summer and autumn. Here the aggregations of stars are the most magnificent, and especially toward the south "the stars pile up in great cumulus masses like summer clouds."

The quotation is from Barnard, whose written and photographic descriptions of these remarkable phenomena are unsurpassed. Fifty of the finest of Barnard's photographs of the Milky Way are contained in his *Photographic Atlas of Selected Regions of the Milky Way*, which was published in 1927, four years after his death. These photographs were made with the 10-inch Bruce doublet, mostly at Mount Wilson in 1905, and the others at the Yerkes Observatory.

The great star-clouds in Sagittarius and the great cloud in Scutum are described by Barnard as the most magnificent of the star-clouds; the latter he styles "the gem of the Milky Way." "In looking at this cloud," he writes, "one can not imagine that it is anything but a real cloud in form, with a depth comparable with its width."

Krieger at the Lick Observatory (1929) finds that the diameter of the Scutum cloud exceeds a thousand light-years, and the depth is from 1500 to 3000 light-years; the center of the cloud is at a distance of about nine thousand light-years.

FIG. 11.22. Region of the Star-Cloud in Scutum. The northern part of the cloud is shown in this photograph. Near its upper edge is the open cluster Messier 11. The entire Scutum cloud appears in Fig. 11.39A. (From a photograph by E. E. Barnard at the Mount Wilson Observatory)

According to the theory that the Milky Way system is a great spiral, the star-clouds in Sagittarius form the nucleus of the spiral. Preliminary measurements appear to show that the distance of the center of these clouds is approximately the same as the distance of the center of the globular cluster system.

The study of the galactic nucleus is made difficult by the presence of the dark clouds which lie in the direction of the center, mostly within a thousand parsecs of the earth. But aside from the obscuring clouds and perhaps other absorbing material near its principal plane, the view through our system is not greatly obstructed; for many exterior systems can be seen in the region of the heavens surrounding the center.

GALACTIC NEBULAE

11.23. Nebulae in General. Cloud-like objects in the heavens which could not be resolved in the telescope into stars have been called *nebulae.* Frequently a " nebula " turned out to be a star-cluster, thereby encouraging the opinion, in former times, that all nebulae are really clusters of stars. William Herschel was firmly convinced that some of the nebulae are not of a starry constitution, but are instead " a shining fluid of a nature unknown to us." His view, however, lost ground in the next generation as more and more of the " nebulae " were resolved into stars by the great telescopes, especially the Earl of Rosse's powerful six-foot reflector.

Beginning in 1864, Huggins examined the spectra of a number of the brighter nebulae, and observed that some of them show bright lines characteristic of the spectrum of a rare gas. But other nebulae, for example, the great nebula in Andromeda, proved to have essentially continuous spectra, such as might be obtained from a cluster of stars. The fact that all nebulae are not unresolved star-clusters was now definitely established.

Modern investigations have shown that nebulae, as distinguished from ordinary star-clusters, fall into two classes having entirely different characteristics, namely, the galactic nebulae and the extra-galactic nebulae. *Galactic nebulae* are found within the galactic system, and in the exterior galaxies also. *Extra-galactic nebulae* are the exterior systems (Chapter XII).

11.24. Types of Galactic Nebulae. Two types of nebulosity are found in the galactic system, the diffuse nebulae and the planetary nebulae. *Diffuse nebulae* are of irregular form, and often of large angular dimensions. Some of them, like the great nebula in Orion (Fig. 11.25), are faintly luminous. The majority are dark; these attract attention by obscuring the view in various directions. The great rift in the Milky Way from Cygnus southward and the many smaller dark patches along its course are well-known examples.

Planetary nebulae have relatively small angular dimensions and, almost without exception, have stars at their centers. The majority have elliptical disks, which accounts for the designation of this type of nebulae; but with this feature the resemblance to the planets ceases.

The Owl Nebula in Ursa Major (Fig. 11.35) and the Ring Nebula in Lyra (Fig. 11.33) are examples of planetary nebulae.

11.25. Bright Diffuse Nebulae. Great variety in form and brightness is presented by the luminous diffuse nebulae. Some, like the great nebula in Orion and the Trifid Nebula in Sagittarius, have the appearance of rather dense clouds with fairly uniform texture, especially in their central parts. Others appear as almost imperceptible h a z e. Photographs with long exposures show the filmiest of nebulosity spread over the whole region of Orion

FIG. 11.24. Network Nebula, N.G.C. 6992, in Cygnus. One of the two brightest parts of the great loop of nebulosity in Cygnus (Fig. 6.25). (From a photograph by C. O. Lampland, Lowell Observatory)

(Frontispiece) and in other places. Still other diffuse nebulae exhibit a great amount of structural detail, suggesting the fibrous cirrus clouds (Fig. 11.24).

The great nebula in Orion is visible to the naked eye; at least, it can be noticed that the middle star of the three in line in Orion's sword is a little too large and hazy to be simply a star. It is a fine object with the telescope on a moonless night. A few other bright diffuse nebulae are interesting objects with the telescope. But photographs with large telescopes and long exposures are required to do justice to most of them.

Diffuse nebulae are actually faint — not faint because of great distance, as a star may be. A star is for us a point source of light; its brightness varies inversely as the square of its distance. On the other hand, a diffuse nebulae is an extended area. As long as it remains so, the nebula has the same brightness per unit angular area, regardless of its distance. Close at hand, it would be as difficult to see as at a great distance.

FIG. 11.25. The Great Nebula in Orion. (From a photograph with the 60-inch reflector, Mount Wilson Observatory)

11.26. The Illumination of Galactic Nebulae. The presence of stars neighboring or actually involved in the bright galactic nebulae is responsible for their shining. In the absence of such stars the nebulae are dark, as a general rule. This fact was clearly demonstrated, in 1922, by Hubble at Mount Wilson.

Hubble has found that particular stars can be selected which are obviously involved in or conspicuously associated with practically every known bright diffuse nebulosity. He has shown also that the angular extent of the illumination of the nebulae depends in a simple way (Fig. 11.26) on the apparent brightness of the star. A star of the first magnitude illuminates the nebula to an angular distance of nearly two degrees, on photographs with an exposure time of one hour, while the illumination of a twelfth magnitude star extends less than a minute of arc.

For the planetary nebulae the relation between the extent of the illumination and the brightness of the involved star is not so simple. Other factors enter. The majority, at least, of these nebulae have central stars.

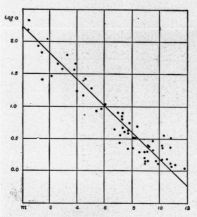

FIG. 11.26. Increase in Extent of Nebular Illumination with Increasing Brightness of the Associated Star. In each case the logarithm of the angular radius, a, of the nebula, on plates exposed one hour, is plotted against the apparent photographic magnitude, m, of the associated star. (From a diagram by Hubble)

The relation between the absolute photographic magnitude, M, of the associated star and the limiting distance, l, in parsecs, to which the nebula is illuminated, as observed on photographs with an exposure time of 160 minutes, is $\log l = - M/5$. Thus a supergiant star $(M = -5)$ illuminates a nebula to a distance of 10 parsecs, or 33 light-years. A star as luminous as the sun $(M = +5.6)$ can light up a nebula to a distance of only 0.24 light-year, or 470 times the mean distance of Neptune from the sun.

11.27. Influence of Stars on Nebular Light.

Some galactic nebulae have spectra containing b r i g h t lines, almost entirely. Others have dark-line spectra. It depends on the spectral class of the associated star, according to Hubble. If the star is hotter than class B1, the nebular spectrum shows bright lines. The great nebula in Orion is an example. Planetary nebulae have bright-line spectra; their central stars are of class O. If the associated star is more advanced than class B1, the nebula has a continuous spectrum interrupted by dark lines. Examples are the nebulae surrounding the Pleiades and ρ Ophiuchi.

The discovery that diffuse nebulae may have dark-line spectra was made by V. M. Slipher at the Lowell Observatory. In 1912, he observed that the nebulosities surrounding Merope and Maia in the Pleiades have advanced class B spectra, like the spectra of the stars themselves. This discovery inaugurated a new point of view concerning the diffuse nebulae, which is still in the process of active development. Slipher made the suggestion that these nebulae in the Pleiades shine by reflected light of the involved stars. He later found other examples elsewhere. Hubble's survey of the diffuse nebulae indicates that they have dark-line spectra as often at least as bright-line spectra.

FIG. 11.27. Diffuse Nebulosity Surrounding Merope, in the Pleiades. (From a photograph at the Mount Wilson Observatory)

11.28. Distribution of Bright Diffuse Nebulae. The dependence of these nebulae on stars for their illumination suggests that they must share the characteristic distribution of the stars. Hubble has shown (Fig. 11.28) that they occur in two distinct belts, of which the first is along the Milky Way. The second belt of nebulae is inclined 20° to the galactic plane, instead of 12° at which the local system is inclined, but with the same nodal points. This double distribution seems to show that the bright diffuse nebulae are concentrated in the local system and in the other star-clouds of the galactic system. They occur in exterior systems also.

The distance of a nebula is nearly the same as the distance of the star that illuminates it; when this distance is known, the dimensions

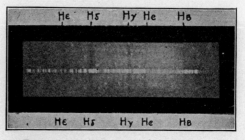

FIG. 11.27A. Spectrum of the Merope Nebula. The spectrum of the nebula resembles that of the involved star, showing dark lines, especially of hydrogen and helium. A comparison spectrum appears in the middle. (From a photograph by V. M. Slipher, Lowell Observatory)

of the nebula can be determined. The great nebula in Orion, at the distance of six hundred light-years, has an apparent diameter of one degree. Its linear diameter is therefore ten light-years. The outer nebulosity is, of course, much greater.

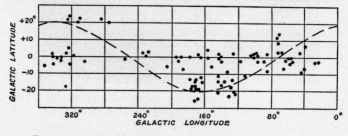

FIG. 11.28. Double Distribution of Galactic Nebulae. They are concentrated along the galactic equator, and in a belt inclined 20° to it. (From a diagram by Hubble)

Measurements of the proper motions and radial velocities of diffuse nebulae have been made in a few cases. They indicate considerable activity within the nebula. In the Crab Nebula in Taurus and in the great loop in Cygnus, whose brightest parts are the filamentary nebulae N. G. C. 6960 and 6992 (Fig. 11.24), the material appears to be moving outward from the center.

11.29. Bright-Line Spectra of Nebulae. The bright lines which characterize the spectra of many diffuse nebulae, and of the planetary nebulae also, are identified with hydrogen, helium, carbon, nitrogen, and oxygen. Some of the lines, including the prominent pairs at λ4959 and λ5007 in the green and at λ3726 and λ3729 in the ultra-violet, have not yet been produced in laboratory spectra of these elements.

Until recently, the possibility was considered that the strictly "nebular lines" which had not been duplicated in the laboratory might belong to the spectrum of an otherwise unknown element. But Wright's observations of the bright-line spectra of many nebulae showed such diversity in the behavior of the nebular lines that they could scarcely be assigned to a single element. Moreover, there is no unoccupied place left in the periodic table for even one new light element. The conclusion that the nebular lines have their origin in known elements under unfamiliar conditions was clearly expressed by Russell. The unfamiliar conditions are the exceedingly low density and great extension of the nebular material.

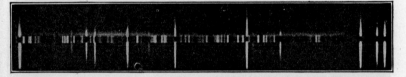

FIG. 11.29. Spectrum of the Orion Nebula. A comparison spectrum runs through the middle. The long bright lines belong to the spectrum of the nebula. The two lines at the extreme right are the green nebular lines at λ4959 and λ5007. The conspicuous line at the extreme left is the combination of the ultra-violet lines at λ3726 and λ3729. The remaining prominent lines are of hydrogen and helium. (From a photograph by W. H. Wright, Lick Observatory)

Bowen at Pasadena, in 1927, presented theoretical evidence to show that the green pair of lines is produced by doubly ionized oxygen, and the ultra-violet pair by singly ionized oxygen. The remaining nebular lines are ascribed mostly to ionized oxygen and nitrogen, and some of the fainter ones are now identified in the laboratory spectra of these elements. Thus the widely discussed problem of "nebulium" is closed, although the precise means by which these lines are produced is still debatable.

11.30. Dark Nebulae. In the course of Barnard's long-continued studies of the Milky Way, the idea gradually took form in his mind that many of its dark markings are caused by the obscuration and not by the absence of stars in these directions. The probability of the existence of vast obscuring dark clouds in the stellar system was definitely set forth in 1910. "It is evident," he wrote concerning one of them, "that we are not looking out into space through an

FIG. 11.29A. The North America Nebula. The striking nebulosity, N.G.C. 7000, is situated in the Milky Way about 3° east of α Cygni. Wolf named it the North America nebula. (From a photograph by M. Wolf, Königstuhl-Heidelberg)

opening in the Milky Way." Barnard's catalogue of dark objects in the sky, assembled by Miss Calvert and published with his *Atlas,* gives the positions and descriptions of 349 dark nebulosities.

All along the Milky Way these dark markings can be found. Some of them are conspicuous without the telescope. The great rift in the Milky Way from Cygnus to Centaurus extends nearly a third of the way around the heavens. The transverse dark streak north of

α Cygni and the "coal sack" near the Southern Cross (Fig. 11.31) are other well-known examples.

On the photographs, large patches and many smaller dark nebulosities of various irregular shapes contrast in a striking manner with the bright star-clouds beyond.   In the region of Ophiuchus dark

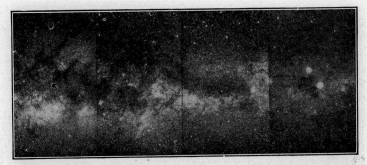

FIG. 11.30.   Great Rift in the Milky Way.   The southern part of the rift, from Sagittarius (left) to Centaurus (right).   These extreme regions are shown on a larger scale in Figs. 11.39A and 11.31.   (From photographs by S. I. Bailey at the Arequipa station of the Harvard College Observatory)

markings are pronounced.   They are found frequently associated with the bright nebulae, and are conspicuous in many exterior systems, showing especially well as dark streaks across the spiral nebulae which are presented edgewise to the earth (Fig. 12.8).

11.31. Nature of Diffuse Nebulae.   Great extension and extremely low density are characteristics of these nebulae.   They are certainly far more rarefied than the best vacuum which can be produced in the laboratory.   The temperature must be very low.   It has already been mentioned that nebulae shine only when they are excited to luminescence by neighboring stars, or perhaps, in the case of nebulae having dark-line spectra, when they are sufficiently illuminated by stars.   The problem of the light of nebulae seems to have much in common with the problems of the light of comets and of the aurora.

Diffuse nebulae are believed to be composed of gas and fine dust. Rare gas can account for the bright-line spectrum, and the dust for the reflected starlight, and for the obscuration of the stars behind the nebulosity.   The observed phenomena appear to require the presence of both gas and dust, but they have given thus far little information concerning larger solid bodies in the nebulae. Such bodies may be present also. Altogether, the amount of material is considerable. Russell estimates that the mass of the great nebula in Orion is equal to that of several stars.

FIG. 11.31. Milky Way in Centaurus and Crux. The Southern Cross is near the center of the photograph. Near it is the "Coal Sack." The two bright stars at the extreme left are α and β Centauri. The globular cluster ω Centauri appears near the upper left corner. (From a photograph by Margaret Harwood at the Arequipa station of the Harvard College Observatory)

11.32. Planetary Nebulae. The number of known planetary nebulae in the galactic system slightly exceeds one hundred. The largest, and probably the nearest, is the helical nebula N.G.C. 7293 in Aquarius; its apparent diameter is about half that of the full moon. Like all the other planetaries, this nebula is too faint to be seen without the telescope. The smallest ones are difficult to distinguish from stars, except by their characteristic spectra.

The large planetary nebulae are found in various parts of the sky, while the small ones are concentrated along the Milky Way, especially in the region of Sagittarius. Evidently the larger planetaries are the nearer. It seems probable that their actual diameters are all of the same order.

Curtis' photographic studies of these objects at the Lick Observatory (1918) have made clear many of their characteristics. The elliptical disks are brighter toward the circumference, so conspicuously in some cases that the appearance of a ring is presented. In some, the light falls off markedly near the extremities of the major axis of the apparent ellipse. Concentric rings and dark patches contribute to the "bewildering complexity" of their structure. As a general rule, there is a star at the center of a planetary nebula.

11.33. Central Stars in Planetary Nebulae. These nuclear stars are of class O. But the luminosities are surprisingly low for stars of this class. The absolute photographic magnitude of a central star is +4.9, with considerable uncertainty, while the corresponding magnitude of the class O star outside the planetaries has been found to be −4.0.

It can scarcely be believed that the light of the central star is diminished nine magnitudes by absorption in the nebular material, so that only 1/4000 of the light is transmitted. Certainly, there is no evidence of selective absorption of the short wave-lengths, for these stars are observed to be especially rich in ultra-violet light. The central stars have the high temperature and low luminosity which characterize the white dwarf stars also. But they are believed to be more massive than the white dwarfs; moreover, the Einstein shift toward the red has not been observed in their spectra.

Hubble's work appears to show that the planetary nebulae are made luminous by excitation from their central stars. Here another mystery appears. The total photographic brightness is, in many cases, a hundred times or more greater than that of the exciting star.

Further researches will doubtless provide the solutions of these perplexing problems.

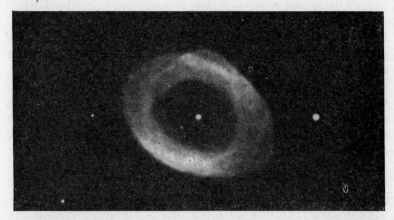

FIG. 11.33. The Ring Nebula in Lyra. The greatest diameter is 83″. Among the features of this well-known object to be noted in the photograph are the elliptical disk, diminished brightness near the extremities of the major axis, complex structural details, and the central star. (From a photograph at the Mount Wilson Observatory)

11.34. Spectra of Planetary Nebulae.

There is little resemblance between the spectra of planetary nebulae and their nuclei. Bright lines characterize the nebular spectra; between these spectra and

FIG. 11.34. Slitless Spectrogram of the Ring Nebula. A separate image of the nebula is formed by each wave-length emitted. The brightest images correspond to the two pairs of "nebular lines" (11.29) in the ultra-violet (left) and in the green (right). (From a photograph by W. H. Wright, Lick Observatory)

those of the bright-line diffuse nebulae there is no essential difference. Since the central stars are always hotter than class B1, the fact that none of the planetaries show a dark-line spectrum is consistent with the rule for the diffuse nebulae (11.27). When they are examined with the slitless spectroscope, so that the bright lines are replaced by images of the nebulae in the separate wave-lengths, it is found that the images have different dimensions in the same nebula (Fig. 11.34).

The inclination of the spectral lines, especially when the slit is placed along the major axis of the elliptical disk, gives additional evidence that planetary nebulae are rotating. Campbell and Moore (1918) have observed the inclination of the lines in the spectra of more than twenty planetaries. If the disk is circular, the lines are not inclined. Evidently in this case the axis is directed so nearly toward the earth that no appreciable Doppler effect accompanies the rotation. The lines are broader in the middle and sometimes divided, as in the reversed lines of some stellar spectra.

Miss Payne suggests the classification of the spectra of all galactic nebulae on the decimal system. On this plan, classes P0 to P9 are arranged in order of diminishing intensity of the bright lines, particularly of the green nebular lines $\lambda4959$ and $\lambda5007$, until they disappear at class P7. Nebulae of class P10 are associated with stars of class B1.5, ordinarily the most advanced class of star which can produce bright lines in the nebular spectra. Classes P11, P12, and onward, in which the spectral lines are dark, are correlated with classes B and A of the associated stars.

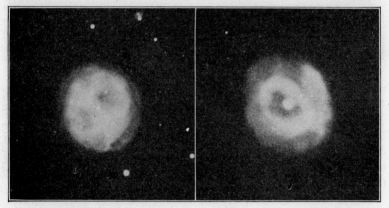

Owl Nebula in Ursa Major.   N.G.C. 7662 in Andromeda.
Diameter 200″   Diameter 30″

FIG. 11.35. Two Planetary Nebulae. (From photographs at the Mount Wilson Observatory)

11.35. Nature of Planetary Nebulae. These objects are ellipsoids of nebulous material assembled around the central stars, and presumably made luminous by these stars. The disk and rings describe their appearance. If they were actually flat disks and rings, some of them would undoubtedly be seen edgewise.

The fact that these nebulae appear as disks, while the angular diameters of the central stars are imperceptible, means, of course, that they are much larger than stars. Their diameters must be reckoned in tens of thousands of astronomical units. More precise values of the diameters can be given as soon as the distances become known with greater certainty. The rotation periods are expressed in

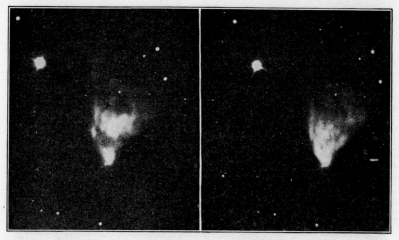

September 18, 1920.   November 1, 1921.

FIG. 11.36. Variable Nebula N.G.C. 2261 in Monoceros. (From photographs with the 100-inch reflector, Mount Wilson Observatory)

thousands of years. On the assumption that the outer parts of the nebulae are in orbital equilibrium, the masses are between 5 and 150 times the sun's mass, of which the greater part must be in the central stars.

The relation between planetary nebulae and other types of objects in the galactic system is not definitely established. They bear some resemblance to the expanding nebulae around novae, and perhaps to the great loop of nebulosity in Cygnus, which, however, has no known central star.

11.36. Nebulae Associated with Variable Stars. Curiosities are found among the nebulae which are associated with variable stars. A very faint nebulosity around the long-period variable R Aquarii, a red star, nevertheless has a bright-line spectrum. The brightness of the nebula does not vary with the fluctuations of the star. But a few variable nebulae are known also.

Two fan-shaped nebulae, N.G.C. 2261 in Monoceros, and N.G.C. 6729 in Corona Australis, vary both in brightness and in apparent form. They have at their apices respectively the irregular variable stars R Monocerotis and R Coronae Australis. On the photographs of the former, by Hubble at Mount Wilson and by Lampland at Flagstaff, the changes are sometimes noticeable from one day to the next. The recurrence of the same mottled pattern suggests that a structure of some permanence is hidden at times and revealed at others. Dark nebulosities are present in the region.

THE STRUCTURE OF THE GALACTIC SYSTEM

Until the distances of many stars became available, the explorations of the galactic system were based entirely on star-counts. While this procedure has given valuable information about the distribution of the stars in the sun's vicinity, it has not contributed greatly, thus far, to knowledge of the form and dimensions of the system as a whole. The recently discovered photometric method of measuring celestial distances, in particular, the use of Cepheid variable stars, affords a new and powerful approach to the solution of the problem.

The photometric method has already produced two achievements of the greatest importance. It has set the galactic system definitely apart from the extra-galactic nebulae, as a unit whose form and size can be investigated. It has given the dimensions of the system of the globular clusters, and has thereby set the upper limit to the dimensions of the Milky Way system.

11.37. The Superstructure of Globular Clusters. The symmetrical arrangement of the globular clusters with respect to the Milky Way clearly shows that they are members of the galactic system, although they appear to avoid the Milky Way itself. Perhaps there are other clusters lurking behind the dark nebulosities which cause the rifts in this luminous stream; but not one of them has yet been seen through the openings in the obscuring clouds.

Almost all of the globular clusters are found in one hemisphere of the sky, having its center in Sagittarius. Shapley, in 1918, gave the reason for the one-sided distribution. Having determined the distances of these clusters, primarily by observations of their Cepheid variables, he showed that they form a spheroidal system 200,000 light-years or more in diameter, whose center is some 50,000 light-years distant from the sun, in Sagittarius. The center lies in galactic longitude 325° near the middle line of the Milky Way.

Since the star-clouds are conspicuously brighter in this direction, and much fainter in the opposite direction, toward Auriga, Shapley reached the conclusion that the system of globular clusters is symmetrical with the galactic system as a whole — that the center of the cluster system is the center of the galactic system.

These results brought out clearly for the first time the enormous size of the galactic system, and the sun's eccentric location within it; they mark a great forward step in our knowledge of the system. Suburban members of the galactic community, the globular clusters appear to enclose the flatter structure of the star-clouds, whose form and dimensions remain to be determined.

11.38. Theories of the Milky Way System. The completion of explorations of the star-fields which are now in progress, combined with a fuller understanding of the absorption of starlight near the galactic plane, should take us a long way toward the solution of the problem. Meanwhile, three theories serve as provisional frames on which to assemble the accumulating observational data:

(1) The system of the star-clouds is a great spiral structure that is concentric with and somewhat smaller than the system of the globular clusters. This theory, which was given prominence by Seares at the Mount Wilson Observatory, in 1928, is preferred by many astronomers.

(2) It is a group of separate star-clouds, including the local system. This "supergalaxy hypothesis" was proposed as an alternate working basis by Shapley at the Harvard Observatory, in 1930.

(3) It is a smaller spiral not concentric with the globular cluster system. This view was suggested by Trumpler at the Lick Observatory, in 1930, as a consequence of his hypothesis of an absorbing layer along the galactic plane (11.12).

11.39. The Galactic System as a Great Spiral. In its general structural relations, the galactic system is pictured by this theory as a vast flat spiral resembling Messier 33, the spiral nebula in Triangulum, though probably larger. It includes a central nucleus, scattered stars

and groups of stars distributed around it along the galactic plane, and
other star-clouds, like the outer condensations of the Triangulum
nebula, which form the two spiral arms. It contains also bright diffuse nebulae and dark dust-clouds, both concentrated near its principal plane. Globular clusters surround the spiral in a considerably
less flattened arrangement.

FIG. 11.39. Spiral Nebula Messier 33, in Triangulum. The nearest of the
spiral nebulae, it is selected tentatively as an example of the appearance of the
galactic system to a very distant observer. (From a photograph at the Mount
Wilson Observatory)

The massive nucleus, near galactic longitude 325°, in Sagittarius,
is partly concealed behind the dark nebulosity which causes the great
rift in the Milky Way. Congeries of stars which appear above and
below the obscuring clouds in the manner familiar in edge-on spirals
(Fig. 12.8) form the two branches of the Milky Way from Cygnus to
Centaurus.

The diameter of the entire system, including the globular cluster
system, is 60,000 parsecs (200,000 light-years) or more. The diameter of the spiral formed by the star-clouds is perhaps between
25,000 and 50,000 parsecs. The local system containing the sun is

FIG. 11.39A Toward the Center of the Galactic System. The Milky Way from Scutum to Scorpio. The Scutum cloud is near the upper left corner. The great cloud in Sagittarius is just below the center of the photograph. To the left of this cloud the inverted bowl of the " Milk Dipper " is conspicuous; to the right are the dark nebulosities of southern Ophiuchus. The pair of stars marking the sting of the Scorpion are near the lower right corner. (From a photograph at the Mount Wilson Observatory)

situated in one of the arms of the spiral, about halfway from the center to the edge. This star-cloud surrounding us may be as much as 2000 parsecs in diameter; it is elongated in the direction at right angles to that of the galactic center.

Like the spiral nebulae, the galactic system is rotating. The character of the rotation suggests strong concentration toward the center, which is the case with many spiral nebulae. But the postulation of spiral structure for our system has as yet little direct observational support; it rests on analogy with the external systems which are spirals, in the majority. Some other arrangement of the galactic star-clouds is, therefore, not altogether improbable.

11.40. The Supergalaxy Theory. If the star-clouds form a spiral structure which is coextensive with the globular cluster system, as was originally supposed, this system is larger than any known spiral nebula. But there is no need for the supposition. The Milky Way system may be considerably smaller than the cluster system; its dimensions must be less, in fact, than those tentatively assigned in the previous Section before our system is freed from the undesirable distinction of being the largest known. Further observations are required for a satisfactory decision.

In view of this objection to the unitary theory, and for other reasons, Shapley proposed an alternate theory in which the star-clouds appear as separate galaxies. The local system, Scutum cloud, Sagittarius cloud, and the others, each of these is a system in itself to be compared with exterior systems. Together, they constitute a group of galaxies, or supergalaxy, analogous to the group of extra-galactic nebulae in Pegasus (Fig. 12.30).

It is evident that the appearance of the Milky Way can be accounted for equally well whether the star-clouds are separate galaxies in nearly the same plane or condensations in a single flat spiral. It is less immediately certain that the supergalaxy theory can interpret other observational data as successfully, in particular, the motions which have been ascribed to galactic rotation.

11.41. The System of the Open Clusters. A third theory views the system of the Milky Way as a flat spiral, similar in size as well as in form to the spiral nebulae. Such an arrangement was envisaged by Curtis and other exponents of the "island universe" theory before the extra-galactic nebulae were established beyond doubt as systems external to our own. It was definitely set forth as a hypothesis by McLaughlin, in 1922; and it was proposed anew by Trumpler, in 1930, on the basis of his measurements of the open clusters.

Trumpler points out that the open clusters appear to be intimately associated with the star-clouds, and frequently to be imbedded in them. Having determined the form and dimensions of the system of open clusters (11.16), with due allowance for the effect of an absorbing layer along the galactic plane, he concludes, therefore, that the results apply in a general way to the Milky Way system as a whole.

The open clusters are distributed through a flattened disk about 10,000 parsecs in diameter and 1000 parsecs thick, whose principal plane is inclined some 2° to the adopted galactic equator. The system of the star-clouds is essentially the same, except that the thickness is twice as great. It is a right-handed spiral as seen from the north galactic pole. Its center is not far from the sun and is, therefore, about 15,000 parsecs distant from the center of the cluster system.

11.42. Surveys of the Star-Clouds. The description of the galactic system depends thus far chiefly on the analysis of star-counts, on the observed arrangements of the globular and open star-clusters, and on the assumption that our system resembles some of the extra-galactic nebulae. But the star-counts relate to a limited part of the system, and the supposition that the cluster systems are coextensive or concentric with the system of the star-clouds gives two quite different pictures of this system, as we have seen. Evidently, a direct attack is required on the star-clouds themselves. Such investigations are now in progress.

A new and extensive survey of the galactic system is being made by Shapley and Miss Swope and their associates at the Harvard Observatory. It is based on the photographic examination of selected regions of the heavens; the majority are in the Milky Way, and especially in the direction of the center in Sagittarius. Many stars in each region prove to be of special types, such as Cepheids and cluster variables, whose distances can be determined by the photometric methods. It is expected that such surveys, when absorption effects are more completely determined and allowed for, will result in a greatly improved understanding of the galactic system.

REFERENCES

Harlow Shapley, *Star Clusters* (Harvard Observatory, 1930).
Harlow Shapley, *Flights from Chaos* (McGraw-Hill, 1930).
Robert H. Baker, *The Universe Unfolding* (Williams and Wilkins, 1932).

The Milky Way in Cepheus.   (From a photograph by F. E. Ross, Yerkes Observatory)

CHAPTER XII

THE EXTERIOR SYSTEMS

EXTRA-GALACTIC NEBULAE — THEIR DISTANCES AND DIMENSIONS —
THEIR DISTRIBUTION — THEIR RADIAL VELOCITIES — CONCLUSION

Extra-Galactic Nebulae

12.1. " Island Universes." In his *Theory of the Heavens* (1755),
Kant presented reasons for his belief that the nebulae are exterior
galaxies of stars. " It is far more natural," he wrote, " to regard
them as . . . systems of many stars, whose distance presents them
in such a narrow space that the light, which is individually imperceptible from each of them, reaches us, on account of their immense
multitude, in a uniform pale glimmer.

" Their analogy with the stellar system in which we find our-
selves, their shape, which is just what it ought to be according to our
theory, the feebleness of their light which demands a presupposed
infinite distance: all this is in perfect harmony with the view that
these elliptical figures are just universes and, so to speak, Milky
Ways, like those whose constitution we have just unfolded."

In recent years, Kant's theory of " island universes " was revived to account for the spiral nebulae which were now sharply set
apart, on a number of considerations, from diffuse and planetary
nebulae. The status of the spirals aroused lively discussion; but
nothing could be definitely established until their distances became
known. The existence of systems beyond the Milky Way was
demonstrated by Hubble, in 1925. He succeeded in measuring the
distance of the spiral nebula Messier 33 (Fig. 11.39), and thereby
showed that it is a separate stellar system of the same order of size
as our own, though somewhat smaller.

12.2. Extra-Galactic Nebulae. It has already been pointed out that
nebulae are of two entirely dissimilar classes, galactic nebulae and
extra-galactic nebulae. The former are concentrated toward the

Milky Way, unless they are members of other systems, while the latter are not so concentrated; in fact, they appear to avoid the Milky Way. But the avoidance is only apparent. The dark nebulae of our system, which congregate in the galactic plane, obscure the remote systems in these directions.

Extra-galactic nebulae are systems exterior to our own. They are exceedingly numerous. Many millions can be photographed with the largest telescope; and they give no indication of thinning out with increasing distance. Three are plainly visible to the naked eye,

FIG. 12.2. Region of the Great Nebula in Andromeda. The only spiral nebula clearly visible to the unaided eye. (From a photograph by E. E. Barnard, Lick Observatory)

namely, the Large and Small Magellanic Clouds, and Messier 31, the great nebula in Andromeda. The first two, which are the nearest of all, do not rise above the horizon in middle northern latitudes.

Spiral nebulae are the most spectacular, and probably the most numerous, of the extra-galactic nebulae.

12.3. Types of Extra-Galactic Nebulae. The exterior galaxies do not conform to a single pattern. Instead, they exhibit considerable variety in their structures; and there is not yet complete agreement among astronomers as to the most convenient basis on which to classify them. Hubble has suggested the division of extra-galactic nebulae into the following types:-

Extra-Galactic Nebulae

Types	Symbols
A. Regular	
1. Elliptical	E0, E1, . . . E7
2. Spiral	
(a) Normal spirals	Sa, Sb, Sc
(b) Barred spirals	SBa, SBb, SBc
B. Irregular	Irr

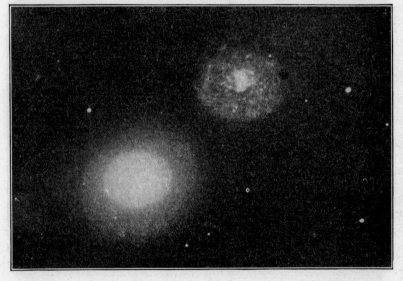

FIG. 12.3. Regular Extra-Galactic Nebulae. Spiral nebula N.G.C. 4647, and elliptical nebula N.G.C. 4649, in Virgo. (From a photograph with the 100-inch reflector, Mount Wilson Observatory)

Regular nebulae are in the great majority. They are characterized by rotational symmetry around a nucleus, and have various degrees of flattening at the poles. They fall into a progressive sequence, from globular masses of unresolved nebulosity to much flattened and widely open spirals whose arms contain a multitude of stars. The great nebula in Andromeda is an example of a regular normal spiral.

Irregular nebulae, such as the Magellanic Clouds and the more
distant cloud N.G.C. 6822, have neither nuclei nor any apparent
rotational symmetry.

The descriptions of the different types of exterior galaxies, which follow,
are based on Hubble's classification; this plan, which is purely descriptive and
independent of any theory of evolution, is especially useful for the nearer
objects, as they appear on photographs made with the large reflecting telescopes.

In connection with the studies of the more distant galaxies, whose structural details are less clearly revealed, Shapley has devised a somewhat different
plan of classification. On this plan, the nebulae are divided into five classes,
distinguished by the capital letters A to E, in order of diminishing apparent
brightness. Six grades, denoted by the small letters a to f, are arranged in
order of increasing concentration of the nebula. Degrees of ellipticity are
indicated by the numbers 1 to 10, in order of decreasing elongation, so that
an object having a circular image receives the number 10. Whenever the
spiral or irregular form can be distinguished, the letter s or i is added as a
prefix. Thus sAb9 denotes a nearly round, bright spiral with very little
central concentration.

These two classifications are among the most recent ones. Somewhat different plans have been employed by Bailey, Wolf, and Reynolds.

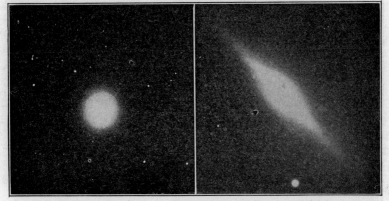

N.G.C. 4486 (E0)   N.G.C. 3115 (E7)

Fig. 12.4. Extreme Types of Elliptical Nebulae. N.G.C. 4486, in Virgo,
has a nearly circular disk. N.G.C. 3115, in Sextans, is among the most flattened elliptical nebulae. (From photographs at the Mount Wilson Observatory)

12.4. Elliptical Nebulae. The objects belonging to the first class of
regular extra-galactic nebulae give no evidence of resolution into
aggregations of stars, with a single possible exception. In these
elliptical nebulae the light fades smoothly from bright nuclei to in-

definite edges; the diameters on the photographs increase with the exposure times.

Degree of flattening, presumably at the poles of rotation, provides about the only mark of distinction between the members of this class. Elliptical nebulae are designated by the symbol E, followed by a number which is the ellipticity — the difference between the major and minor axes divided by the major axis — multiplied by 10. The complete series runs from class E0, showing practically circular disks, to E7 whose members appear like convex lenses viewed edgewise. Here the sequence of elliptical nebulae seems to join the even more flattened spirals.

Evidently, a lenticular nebula presented flatwise to the earth will appear circular; and it might be supposed, at first, that these objects are all decidedly flattened like all the spirals, and oriented in various ways. Hubble finds, however, that the frequencies of the different classes are not consistent with this supposition. Some are really globular, although it is impossible at present to decide for any individual, except one of class E7, whether it is more flattened than it appears to be.

Extreme types of elliptical nebulae, E0 and E7, are represented respectively by N.G.C. 4486 and 3115 (Fig. 12.4). The small companion, Messier 32, to the great nebula in Andromeda (Fig. 12.7), and N.G.C. 4649 (Fig. 12.3) are examples of slightly flattened, class E2, elliptical nebulae.

FIG. 12.5. Spiral Nebula Messier 51, in Canes Venatici. (From a photograph with the 60-inch reflector, Mount Wilson Observatory)

12.5. Spiral Nebulae. The spiral form of this type of nebula was discovered, in 1845, by the Earl of Rosse with his 6-foot reflecting telescope, then and for many years afterward the greatest telescope in the world. The whirlpool nebula Messier 51 (Fig. 12.5), in Canes Venatici, was the first to be distinguished as a spiral.

Spiral nebulae of the normal type have central condensations, from opposite sides of which two spiral arms emerge and coil in the same direction and in the same plane. These flattened, nearly circular structures are presented to the earth in various ways, so that some appear nearly circular, some appear as ellipses, and others are seen edgewise. The nuclear regions are generally much brighter than the arms; they are in many cases easily visible with the telescope. But the arms, especially with respect to their spiral character, can be viewed to advantage only on photographs.

Roberts, in England, was one of the first to successfully delineate the spiral nebulae photographically. Keeler, with the Crossley reflector at the Lick Observatory, Ritchey, with the reflecting telescopes of the Yerkes and Mount Wilson Observatories, and Hubble with the 100-inch reflector have secured many remarkable photographs of these objects.

12.6. Normal Spirals. All regular nebulae having ellipticities greater than that represented by class E7 are spirals, and no spirals are known with ellipticities less than this limit. If they appear more nearly circular, it is because they are not presented edgewise. The circular spirals are evidently those whose equatorial planes are perpendicular to the line of sight.

Spiral nebulae of the normal type are divided into three classes: *Class Sa* comprises spirals having large nuclear regions and closely coiled arms which have not been resolved into stars. An example is N.G.C. 4594 (Fig. 12.8). In *class Sb* the nuclei are smaller, and the arms are wider open and, in the nearer spirals of this group, resolved into stars, especially in the outer regions. The great nebula in Andromeda (Fig. 12.7) is typical of the group. In *class Sc* the nuclei are inconspicuous; the arms are loosely coiled and gathered into knots which, in the nearer spirals, are found to be aggregations of stars. Messier 33 in Triangulum (Fig. 11.39) and Messier 101 in Ursa Major (Fig. 12.20) are representative of this class.

12.7. The Great Nebula in Andromeda. Messier 31 (N.G.C. 224), the great nebula in Andromeda, is the only spiral nebula clearly visible to the naked eye. It is, in fact, the most distant celestial object that can be seen without the telescope. A hazy patch about 30′ long and 15′ wide, it was placed on some of the star charts before

FIG. 12.7.   Great Nebula in Andromeda.   (From a photograph by G. W. Ritchey, with the 24-inch reflector, Yerkes Observatory)

the telescope came into use.   As early as 1612, Marius observed it with the telescope and described its appearance as that of a candle shining through horn.

The equatorial plane of the Andromeda nebula is inclined 15° to the line of sight, enough to reveal the structure clearly.   It is the nuclear region, for the most part, that appears to the naked eye.   The entire nebula is 2° 40′ in length and 40′ wide, occupying an angular area in which a row of five full moons could easily be placed.

The distance of Messier 31 is 247,000 parsecs, or about 800,000 light-years (12.14). Its diameter is 11,500 parsecs, and its mass is estimated to be thirty-five hundred million times the sun's mass.

12.8. Edgewise Spirals. Many spirals are presented edgewise, or nearly so, as would be expected. They show clearly (Fig. 12.8) the polar flattening of the nuclear regions and the fidelity with which the

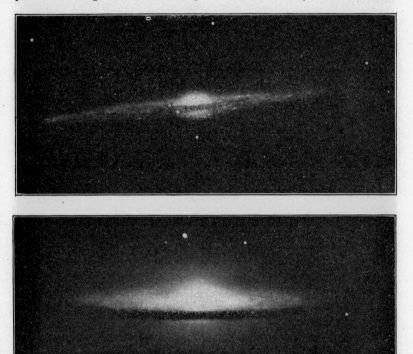

FIG. 12.8. Spiral Nebulae on Edge. (Above) N.G.C. 4565, in Coma Berenices. (Below) N.G.C. 4594, in Virgo. (From photographs with the 60-inch reflector, Mount Wilson Observatory)

material of the arms keeps to the principal plane. A remarkable feature of the edgewise spiral is the dark streak extending across its long dimension.

The existence of the dark lanes has been recognized for a long time. Curtis found (1918) as many as thirty-eight instances of this sort among the nearly edgewise spirals, and concludes that they are the rule and not the exceptions. These long, curving clouds of dark nebulosity are peculiarly associated with the spirals; they are apparently similar to the cloudy region between the earth and the center of the galactic system, which causes the great rift in the Milky Way. The rifts in some of the edgewise spirals seem to cut them sharply in two.

12.9. Barred Spirals. About twenty per cent of the spirals do not follow the normal pattern, in which the arms emerge directly from opposite sides of the nucleus. Instead, the arms begin abruptly at

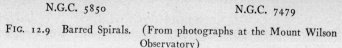

N.G.C. 5850   N.G.C. 7479

FIG. 12.9   Barred Spirals.   (From photographs at the Mount Wilson Observatory)

the extremities of a luminous bar which extends across the nucleus and beyond it. These barred spirals were first described by Curtis who designated them as ϕ-type spirals.

Hubble finds that the barred spirals fall into a sequence parallel to that of the normal spirals. Large nuclear regions and undifferentiated arms characterize the first class, SBa. Aside from the nucleus they resemble the Greek letter θ. At the other extreme are the small nuclei and wide open arms of the S-shaped spirals. The significance of these strange forms is not known.

12.10. The Magellanic Clouds. The nearest of the extra-galactic aggregations are the two Magellanic Clouds, which are plainly visible to the naked eye, although they are too close to the south celestial pole to be seen north of the tropical zone. The Large Cloud is in the constellation Doradus, having its center of figure in right ascension 5ʰ 26ᵐ, declination −69°, and 33° from the galactic equator; its angular diameter is about seven degrees. The Small Cloud is in

Fɪɢ. 12.10.   Large Magellanic Cloud.   (From a photograph at the Union Observatory, Johannesburg, South Africa)

Tucana, in right ascension 0ʰ 50ᵐ, declination −73°, and in galactic latitude − 44°; its angular diameter is about half that of the other.

The distance of the Large Cloud is 26,200 parsecs, or 86,000 light-years, according to Shapley, and the diameter is 3300 parsecs. The Small Cloud is somewhat farther away, at the distance of 29,000 parsecs; its diameter is 1800 parsecs, and it is about 10,000 parsecs distant from the larger cloud. There appears to be no material connection between the two.

The Magellanic Clouds do not exhibit the rotational symmetry which is characteristic of most extra-galactic objects. They are aggregations of stars, star-clusters, and nebulosities, resembling in appearance and in the order of their dimensions the star-clouds of the Milky Way. For the present, it would be unsafe to say that they are detached portions of the galactic system, or that they are not.

12.11. Irregular Nebulae. About three per cent of the extra-galactic nebulae lack both the conspicuous nuclei and the rotational symmetry of the others; they are classed as *irregular nebulae*. The

nearest of these are the Magellanic Clouds. Next, in order of distance, is N.G.C. 6822 (Fig. 12.11), first mentioned by Barnard in 1884, and extensively studied by Hubble (1925). It was the first object definitely assigned to the region outside the galactic system, by Shapley's estimate in 1923.

N.G.C. 6822 is near the northern border of Sagittarius, in right ascension 19^h 41^m, declination —15°, having an angular area about 20′ × 10′. The distance is 192,000 parsecs, or about 625,000 light-years. It bears a close resemblance to the Magellanic Clouds, but it is smaller; the greatest diameter is 1120 parsecs.

FIG. 12.11. Distant Star-Cloud N.G.C. 6822, in Sagittarius. (From a photograph by Edwin Hubble, Mount Wilson Observatory)

Irregular nebulae contain variable stars, star-clusters, and diffuse nebulae, generally similar to those of the galactic system. Many highly luminous stars are found in them and, perhaps on this account, bright diffuse nebulae of great size. The diffuse nebula 30 Doradus (N.G.C. 2070) in the Large Cloud is the largest object of this kind anywhere, according to Shapley. It is eighty parsecs in

diameter. These bright nebulosities have bright-line spectra resembling the corresponding type in the galactic system.

12.12. Resolution of Spiral Nebulae. Previous to 1925, the knots
in the arms of spiral nebulae, which are conspicuous in the photographs, were variously interpreted, as stars in the process of formation, as nebulous stars, and sometimes as unresolved aggregations of

FIG. 12.12. Enlarged Portion of Messier 31. Region in the arms of the
great nebula in Andromeda, near the upper extremity of the nebula, as it appears
in Fig. 12.7. Individual stars in the arms of the spiral are clearly shown. (From
a photograph at the Mount Wilson Observatory)

ordinary stars. These photographs were taken generally with the
nucleus of the nebula central in the field, so that the outer parts of
the nebular arms were not shown under conditions most favorable
for the best definition.

The resolutions of outer portions of Messier 33, and of Messier 31
soon afterward, into stars was accomplished by Hubble on photographs with the 100-inch reflector, in which these outer regions were

placed centrally on the plates. This achievement opened up a new field of investigation which has already yielded important contributions to our knowledge of the spiral nebulae. The nuclei have not been resolved into stars, nor have any portions of the compact Sa spirals and elliptical nebulae.

The stars which the recent photographs show in the nebular arms are, in general, super-giants. Many Cepheid variables and a few long-period or irregular variable stars have been found among them. Inasmuch as the Cepheids are especially valuable for distance determinations, it is fortunate that they are stars of high luminosity. Novae frequently make their appearance also.

12.13. Novae in Extra-Galactic Nebulae. The temporary stars which flare out in the exterior galaxies and then fade away gradually are divided into two classes:

FIG. 12.13. Novae in a Spiral Nebula. Comparison of two photographs of the spiral nebula N.G.C. 4321, taken in 1901 and 1914, shows two novae, to which the arrows point. (From photographs at the Lick Observatory)

(1) Occasional novae whose luminosities at maximum are considerable fractions of the total luminosities of the nebulae in which they appear. The first known nova of this class, S Andromedae, was discovered in August, 1885, in the great nebula in Andromeda; at maximum brightness it shone as a star of the eighth magnitude, near the nucleus of the nebula.

(2) The more numerous novae which resemble the galactic novae in the order of the luminosity at maximum, and the character of

the light variation. Owing to their great distances, these novae are very faint objects even at maximum, and are therefore almost entirely beyond the reach of the spectroscope at present. Humason's slitless spectrogram of a nova in the Andromeda nebula shows faint patches of emission suggestive of the spectrum of a galactic nova.

In 1931, as many as one hundred novae of the familiar type had been discovered in the great nebula in Andromeda, the majority of them by Hubble who estimates that novae appear in this spiral alone at the rate of thirty a year. The most frequent photographic magnitude at maximum is −5.7, which is not far from the estimated average of galactic novae at maximum. Since the distance factor is practically eliminated, the relations between the novae in Messier 31 are more clearly exhibited than are those between the galactic novae whose distances are not very well known.

12.14. Suggested Relation of Elliptical and Spiral Nebulae.
Jeans has proposed a theory of the development of extra-galactic nebulae, in which the observed types of regular nebulae are regarded as successive stages of the process.

A great ball of gas, originally in slow rotation, passes, as it shrinks, through a sequence of spheroidal forms of increasing ellipticity. These, according to the theory, are the elliptical nebulae. At length, the degree of ellipticity is reached at which the equatorial region becomes unstable, and rises to a sharp edge, as in class E7. Owing to the slightly stronger attraction of neighboring bodies in one direction, two streams of gas emerge from opposite points of the equator, and are whirled by the rotation to form the beginnings of the spiral arms. This process continues, once it has begun. More and more of the gaseous material of the nucleus moves out into the arms, where it further separates, and condenses into clusters of stars. Thus we have the sequence of spiral nebulae of decreasing nuclei, and increasing content and spread of arms. The successive stages in the supposed process are the various types of Hubble's descriptive classification.

This nebular hypothesis does not undertake to explain the special forms of the arms in the normal and barred spirals. It clearly regards the elliptical nebulae and the nuclei of spiral nebulae as gaseous, and not as aggregations of stars. On this ground it seems to stand or fall. The usefulness of the descriptive classification is not affected by the success or failure of any theory of evolution.

12.15. The Brightest Extra-Galactic Nebulae. Table 12.I lists the 20 photographically brightest exterior systems, according to the recent survey by Shapley and Miss Ames at the Harvard Observatory. All except the Magellanic Clouds, the most conspicuous of all, rise above the horizon of latitude 40° north, though three or four others are never high enough to be well seen.

The brightest exterior systems include examples of all recognized types and their subdivisions, except the barred spirals. Normal spirals of different degrees of concentration appear among them, from the highly condensed N.G.C. 4594 to the more loosely knit Messier 33. These spirals have various degrees of orientation, ranging from the flatwise Messier 101, which appears circular, to N.G.C. 4631 which is presented so nearly edgewise that its major diameter exceeds the minor diameter ten times.

Messier 31, the great nebula in Andromeda, is brightest of the spirals. The second in order is N.G.C. 253, in Cetus (12.20); it is too far south to have a place in Messier's catalogue. The Magellanic Clouds are by far the brightest of the irregular nebulae. It is inter-

TABLE 12.I. THE BRIGHTEST EXTRA-GALACTIC NEBULAE

Name		Right Ascension	Declination	Diameter Major	Diameter Minor	Photg. Mag.	Type
Large Magellanic Cloud		5^h 26^m	− 69°	432′	432′	0.5	I
Small Magellanic Cloud		0 50	− 73	216	216	1.5	I
N.G.C. 224 Messier 31		0 40	+ 41	160	40	5	Sb
253		0 45	− 26	22	6	7.0	Sc
5128		13 22	− 43	10	8	7.2	I
598	33	1 31	+ 30	60	40	7.8	Sc
55		0 12	− 40	25	3	7.8	S
5236		13 34	− 30	10	8	8.0	Sc
4826	64	12 54	+ 22	8	4	8.0	Sb
4594		12 37	− 11	7	2	8.1	Sa
3031	81	9 52	+ 69	16	10	8.9	Sb
5457	101	14 01	+ 55	22	22	9.0	Sc
4736	94	12 49	+ 41	5	4	9.0	Sb
4945		13 02	− 49	12	2	9.2	S
3034	82	9 52	+ 70	7	2	9.4	I
221	32	0 40	+ 41	3	2	9.5	E
4631		12 40	+ 33	12	1	9.6	Sc
7793		23 55	− 33	6	4	9.7	S
3115		10 03	− 7	4	1	9.8	E
3627	66	11 18	+ 13	8	2	9.9	Sb

esting that one fifth of the brightest objects are of this infrequent type. Elliptical nebulae are fainter owing to their smaller dimensions; the brightest of this type is Messier 32, companion of the Andromeda nebula.

THEIR DISTANCES AND DIMENSIONS

12.16. Further Use of the Period-Luminosity Relation. The clustering of celestial objects within the galactic system, into separate galaxies, and, as we shall see, into galaxies of galaxies is a fortunate characteristic for the investigator. In general, the differences in the distances of the individuals in a group are so small in comparison with the distance of the group as a whole that they can be neglected. Under these conditions, relations of apparent brightness and of absolute brightness are practically identical. Thus the discovery of the nearly linear relation between period and apparent brightness of Cepheid variable stars in the Small Magellanic Cloud served as the foundation of the period-luminosity relation (9.35).

It might be expected that the relation between the periods and median absolute magnitudes of typical Cepheids in spiral nebulae would be represented by a curve similar in form to the period-luminosity curve. Hubble has shown that this is indeed the case. Thus the way is open for the determination of the distances of all extra-galactic nebulae in which these variable stars can be observed.

The curve defined by the Cepheids in an extra-galactic nebula is displaced vertically with respect to the period-luminosity curve by a number of magnitudes, $m - M$, which has been called the *modulus*. When the modulus has been determined, the parallax, p, of the nebula can be calculated by the formula (9.22): $m - M = 5 + 5 \log p$. The distance of the Small Magellanic Cloud, given above, is derived from the modulus 17.32. The distances of other extra-galactic systems, as determined by Hubble, are referred to this value.

The distances are expressed in terms of a unit defined by the zero-point of the period-luminosity relation. Some revision of the zero-point, which new data may suggest, would not alter the relative distances.

12.17. Distances of Extra-Galactic Nebulae. Seven extra-galactic aggregations are known to be within 300,000 parsecs, or one million light-years from the earth. Their distances, as determined from observations of their Cepheid variable stars, and the use of the period-luminosity relation, subject to possible alterations in the zero point of this curve are:

	Distance in Parsecs	Maximum Diameter in Parsecs
Large Magellanic Cloud	26,200	3,300
Small Magellanic Cloud	29,000	1,800
N.G.C. 6822 (Sagittarius)	192,000	1,120
Messier 33 (Triangulum)	236,000	4,100
Messier 31 (Andromeda)	247,000	11,500
Messier 32 companions of		
N.G.C. 205 Messier 31		

In addition, the distances of the spiral nebulae Messier 101, N.G.C. 2403, and Messier 81 are made known by their variable stars as 400,000, 630,000, and 730,000 parsecs respectively, though somewhat less reliability is claimed for them.

The very brightest stars in these nebulae, which are not variable stars, have nearly the same absolute photographic magnitude, -6.1. For more remote nebulae, where only the brightest stars can be seen, this value is employed in calculating the distances. But most of the exterior systems show no stars at all to present telescopes. Their distances are derived for statistical purposes by supposing that all have equal total absolute magnitudes, or the same surface brightness. As measures of the radial velocities of the remoter systems accumulate, their distances can be determined with considerable confidence from the velocity-distance relation (12.27).

12.18. Dimensions of Extra-Galactic Nebulae. For the nearest extra-galactic nebulae whose distances are well determined, the diameters are established with equal reliability. These are given in the preceding Section. With these exceptions, the diameters of individual systems are not, at present, subject to accurate determination. Hubble has found reasons for supposing that all extra-galactic nebulae of the same type have, in general, approximately the same size and surface brightness. On this basis he has calculated the diameters for the different types of his classification.

According to these calculations, the mean maximum diameters increase along the sequence of elliptical nebulae, from 300 parsecs for type Eo to 1000 parsecs for type E7. For the normal spirals the diameters are: Sa, 1300 parsecs; Sb, 1700 parsecs; Sc, 2200 to 2600 parsecs. Barred spirals of corresponding types are slightly smaller. The mean maximum diameter for the irregular nebulae is given as 1350 parsecs.

It is important to notice that these mean diameters are much smaller than the diameter of the Milky Way system, which has been estimated as between 25,000 and 50,000 parsecs. The mass of the normal extra-galactic system is believed to be of the order of 260 million times the sun's mass, which is far below that of the galactic system.

12.19. Globular Clusters in Messier 31.

On photographs of the Andromeda nebula Hubble finds (1932) 140 objects having the appearance of nebulous stars projected against and near the borders of the spiral. Their numbers and roughly symmetrical distribution around the nucleus suggest association with the nebula. One of these objects, examined spectroscopically, has high velocity of approach, of the same order as that of the nebula itself.

They are designated provisionally as globular clusters, like those that lie on the outskirts of the galactic system. They range in diameter from 4 to 16 parsecs. Their absolute photographic magnitudes average −5.3 which is somewhat fainter than the corresponding integrated magnitudes of the galactic globular clusters. In their colors and structures also they do not differ widely enough from these clusters to cast doubt on the identification. The cluster system of Messier 31 has a diameter of 30,000 parsecs, or 100,000 light-years, nearly three times greater than the accepted diameter of the spiral proper.

Eight of the "nebulous objects" are found near N.G.C. 205, an elliptical nebula, the fainter companion of Messier 31. None are seen, however, in the vicinity of its brighter companion, Messier 32, also an elliptical nebula. A few objects of similar appearance are associated with the spirals Messier 33, in Triangulum, Messier 81 and 101 in Ursa Major, and perhaps also with the irregular nebula N.G.C. 6822. A number of globular clusters are recognized in the Magellanic Clouds. Thus we find them connected with elliptical and irregular nebulae as well as with spirals.

The discovery of globular clusters in Messier 31 does not show, of course, that our system has the spiral structure. But it adds an-

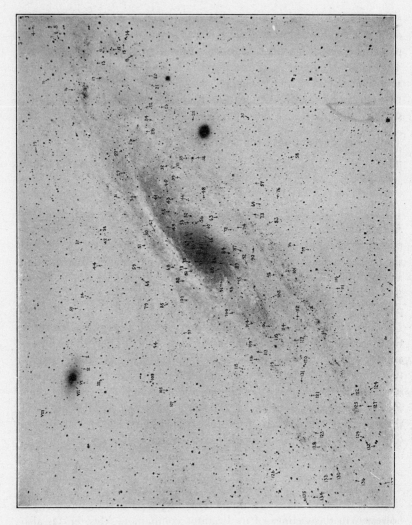

FIG. 12.19. Globular Clusters in Messier 31. On this negative of Ritchey's photograph of the great nebula in Andromeda (Fig. 12.7) Hubble has marked the positions of 140 "nebulous objects" which he identifies provisionally as globular clusters. Eight of these objects are associated with N.G.C. 205, in the lower left corner, and none at all with Messier 32, directly above the nucleus of the large system. (By courtesy of the Mount Wilson Observatory)

other impressive similarity to the list. To an observer in the Andromeda nebula, located halfway out from its center, a milky way
would be a striking feature of the heavens, brightening more than
ours in the direction of the nucleus. Doubtless it would be divided
into two branches along part of its course, and marked with other dark
rifts caused by smaller obscuring clouds, a region generally avoided by
globular clusters and external systems.

12.20. Comparison with the Galactic System. Extra-galactic nebulae, so far as they have been resolved, bear a close resemblance to
the galactic system in the kinds of objects which they contain. The
brightest stars have the same order of luminosity as in our system.

FIG. 12.20.   Spiral Nebulae at Different Inclinations.   (Left) N.G.C.
253, in Cetus. (From a photograph by C. O. Lampland with the 42-inch reflector, Lowell Observatory.) (Right) N.G.C. 5457. Messier 101, in Ursa
Major. (From a photograph by G. W. Ritchey with the 60-inch reflector,
Mount Wilson Observatory)

Variable stars of familiar types are present. The majority of the
novae seem to resemble the galactic novae. Patches of bright diffuse nebulosity are to be seen, or make their presence known by their
spectra. Large dark nebulae are abundant in the spirals, and are
especially noticeable in the edgewise spirals.

What is already known about the organization of the galactic
system is interpreted plausibly by analogy with the spiral nebulae of
the type of Messier 33. Even the superstructure of globular clusters

seems to have its counterpart in outside systems, notably in the Andromeda nebula.

The outstanding discrepancy between the spiral nebulae and the galactic system is in their dimensions. Messier 31, one of the largest of the spirals, has only one half to one fourth the diameter of the Milky Way system, as it is provisionally estimated (11.39); the average spiral is much smaller. The assemblage of globular clusters around the Andromeda nebula, according to Hubble's estimate, has not more than half the size of the galactic globular cluster system.

Is our own system, then, a continent among the "island universes"? It is proper to look with suspicion upon a conclusion which makes the observer's location in the universe conspicuous in any way. Shapley's supergalaxy theory (11.40) avoids the difficulty by regarding the galactic system as a group of "islands." Trumpler's theory (11.41) brings the dimensions into better agreement at the expense of the symmetry between the star-cloud and globular cluster systems.

Their Distribution

12.21. The Nearer Extra-Galactic Nebulae. There are 1025 external systems brighter than photographic magnitude 13, according to the recent survey by Shapley and Miss Ames, in which special attention was given to measurements of the integrated magnitudes. These objects are bright enough to show satisfactorily on photographs with a camera having a 2-inch lens with exposures not exceeding an hour and a half. They comprise all systems of normal luminosity within a distance of 3 million parsecs.

Excluding 78 of undetermined type, 23 per cent are elliptical nebulae, 66 per cent are ordinary spirals, 8 per cent are barred spirals, and 3 per cent are irregular. Thus among the nearer systems, the spirals outnumber elliptical and irregular nebulae three to one.

On the average, there is one of these systems in every cube of space 400,000 parsecs on a side; and there is no evidence of wider spacing with increasing distance from the earth. The fact that more than the average number are found within the radius of half a million parsecs around us may lend some support to the idea that the galactic system is one of an associated group of systems. But the distribution of the nearer extra-galactic nebulae is far from uniform, as is easily seen from their arrangement over the face of the heavens (Fig. 12.21).

Almost no exterior systems are found within 10° of the galactic equator. Their absence here is reasonably ascribed to their obscuration by intervening dust-clouds. Above galactic latitude 30°, however, where absorption within our system must be slight, their dis-

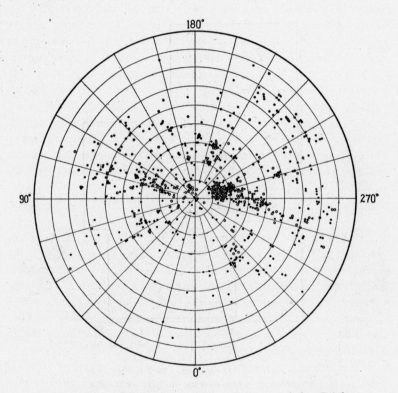

FIG. 12.21. Distribution of Extra-Galactic Nebulae Brighter than Photographic Magnitude 13 in the Northern Galactic Hemisphere. The positions of 538 nebulae are indicated by dots. The outer circle represents the galactic equator. The Virgo cluster is seen at the right of the center which marks the north galactic pole. (From *Harvard College Observatory Annals*)

tribution is patchy; there are relatively vacant areas, and regions richer than average. In addition, definite clusters of extra-galactic nebulae are to be seen. The nearest and largest of known clusters appears in the constellation Virgo, near the north galactic pole (near the center of Fig. 12.21).

12.22. The Virgo Clusters. Shapley and Miss Ames have made a special study of the clustering of extra-galactic nebulae in the region of Coma Berenices and Virgo. In an area mostly between right ascensions 12ʰ 0ᵐ and 12ʰ 40ᵐ, and declinations +5° and +20°, 2775 extra-galactic nebulae appear on long-exposure plates taken with the

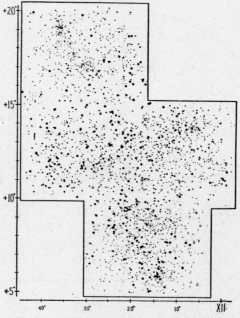

FIG. 12.22. Extra-Galactic Nebulae in the Coma-Virgo Region. The positions of 2775 nebulae are indicated by dots. Relative apparent brightness is represented by the size of the dot. The brightest cluster spreads over the entire area. Two faint, distant clusters are shown near the top of the diagram. (From *Harvard College Observatory Bulletin* 865)

24-inch telescope at the Arequipa station. These plates show nebulae as faint as the eighteenth magnitude.

Four, and perhaps six, distinct clusters are found in this region. Practically all the nebulae brighter than the fifteenth magnitude, two or three hundred in all, belong to the principal Virgo cluster which is ten degrees or more across, and centered in right ascension 12ʰ 24ᵐ, declination +12°. Further investigations have shown that this cluster is part of a long stream which extends far to the south. Open spirals are exceptionally numerous in the Virgo cluster as compared with the clusters generally, where elliptical nebulae and closely coiled spirals occur with more than average frequency.

Between magnitudes 15 and 16 the second group appears; it is three degrees in diameter, and three or four times more remote than

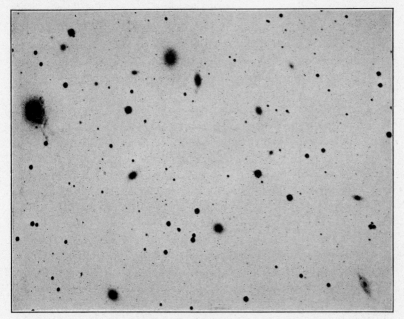

FIG. 12.23. Part of the Perseus Cluster of Extra-Galactic Nebulae. (From a photograph at the Mount Wilson Observatory)

the brighter cluster. The faintest nebulae on the plates of this region exhibit two distinct clusters, each about a degree in diameter and evidently several times more distant than the second group.

12.23. Clusters of Extra-Galactic Nebulae.

The clustering of the celestial bodies is a pronounced characteristic. Stars are assembled into clusters, clouds, and galaxies. Galaxies themselves are gathered into clusters, to which Shapley has applied the picturesque term "galaxies of galaxies." In addition to the Virgo clusters, many others are being recognized as the explorations proceed. The following notes refer to some of the larger clusters:

The Cancer cluster contains about 150 members. It occupies an area about a degree square, centered near N.G.C. 2562. This cluster has been studied by Carpenter, at the Steward Observatory, Arizona, and by the Mount Wilson astronomers.

The Perseus cluster (Fig. 12.23) has a membership of 500, mostly elliptical, nebulae. It was discovered by Wolf, in 1905. The cluster is distributed over an area 2° in diameter, to the east of Algol. Only 13° from the galactic equator, its nebulae are apparently somewhat dimmed and reddened by absorbing material in the galactic system.

The Coma cluster, only 3° from the north galactic pole, was investigated by Wolf, in 1901; he counted a hundred nebulae in an area no larger than that covered by the full moon. The cluster has 800 members. Its diameter is 1°.7.

The Ursa Major cluster is located in the bowl of the Great Dipper. It has been studied by Baade, at Hamburg, and by Hubble and Humason. About 300 nebulae occupy an area of the sky 0°.7 in diameter.

The Leo cluster, east of Regulus, covers an angular area slightly larger than that of the full moon. It includes 300 nebulae, and probably many more too faint to be recorded on the photographs. This cluster was discovered by Christie at Mount Wilson (1931).

The Centaurus cluster, centered in R.A. 13ʰ 24ᵐ, Decl. −31°.1, has been studied by Shapley on three Bruce plates of the region. About 300 nebulae are found in an oval area 2°.8 × 0°.8. Doubtless many more are too faint to appear on the photographs. The total membership is estimated to be ten times that of the Virgo cluster; the distance is 14 times as great. Its largest members are believed to be comparable in size with the great nebula in Andromeda.

12.24. Surveys of the External Systems. The Harvard Observatory is making a survey of the extra-galactic nebulae down to about photographic magnitude 18. Long-exposure photographs with the Bruce telescope at Bloemfontein, in South Africa, are employed in the survey. Each photograph covers effectively more than 25 square degrees of the sky. The work consists in determining the positions, magnitudes, diameters, and classifications of these objects, tens of thousands of which are being observed for the first time.

This survey, which is confined for the present largely to the southern hemisphere, will provide data for the study of that part of the vast metagalactic system which lies within 15 million parsecs, or 50 million light-years, of the earth. More than a sixth of the whole sky has already (1933) been examined on the Bruce photographs. The conclusions concerning the distribution of the exterior systems are in substantial agreement with the findings for the nearer systems (12.21).

Excluding the clusters and the absorbing regions in low galactic latitudes, the distribution still seems far from uniform. Taken all together, however, the nebulae increase in number four times for each fainter magnitude that is added, as they should, if there is no thinning out per unit volume of space with increasing distance.

A second survey for the northern hemisphere is in progress, chiefly at Mount Wilson. Photographs with the 100-inch telescope carry the explorations to fainter magnitudes, and so to greater distances. To distances of the order of 60 million parsecs, Hubble finds no evidence that the exterior systems are thinning out. At these distances, where the great systems are reduced to minute dots even with the largest telescope, there is nothing to show that appreciable progress has been made toward the border of the metagalactic system.

THEIR RADIAL VELOCITIES

12.25. Spectra of Extra-Galactic Nebulae. As early as 1899, Scheiner photographed the spectrum of the Andromeda nebula; he found that it is a dark-line spectrum of about the solar type, and concluded that this nebula must be a system of stars. Similar photographic evidence is now available for other extra-galactic nebulae.

It has not been a simple matter to secure the spectrograms. The low surface brightness of these objects and their nearly white light, as contrasted with the concentration of the light of many diffuse nebulosities into a few bright lines, make the photography of their spectra a slow process. The exposure of a single plate is likely to be prolonged through the available time of several nights. Even then, it is only the nucleus of the spiral that makes a distinct spectral impression; the light from the arms is too faint.

The spectra of spiral nebulae, and of elliptical and irregular nebulae also, are composites of about class G, resembling the spectrum of an aggregation of stars, such as the star-clouds of the Milky Way. The dark Fraunhofer lines are wide and rather weak; probably they are spread by the different radial velocities of the individual stars in the system. In addition, the occasional appearance of bright nebular lines on the spectrograms shows the presence of patches of bright nebulosity in some of these aggregations.

12.26. Rotation Shown by the Spectra. The flattened forms of elliptical nebulae and of the nuclei of spiral nebulae suggest that they are rotating. Spectroscopic proof of the rotation of spirals was first presented, about 1914, by Slipher in the case of the nearly edgewise nebula N.G.C. 4594, and by Wolf from the spectrum of the inclined nebula Messier 81.

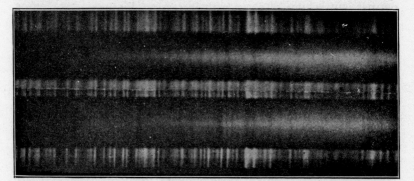

FIG. 12.26. Spectra of Two Spiral Nebulae. (Above) Spectrum of N.G.C. 4594, in Virgo (12.8). (Below) Spectrum of Messier 31, in Andromeda (12.7). The dark lines resemble those in the solar spectrum. They are displaced toward the violet in the lower spectrum, and toward the red in the upper one. In the upper spectrum also the dark lines are slanting, showing that the nebula is rotating. Bright comparison lines of vanadium and iron appear above and below the nebular spectra. (From photographs by V. M. Slipher, Lowell Observatory)

If the equatorial plane of the rotating spiral is not perpendicular to the line of sight, one side of the major axis is approaching, and the other is receding with respect to its center. When the slit of the spectrograph is placed along the major axis, the lines in the spectrum slant (Fig. 12.26), in accordance with the Doppler principle, at an angle which increases with the speed of the rotation. It is the same effect as that shown in spectra of planets (5.38).

For the great nebula in Andromeda, Pease has determined from spectroscopic observations that the rate of rotation is $0.48x$ km./sec., where x is the distance from the center, measured in seconds of arc. Thus, at the distance of 150″ from the center, the nebula rotates at the rate of 45 miles a second; and all parts of the nuclear region rotate at the same angular rate, once around in 16 million years. At the distance of 120" from the center of N.G.C. 4594, the rate of rotation is 200 miles a second.

12.27. The Velocity-Distance Relation. The radial velocities of about a hundred extra-galactic nebulae have been determined (1933), chiefly by V. M. Slipher at the Lowell Observatory, and by the Mount Wilson astronomers. Except for the very nearest ones, they are velocities of recession; and with increasing distance they run into tens of thousands of kilometers a second.

With respect to the exterior systems, according to Hubble, the sun is moving at the rate of 280 km./sec. approximately toward right ascension $18^h 28^m$, declination $+36°$. The speed is similar to that previously assigned as the sun's share in the galactic rotation (8.24), though the direction is considerably different. Having corrected the nebular velocities for this solar motion, Hubble showed, in 1929, that they vary directly as the distances; the velocities of recession of extra-galactic nebulae increase at the rate of 560 km./sec. per million parsecs of their distance from the earth (Fig. 12.28).

The validity of this remarkable relation is convincingly supported by more recent data by Hubble and Humason (Table 12.II). With increasing distances of the nebulae the velocities become enormous. Clusters of nebulae are employed in these determinations as far as possible, so that each distance and radial velocity may be the average for a number of objects. Only the smallest scale spectra can be obtained in the light of objects as faint as these, even with the 100-inch telescope.

TABLE 12.II. DISTANCES AND RADIAL VELOCITIES OF EXTRA-GALACTIC NEBULAE (HUBBLE AND HUMASON)

Cluster	Right Ascension	Declination	Distance in parsecs	Velocity in km./sec.
Virgo	$12^h 25^m$	$+ 12°$	2	890
Pegasus	23 17	$+ 8$	7	3810
Pisces	1 35	$+ 32$	7	4630
Cancer	8 16	$+ 21$	9	4820
Perseus	3 15	$+ 41$	11	5230
Coma	12 56	$+ 28$	14	7500
Ursa Major	11 43	$+ 57$	22	11800
Leo	10 24	$+ 11$	· 32	19600
Gemini	.. ...	..	41	24000

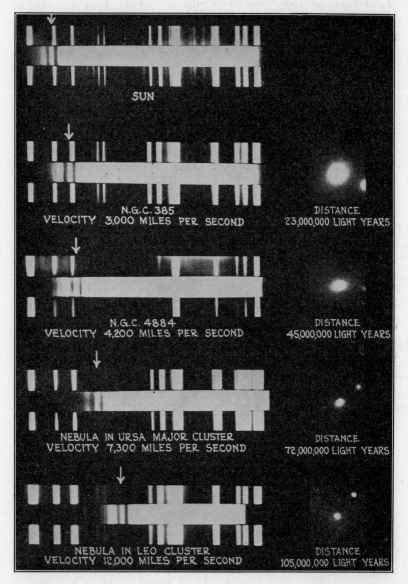

FIG. 12.27. The Red Shift in the Spectra of Distant Extra-Galactic Nebulae. Arrows point to the H and K lines of calcium. Direct photographs of the nebulae are shown at the right. (From photographs by Edwin Hubble and M. L. Humason, Mount Wilson Observatory)

12.28. Significance of the Velocity-Distance Relation. It is an open question whether the enormous shifts to the red in the spectra of extra-galactic nebulae (Fig. 12.27) are Doppler effects representing equally enormous velocities of recession. As an alternative it might be imagined, for example, that the quanta are stepped down in their journey through space, but so gradually that the effect is appreciable only for exceedingly remote objects. Since the speed of light is constant, the effect would be a reduction in its frequency, or a shift to the red of its spectrum, which might well be proportional to the distance.

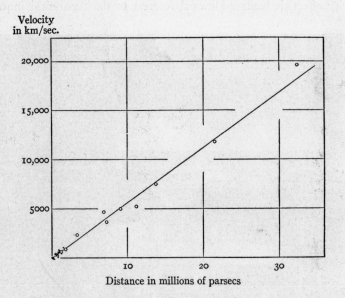

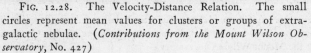

FIG. 12.28. The Velocity-Distance Relation. The small circles represent mean values for clusters or groups of extra-galactic nebulae. (*Contributions from the Mount Wilson Observatory*, No. 427)

The speed of light is not altered through these great distances. Van Biesbroeck at the Yerkes Observatory and Strömberg at Mount Wilson find that the aberration constant (2.10) is the same for a nebula in the Ursa Major cluster as for nearby stars, despite its distance of 70 million light-years, and its velocity of recession of nearly 7500 miles a second.

As a hitherto unexpected effect, the velocity-distance relation demands interpretation. But as an unexplained relation it still has great importance as a means of determining the distances of exterior systems, particularly of more remote ones whose separate stars are invisible. The procedure is to photograph the spectrum of the nebula, to measure the shift of its lines toward the red, and to calculate easily from this shift the velocity of recession. When the velocity has been corrected for the solar motion, the distance is obtained by the rule: distance in parsecs = 1790 × velocity in km./sec.

12.29. The " Expanding Universe." If the red-shift is really a velocity effect, it lends additional interest to the theoretical inquiries

FIG. 12.29. A Group of Extra-Galactic Nebulae. A small region in Pegasus, showing several extra-galactic nebulae of different types. (From a photograph at the Mount Wilson Observatory)

concerning properties of space which have been frequent since the formulation of the theory of relativity. In 1917, Einstein added to his law of gravitation (4.34) a small " cosmical term "; it was equivalent to adding to the Newtonian law a repulsive force varying directly as the distance from the sun. Negligible in its effect on the nearer bodies it becomes overwhelmingly predominant for the remote extra-galactic nebulae. In the interest of stability it was compensated by Einstein's assumption of a spherical universe filled with a medium of uniform density which produced an attractive force varying directly as the distance.

As the other extreme, de Sitter, in Holland, studied the properties of an empty universe, in which the repulsive force operates uncontrolled. Lemaître, in Belgium, in 1927, published an intermediate solution, which Eddington has investigated also. He showed that Einstein's model is unstable, so that it may expand or contract, and discussed the former case. In his solution the universe is expanding, like a balloon in the process of inflation, and approaching the de Sitter model as the limit. From any point of observation whatever, the external systems should retreat with velocities proportional to their distances, as they are observed to do; but they should not themselves expand.

Conclusion

12.30. The Physical Universe. The unfolding of knowledge of the physical universe reveals a picture of ever increasing grandeur. It begins, in Chapter I, with the homocentric view of the universe. The observer is the central figure. Around him is the earth, and over him bends the sky full of stars which rise and set, and march westward with the changing seasons.

In the geocentric view, upheld by Hipparchus and Ptolemy, the central earth is the dominating feature. The other members of the solar system, revolving around it, are now set distinctly apart from the more distant sphere of the " fixed stars." Next, the heliocentric view, dating formally from the time of Copernicus, establishes the solar system on an approximately correct basis, leaving the sphere of the stars, at first, unchanged.

Then emerges gradually the realization that the sun is only one of the stars; and the attention turns to the system of the stars, with the sun still occupying a central position, by virtue of tradition and from the lack of any information to the contrary. With William Herschel, the founder of sidereal astronomy, details of the stellar system begin to appear. The sun's motion in the stellar system, the existence of physically related pairs of stars, the vast numbers of star-clusters and of nebulae, some of them " not of a starry nature," the first attempts to survey the galactic system — all these developments aroused interest in the regions beyond the solar system. For the successful exploration of these remote regions, the greatest ingenuity has been required. The spectroscope, photographic plate, photometer, interferometer, and other devices have been called upon to supplement the eye at the telescope.

In recent years, as we have seen, the picture of the universe has developed with spectacular rapidity. The galactic system, with the sun no longer central, now stands out sharply. The hitherto mysterious spirals and others among the nebulae, altogether perhaps as numerous as thirty millions within the reach of present telescopes, are established as exterior systems; and many of them are gathered into greater systems.

Whether all these galaxies and clusters of galaxies are organized into a super-system which is again a unit in a still more gigantic structure we can for the present only imagine.

The Bruce Telescope at the Southern Station of the Harvard Observatory, Bloemfontein, South Africa.

ASTRONOMICAL CONSTANTS

		Section
Constant of aberration	$20''.47$	2.10
Velocity of light	299,796 km./sec., or 186,284 mi./sec.	2.12
Constant of nutation	$9''.21$	2.31
General precession	$50''.2564 + 0''.000222(t - 1900)$	2.32
Obliquity of the ecliptic	$23° 27' 8''.26 - 0''.4684(t - 1900)$	1.17
Constant of gravitation	6.670×10^{-8} dynes	4.14
Sidereal day	$23^h 56^m 4^s.091$ of mean solar time	2.17
Synodic month	$29^d 12^h 44^m 2^s.8$	3.29
Sidereal month	$27^d 7^h 43^m 11^s.5$	3.29
Tropical year	$365^d 5^h 48^m 46^s.0$	2.33
Sidereal year	$365^d 6^h 9^m 9^s.5$ (31,558,149.5 seconds)	2.33
Earth's equatorial diameter	12,756.78 km., or 7926.68 miles	3.3
Sun's diameter	1,390,600 km., or 864,100 miles	
Earth's mass	5.98×10^{27} grams, or 6.6×10^{21} tons	3.8
Sun's mass	1.983×10^{33} grams	4.16
1 astronomical unit	149,450,000 km., or 92,870,000 miles	4.25
1 light-year	9.461×10^{12} km., or 5.88×10^{12} miles	8.4
1 parsec	3.258 light-years, or 1.92×10^{13} miles	8.4
1 radian	$57°.30$, $3437'.7$, or $206,264''.8$	4.24
1 mile	1.609347 km.	
1 inch	2.540005 cm.	
1 pound	453.59243 grams	
$x°$ Fahrenheit (F.)	$5/9(x - 32°)$ Centigrade (C.)	
Absolute temperature (K)	$C. + 273°$	

INDEX OF NAMES

507

INDEX OF SUBJECTS